# OXFORD

# GCSE Maths

## For Edexcel

### SPECIFICATION B

### FOUNDATION

### Modular

Dave Capewell
Geoff Fowler
Peter Mullarkey
Katherine Pate

OXFORD
UNIVERSITY PRESS

# OXFORD
## UNIVERSITY PRESS

Great Clarendon Street, Oxford OX2 6DP
Oxford University Press is a department of the University of Oxford.
It furthers the University's objective of excellence in research, scholarship,
and education by publishing worldwide in
Oxford   New York
Auckland  Cape Town  Dar es Salaam  Hong Kong  Karachi
Kuala Lumpur  Madrid  Melbourne  Mexico City  Nairobi
New Delhi  Shanghai  Taipei  Toronto
With offices in
Argentina  Austria  Brazil  Chile  Czech Republic  France  Greece
Guatemala  Hungary  Italy  Japan  South Korea  Poland  Portugal
Singapore  Switzerland  Thailand  Turkey  Ukraine  Vietnam
Oxford is a registered trade mark of Oxford University Press
in the UK and in certain other countries

British Library Cataloguing in Publication Data
Data available
ISBN 9780199139460
10 9 8 7 6 5 4 3 2 1
Printed in Spain by Cayfosa (Impresia Iberica)

Paper used in the production of this book is a natural, recyclable product made from wood
grown in sustainable forests. The manufacturing process conforms to the environmental
regulations of the country of origin.

Acknowledgements
The Publisher would like to thank Edexcel for their kind permission to reproduce past exam
questions.
Edexcel Ltd, accepts no responsibility whatsoever for the accuracy or method of working in
the answers given

The Publisher would like to thank the following for permission to reproduce photographs:

P20 Derek Holloway; p40 Oxford University Press; p77 Justin Case/Alamy; p78 Tim Graham/
Alamy; p102 all Oxford University Press; p114 Oxford University Press; p134 Oxford
University Press; p141 Sami Sarkis/Alamy; p148 Oxford University Press; p173 Peter Adams
Photography/Alamy; p209 Oxford University Press; p254 Ingram/Oxford University Press;
p300 Photodisc/Oxford University Press; p317 Oxford University Press; p319 Elizabeth A
Whiting/Corbis; p364 Photodisc/Oxford University Press; p388 Hemera/Oxford University
Press; p410 Oxford University Press; p437 Araldo de Luca/Corbis.

The Publisher would also like to thank Anna Cox for her work in creating the case studies.
The charts on pages 45-46 are reproduced courtesy of the Meteorological Office; the bar
chart on page 152 is reproduced courtesy of Defra; the data on page 250 is reproduced
courtesy of the IAAF.

Figurative artwork is by Peter Donnelly

# About this book

This book has been specifically written to help you get your best grade in your Edexcel GCSE Mathematics examinations. It is des for students who have achieved level 4 or below at Key Stage looking to progress to a grade E at GCSE Foundation tier.

The authors are experienced teachers and examiners who h excellent understanding of the Edexcel specification and so qualified to help you successfully meet your objectives.

The book is made up of chapters that are based on Edexcel specification B, and is organised clearly into the three units that will make up your assessment:

Unit 1 **Statistics and probability** (plus elements of Number,
algebra, geometry and measures common to unit 2) **pages 2 – 131**
Unit 2 **Number, algebra, geometry and measures** **pages 132 – 291**
Unit 3 **Number, algebra, geometry and measures** **pages 292 – 407**

Towards the end of the book, the **C Booster** section provides targeted access to grades C and D. References to this section are made throughout the book, so you can skip ahead and improve your grade potential. **Functional maths** and **problem-solving** are flagged in the exercises throughout.

- In particular there are **case studies**, which allow you apply your GCSE knowledge in a variety of engaging contexts.

- There are also **rich tasks**, which provide an investigative lead-in to the chapter – you may need to study some of the techniques in the chapter in order to be able to complete them properly.

Also built into this book are the new **assessment objectives:**
**AO1**   recall knowledge of prescribed content
**AO2**   select and apply mathematical methods in a range of contexts
**AO3**   interpret and analyse problems and select strategies to solve them
AO2 and AO3 are flagged throughout, particularly in the regular **summary assessments**, as these make up around 50% of your assessment.

Finally, you will notice an icon that looks like this:

This shows opportunities for **Quality of Written Communication**, which you will also be assessed on in your exams.

Best wishes with your GCSE Maths – we hope you enjoy your course and achieve success!

# Finding your way around this book

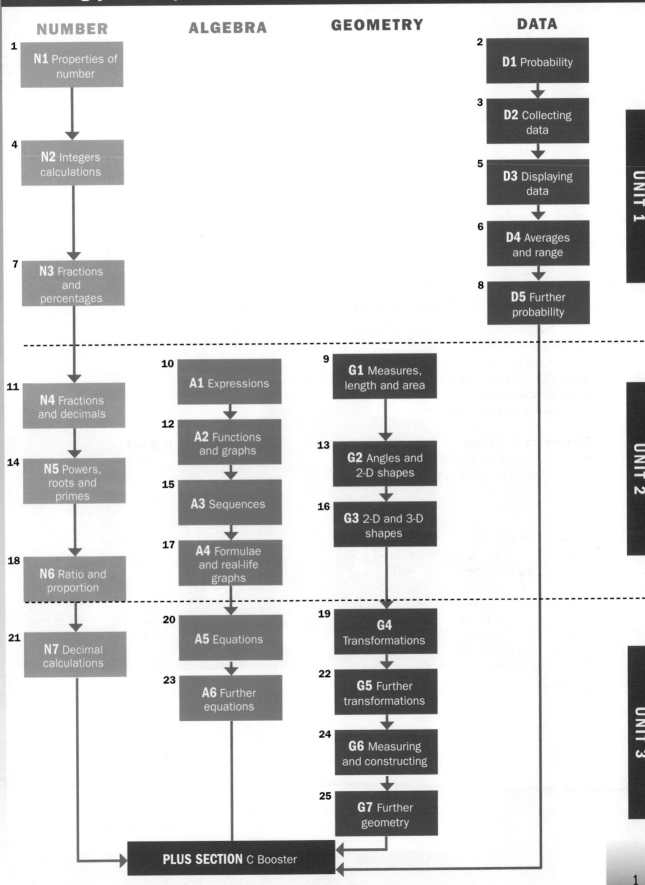

**NUMBER**

1  **N1** Properties of number

4  **N2** Integers calculations

7  **N3** Fractions and percentages

11  **N4** Fractions and decimals

14  **N5** Powers, roots and primes

18  **N6** Ratio and proportion

21  **N7** Decimal calculations

**ALGEBRA**

10  **A1** Expressions

12  **A2** Functions and graphs

15  **A3** Sequences

17  **A4** Formulae and real-life graphs

20  **A5** Equations

23  **A6** Further equations

**GEOMETRY**

9  **G1** Measures, length and area

13  **G2** Angles and 2-D shapes

16  **G3** 2-D and 3-D shapes

19  **G4** Transformations

22  **G5** Further transformations

24  **G6** Measuring and constructing

25  **G7** Further geometry

**DATA**

2  **D1** Probability

3  **D2** Collecting data

5  **D3** Displaying data

6  **D4** Averages and range

8  **D5** Further probability

**PLUS SECTION** C Booster

UNIT 1

UNIT 2

UNIT 3

1

# Introduction

Negative numbers have been the source of great controversy in the history of mathematics. Because negative numbers could not represent real quantities people were reluctant to accept them. The Greeks, who understood equations, called any equation with a negative solution absurd!

## What's the point?

In the present day, negative numbers have lots of 'real' meanings such as representing temperatures below zero, indicating losses on the stock market, and showing that something is moving or flowing in the opposite direction to normal.

## Check in

1 Write the number three hundred and four in figures.

2 Calculate
   **a** $7 \times 10$     **b** $5 - 17$     **c** $40 \div 8$

3 What is the temperature on this thermometer?

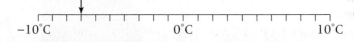

**Orientation**

| What I need to know | What I will learn | What this leads to |
|---|---|---|

Key stage 3 →

- ■ Understand place value
- ■ Read scales, dials and timetables
- ■ Calculate with negative numbers, including in context
- ■ Round whole numbers and decimals

→ N2 + 5

**Rich task**

Temperature can be measured in both Centigrade and Fahrenheit.
A temperature of −20 degrees Centigrade is equal to −4 degrees Fahrenheit.
A temperature of +20 degrees Centigrade is equal to +68 degrees Fahrenheit.
How many degrees Centigrade is 41 degrees Fahrenheit?

This spread will show you how to:

- Understand place value and order positive numbers
- Multiply and divide by powers of 10

**Keywords**
Digit
Order
Place value

- The value of each **digit** in a number depends upon its place in the number. This is called its **place value**.

In the number 4207

| Thousands | Hundreds | Tens | Units |
|:---:|:---:|:---:|:---:|
| 4 | 2 | 0 | 7 |

The digit 4 stands for 4 thousands

The digit 2 stands for 2 hundreds

The digit 7 stands for 7 units

You write this number in words as four thousand, two hundred and seven.

You can compare numbers using a place value table. Compare the place values of the first non-zero digits. If they are the same, compare the second digits. Keep comparing digits until you find a difference.

**Example**

Put these numbers in **order** from lowest to highest.
17   6300   5993   2330   2426   12 540
......................................................................................

Put the numbers in a place value table.

| Ten Thousands | Thousands | Hundreds | Tens | Units |
|:---:|:---:|:---:|:---:|:---:|
| | | | **1** | 7 |
| | **6** | 3 | 0 | 0 |
| | **5** | 9 | 9 | 3 |
| | **2** | 3 | 3 | 0 |
| | **2** | 4 | 2 | 6 |
| **1** | 2 | 5 | 4 | 0 |

Look at the first non-zero digits (in bold).
You can now put all the numbers in order except for 2330 and 2426.

For these two numbers you need to look at the second digit
    2330      2426
In order the numbers are 17, 2330, 2426, 5993, 6300, 12 540.

You can use a place value table to multiply and divide by 10 or 100.

- To multiply a number by 10 all the digits move one place to the left.

- To divide a number by 100 all the digits move two places to the right.

 p.224

$37 \times 10 = 370$

| Hundreds | Tens | Units |
|:---:|:---:|:---:|
| | 3 | 7 |
| 3 | 7 | 0 |

$\times 10$

The **0** holds the digits in place.

$4850 \div 100 = 48.5$

| Thousands | Hundreds | Tens | Units | • | tenths |
|:---:|:---:|:---:|:---:|:---:|:---:|
| 4 | 8 | 5 | 0 | • | |
| | | 4 | 8 | • | 5 |

$\div 100$

**1** Write each of these numbers in figures.
  **a** eighty-seven
  **b** one hundred and forty-three
  **c** four hundred and six
  **d** four hundred and sixty
  **e** two thousand and fifty-three
  **f** eight thousand, five hundred and three
  **g** eight thousand, five hundred and thirty
  **h** thirty-four thousand, six hundred and forty
  **i** thirty thousand, four hundred and sixty-four
  **j** two hundred and six thousand, five hundred and three

**A02 Functional Maths**

**2** These are the areas of eight countries in square kilometres.
  Write each number in words.
  **a** Algeria    2 381 741      **b** Chile           756 950
  **c** France       543 965      **d** India         3 166 829
  **e** China      9 596 960      **f** United Kingdom  244 100
  **g** USA        9 368 900      **h** Australia     7 682 300

**DID YOU KNOW?**

RUSSIA

Russia is the largest country in the world with an area of 17 075 000 km$^2$.

**3** Put each list of numbers in order, starting with the smallest.
  **a** 56    34    9    112    178    89    139
  **b** 2372    1784    2386    1990    3233    3022
  **c** 40 500    45 045    4555    4005    40 545    44 054
  **d** 240 440    204 044    24 445    245 004    42 024    242 404

**4** Draw a place value table to calculate each of these.
  The first one has been started for you.
  **a** 29 × 10

| Thousands | Hundreds | Tens | Units | • | tenths | hundredths |
|---|---|---|---|---|---|---|
|  |  | 2 | 9 | • |  |  |
|  |  |  |  | • |  |  |

  **b** 132 × 10        **c** 590 ÷ 10        **d** 17 × 100
  **e** 6400 ÷ 10       **f** 73 ÷ 10         **g** 345 ÷ 100

**5** Calculate
  **a** 12 × 10      **b** 4 × 100      **c** 320 ÷ 10     **d** 4600 ÷ 100
  **e** 30 × 10      **f** 4.6 × 10     **g** 230 ÷ 100    **h** 659 ÷ 10
  **i** 34 × 1000    **j** 3.56 × 100   **k** 23.6 ÷ 10    **l** 0.345 × 100

This spread will show you how to:

- Represent numbers as positions and transitions on a number line
- Read measurements and information from scales, dials and timetables

- Every number can be represented as a position on a **number line**.

Most of the **scales** you read are number lines.

You use a ruler to measure lengths. You use a weighing scale to measure weight or mass. You use a measuring jug to measure a volume of liquid.

**Example**

Write the reading shown on each scale.

**a**
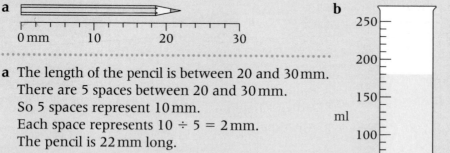
0 mm     10     20     30

**b**

**a** The length of the pencil is between 20 and 30 mm.
There are 5 spaces between 20 and 30 mm.
So 5 spaces represent 10 mm.
Each space represents $10 \div 5 = 2$ mm.
The pencil is 22 mm long.

**b** The reading is between 150 and 200 ml.
There are 5 spaces between 150 and 200 ml.
So 5 spaces represent 50 ml.
Each space represents $50 \div 5 = 10$ ml.
The reading is 180 ml.

p.140

- You can **estimate** a measurement from a scale.

You need to be able to read **timetables** for buses and trains.

**Example**

| Station | Depart | Depart | Depart |
|---|---|---|---|
| Penrith | 08:00 | 09:00 | 10:00 |
| Kendal | 08:20 | 09:20 | 10:20 |
| Lancaster | 08:35 | 09:35 | 10:35 |
| Preston | 08:55 | 09:55 | 10:55 |
| Warrington | 09:15 | 10:15 | 11:15 |

How long does it take the 09:20 train from Kendal to get to Warrington?

The train leaves Kendal at 09:20 and arrives at Warrington at 10:15.
The journey time is:

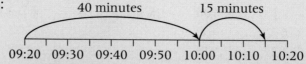

40 minutes      15 minutes

09:20   09:30   09:40   09:50   10:00   10:10   10:20

From 09:20 to 10:00  = 40 minutes
From 10:00 to 10:15  = 15 minutes
Total time           = 55 minutes

Unit 1

**1** Write the number each of the arrows is pointing to.

**a**

**b**
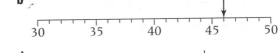

**c**
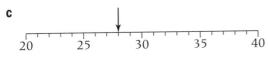

**d**
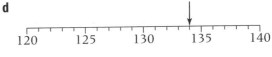

**e**
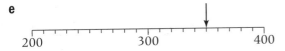

**f**
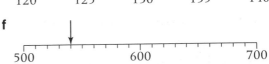

**2** Write the reading shown on each scale.

**a**
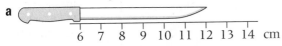

**b**
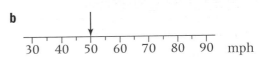

**c**
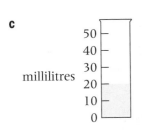

**d**
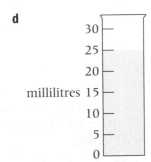

**3** Write the readings on each scale.

**a**        **b**        **c**        **d**
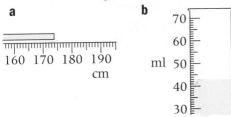
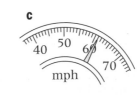

**Functional Maths**

**AO2**

**4**

| Lancaster–Keswick bus timetable | | | |
|---|---|---|---|
| Lancaster | 12:30 | 14:20 | 17:25 |
| Kendal | 13:35 | 15:30 | 18:35 |
| Windermere | 14:03 | 15:58 | 19:03 |
| Ambleside | 14:18 | 16:18 | 19:23 |
| Grasmere | 14:36 | 16:36 | 19:41 |
| Keswick | 14:56 | 16:56 | 20:01 |

**a** What time does the 12:30 bus from Lancaster arrive in Keswick?
**b** A bus arrives in Grasmere at 19:41.
   At what time did it leave Kendal?
**c** How many minutes does it take the 13:35 bus from Kendal to get to Ambleside?
**d** Karen catches the 17:25 bus from Lancaster. How long does it take her to travel
   to Windermere?

This spread will show you how to:

- Order temperatures and position them on a number line
- Calculate changes in temperature

**Keywords**
Degrees Celsius
Negative
Number line
Temperature

- You use **negative** numbers for **temperatures** below 0°C.

These readings show the temperatures in Sydney and Moscow.

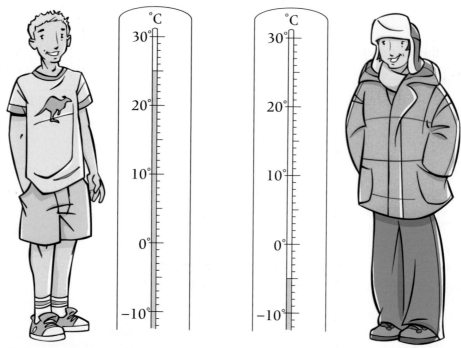

Sydney, Australia    Temperature is 25°C    Temperature is –5°C    Moscow, Russia

The temperature scale is a **number line**.

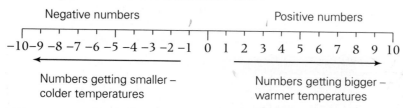

Negative numbers                    Positive numbers

−10 −9 −8 −7 −6 −5 −4 −3 −2 −1  0  1  2  3  4  5  6  7  8  9  10

Numbers getting smaller –            Numbers getting bigger –
colder temperatures                  warmer temperatures

**Example**

The temperature in London is 13 °C. During the night the temperature falls by 18°. What is the night-time temperature in London?

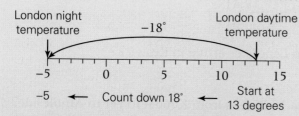

London night
temperature              −18°              London daytime
                                           temperature

−5          0          5          10          15

−5    ←    Count down 18°    ←    Start at
                                  13 degrees

The night-time temperature in London is −5°C.

1  Write the temperature on each of these thermometers.

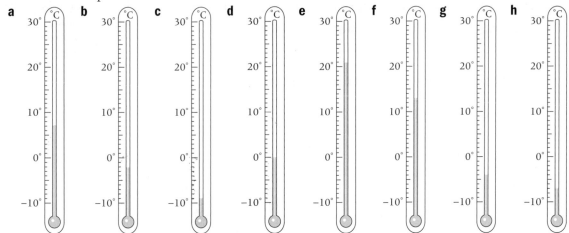

2  Write the hottest and coldest temperatures in each of these lists.
   All the temperatures are in degrees Celsius.

| | | | | | |
|---|---|---|---|---|---|
| **a** −3 | −6 | 0 | 7 | −2 | 12 |
| **b** 0 | −12 | −15 | −8 | −3 | −17 |
| **c** 12 | 21 | −2 | 14 | 9 | 3 |
| **d** −12 | 15 | 19 | −31 | 28 | 8 |

3  What temperature is
   **a** 5 degrees higher than 7 °C    **b** 10 degrees higher than 2 °C
   **c** 4 degrees higher than −1 °C    **d** 12 degrees higher than −15 °C
   **e** 4 degrees lower than 12 °C    **f** 5 degrees lower than 2 °C
   **g** 8 degrees lower than −3 °C    **h** 15 degrees lower than 7 °C?

A02    Functional Maths

4  This table shows the highest and lowest temperatures, in °C, in several cities
   around the world.

| City | Perth | Cape Town | Copenhagen | Calgary | Manchester |
|---|---|---|---|---|---|
| Highest summer temperature | 36 | 40 | 21 | 16 | 28 |
| Lowest winter temperature | 12 | 15 | −12 | −25 | −2 |

   **a** Which city had the highest summer temperature?
   **b** Which city had the lowest winter temperature?
   **c** Which city had the biggest difference in temperature between summer and winter?
   **d** Which city had the smallest difference in temperature between summer and winter?

This spread will show you how to:

- Order negative numbers and position them on a number line
- Add, subtract and multiply with negative numbers

**Keywords**
Add
Multiply
Negative number
Number line
Subtract

- You can order negative numbers using a **number line**.

**Example**

Place these numbers in order, starting with the smallest.

−3    −4    2    −5    −2    4

Using a number line

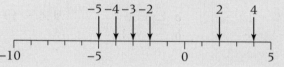

The correct order is −5, −4, −3, −2, 2, 4.

−5 is further away from zero than −4, so it is smaller.

You can use a number line to **add** and **subtract negative numbers**. There are two rules to remember.

- Adding a negative number is the same as subtracting a positive number.

- Subtracting a negative number is the same as adding a positive number.

**Example**

Calculate
**a** $8 + -3$          **b** $-8 - -3$

**a** Start at 8 and subtract 3 (move to the left).

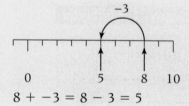

$8 + -3 = 8 - 3 = 5$

**b** Start at −8 and add 3 (move to the right).

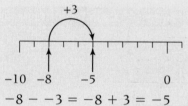

$-8 - -3 = -8 + 3 = -5$

You can **multiply** with negative numbers.
There are two rules to remember.

- Negative number × positive number = negative number

     $-3 \times 4 = -12$

- Negative number × negative number = positive number

     $-3 \times -4 = 12$

**1** Copy and complete this table, working out the new temperature in each case.

| Start temperature (°C) | Change in temperature | New temperature (°C) |
|---|---|---|
| 14 | −11 | |
| 7 | −10 | |
| 13 | −6 | |
| −5 | +11 | |
| −8 | −5 | |

**2** Calculate
  **a** 3 + 5     **b** 15 − 12     **c** 7 − 10     **d** 4 − 13     **e** 14 − 17
  **f** 12 − 9     **g** −4 + 8     **h** −3 + 12     **i** −15 + 11     **j** −3 + 7
  **k** −8 − 2     **l** −3 + 5     **m** −2 − 6     **n** −9 − 7     **o** −3 + 8
  **p** −21 + 14   **q** 21 − 14    **r** −21 − 14   **s** −13 − 23   **t** −16 + 34

**3** Calculate
  **a** 16 + −3   **b** 8 + −6    **c** 13 + −5    **d** −7 + −3    **e** −6 + −7
  **f** −4 + −8   **g** −8 + −2   **h** 12 − −7    **i** 5 − −11    **j** −3 − −6
  **k** −9 − −2   **l** −4 − −2   **m** −6 − −10   **n** −3 + −2   **o** −3 − −2
  **p** 15 + −11  **q** 17 − −13  **r** 14 + −13   **s** 15 − −11   **t** −11 + −14

**4** Calculate
  **a** 3 × 5     **b** −3 × 4     **c** −2 × 10    **d** −3 × 8     **e** −4 × 5
  **f** −3 × −2   **g** −4 × −2   **h** −6 × −3   **i** −5 × 2    **j** −7 × −3

A03 Problem

**5** In these pyramids the brick that sits directly above two bricks is the sum of those two bricks. For example:

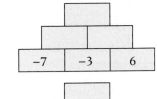

Copy and complete these pyramids.

**a**
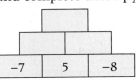

**b**

**c**
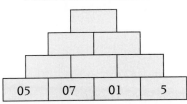

**d**

11

This spread will show you how to:

- Round positive whole numbers to the nearest 10, 100 or 1000 and decimals to the nearest whole number
- Estimate the answer to problems

**Keywords**
Approximate
Estimate
Rounding
Whole number

**Rounding** gives you the **approximate** size of a number.
When rounding numbers to a given degree of accuracy, look at the next digit.
If it is 5 or more, the number is rounded up.
Otherwise it is rounded down.

You can round a number to the nearest 10, 100 or 1000.

You can round a decimal to the nearest whole number.

**Example**

**a** Round 4639 to the nearest 100.
**b** Round 235.723 to the nearest whole number.

p.172

**a** Look at the **tens** digit.

| Thousands | Hundreds | Tens | Units |
|-----------|----------|------|-------|
| 4 | 6 | 3 | 9 |

**4639**

4500    4600    4650    4700    4800

The **tens** digit is **3**, so the number is rounded **down** to 4600.

You can say that 4639 ≃ 4600 (to the nearest 100).

**b** Look at the **tenths** digit.

| Hundreds | Tens | Units | • | tenths | hundredths | thousandths |
|----------|------|-------|---|--------|------------|-------------|
| 2 | 3 | 5 | • | 7 | 2 | 3 |

**235.723**

234    235    235.5    236    237

The **tenths** digit is **7**, so the number is rounded **up** to 236.

You can say that 235.723 ≃ 236 (to the nearest whole number).

This topic is extended on page 408.

- You can estimate the answer to a calculation by rounding the numbers.

**Example**

John brings 324 tin cans to the recycling centre.
Habib brings 387 tin cans to the recycling centre.
**About** how many tin cans do the two boys bring to the recycling centre?

You can round each number to the nearest 100 to make a good estimate.

324 ≃ 300 (nearest 100)
387 ≃ 400 (nearest 100)

The boys bring about 300 + 400 = 700 tin cans to the recycling centre.

You have to decide whether to round the numbers to the nearest 10, 100 or 1000.

**1** Round each of these numbers to the nearest 10.
  **a** 48  **b** 89  **c** 483  **d** 792  **e** 2638  **f** 6193

**2** Round each of these numbers to the nearest 100.
  **a** 343  **b** 484  **c** 882  **d** 2732  **e** 5678  **f** 16 491

> You could use a number line sketch to help you.

**3** Round each of these numbers to the nearest 1000.
  **a** 3448  **b** 2895  **c** 4683  **d** 36 927  **e** 62 532  **f** 261 932

**4** Round each of these numbers to the nearest
  **i** 1000  **ii** 100  **iii** 10.
  **a** 3472  **b** 81 382  **c** 1236.4  **d** 283.4  **e** 13 998  **f** 9999

**5** Round each of these numbers to the nearest whole number.
  **a** 4.8  **b** 3.9  **c** 11.6  **d** 25.074  **e** 16.286  **f** 435.972

**6** Here are some statistics about eight footballers.

| Name | Goals scored in a season | Passes completed in a match | Maximum shot speed (km/h) | Time to run 100 m (s) | Distance run in a match (m) |
|---|---|---|---|---|---|
| Peter Beattie | 3 | 23 | 97.2 | 10.2 | 1623 |
| Thierry Angel | 26 | 52 | 89.6 | 10.95 | 12 453 |
| Frank Schmiechal | 1 | 38 | 69.2 | 13.7 | 11 276 |
| Rudi Baros | 18 | 29 | 93.9 | 11.03 | 13 789 |
| Jan van Nistelroo | 12 | 68 | 92.3 | 12.37 | 8673 |
| Milan Dickov | 5 | 15 | 78.3 | 16.4 | 9374 |
| Paul Henry | 21 | 33 | 83.7 | 11.06 | 9898 |
| Phil Lampard | 19 | 46 | 91.7 | 12.6 | 10 372 |

For each player round
  **a** the distance run in a match to the nearest 1000 m
  **b** the maximum shot speed to the nearest 10 km/h
  **c** the time to run 100 m to the nearest 1 second.

A02 Functional Maths

**7** Use rounding to **estimate** the answer to each of these calculations.
  **a** 43 + 189  **b** 1563 + 28  **c** 1602 + 2654

13

## Summary

### Check out
You should now be able to:

- Understand place value for whole numbers
- Multiply or divide by powers of 10
- Order positive and negative whole numbers
- Add, subtract and multiply negative numbers
- Round whole numbers to the nearest 10, 100 or 1000
- Round decimals to the nearest whole number
- Read and interpret scales, dials and timetables

### Worked exam question

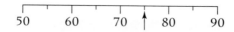

a  Write down the number marked by the arrow.  (1)

b  Find the number 530 on the number line.

   Mark it with an arrow (↑).  (1)

c  Put these numbers in order of size.
   Start with the smallest.

   52    31    1007    180  (1)

(Edexcel Limited 2007)

a

   75

   Put the answer here NOT on the scale.

b

   Use an arrow with the point exactly on 530

c

   31    52    180    1007

   There should be 4 numbers in your answer.

# Exam questions

1. **a** Write the number 7360 in words. (1)
   **b** Write 14 390 to the nearest thousand. (1)
   **c** Write down the value of the 4 in the number 21 840. (1)

2. Write these numbers in order of size.
   Start with the smallest number.
   56   79   28   121   45 (1)

3. Here is part of a train timetable from Peterborough to London.

   | Station | Time of leaving |
   |---|---|
   | Peterborough | 08 44 |
   | Huntingdon | 09 01 |
   | St Neots | 09 08 |
   | Sandy | 09 15 |
   | Biggleswade | 09 19 |
   | Arlesey | 09 24 |

   **a** Which station should the train leave at 09 01? (1)

   The train arrives in Sandy at 09 12
   **b** How many minutes should the train wait in Sandy? (1)

   The train should take 41 minutes to travel from Arlesey to London.
   **c** What time should the train arrive in London? (1)

   (Edexcel Limited 2008)

4. The table shows the temperatures in three cities at noon one day.

   | Oslo | New York | Cape Town |
   |---|---|---|
   | −13°C | −5°C | 9°C |

   **a** Work out the difference in temperature between Oslo and New York. (1)
   **b** Work out the difference in temperature between Cape Town and Oslo. (1)

   (Edexcel Limited 2008)

A02

5. Music videos cost £1.79 to download.
   Rehan downloads 21 videos.
   **Estimate** how much money Rehan pays.
   Show your working clearly. (3)

# Introduction

There are many things in life which are uncertain. Will it be sunny tomorrow? Will my football team win the Premier League? Will I be able to afford a house in the future? The mathematics used to deal with uncertainty is called probability.

## What's the point?

When the Met Office gives a weather forecast, they use a complex mathematical model to predict the probability of sunshine in a particular region.

## Check in

1 Order these decimals in size, smallest first.

   **a** 0.25        0.2        0.3

   **b** 0.7         0.8        0.75

   **c** 0.85       0.8        1

2 State the shaded part of each diagram as a fraction.

   **a**       **b**

3 Work out each of these fraction calculations.

   **a** $\frac{1}{3} + \frac{2}{3}$        **b** $\frac{3}{10} + \frac{7}{10}$

   **c** $1 - \frac{9}{10}$        **d** $1 - \frac{4}{5}$

   **e** $1 - \frac{3}{4}$

4 Work out each of these decimal calculations.

   **a** $1 - 0.2$      **b** $1 - 0.7$

   **c** $1 - 0.9$

**Rich task**

Two people can play an old game called Rock, Paper, Scissors.
In the game,
- rock is a closed fist
- paper is palm on palm,
- and scissors is the number two horizontally.

The players reveal their 'hand' simultaneously.
A rock beats scissors.
Paper beats rock, and scissors beats paper.

Is the game fair?

This spread will show you how to:

● Understand and use the vocabulary of probability

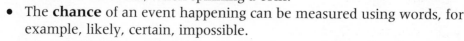

● The **outcomes** of spinning a coin are a Head and a Tail.
● An **event** is one or more outcomes. A Head is an event, when spinning a coin.
● The **chance** of an event happening can be measured using words, for example, likely, certain, impossible.

The event may be

| impossible | possible | certain |
|:---:|:---:|:---:|
| Choosing a blue ball | Choosing a blue ball | Choosing a blue ball |

● You can use words to describe how likely it is that an event will happen.

more and more likely to happen

| **impossible** | **unlikely** or poor chance | **even chance** | **likely** or good chance | **certain** |
|:---:|:---:|:---:|:---:|:---:|

| The event will never happen | | The event has the same chance of happening as not happening | | The event will definitely happen |

**Example**

Use impossible, unlikely, even chance, likely or certain to describe these events.

**a** You get a Head when you spin a coin.
**b** A baby will be born tomorrow.
**c** It will snow on the Costa del Sol in Spain next winter. (It did in 2005!)

. . . . . . . . . . . . . . . . . . . . . . . . . . . . . . . . . . . . . . . . . . . . . . . . . . . . . . . . . . . . . . . .

**a** Even chance
**b** Likely
**c** Unlikely

**1**

impossible    unlikely    even    likely    certain
or    chance    or
poor chance    good chance

Use impossible, unlikely, even chance, likely or certain to describe these events.

**a** The day after Christmas Eve is Christmas Day.
**b** The day after Thursday is Wednesday.
**c** The sun will rise tomorrow.
**d** You get a Tail when you spin a coin.
**e** You are dealt a red card from a shuffled pack of cards.
**f** It will rain sometime next year.
**g** You will climb to the top of Mount Everest tomorrow.
**h** You will roll a 7 on an ordinary dice.
**i** You will roll an even number on a dice.
**j** You will roll a 6 on a dice.
**k** You will pick a red ball from a bag that contains 8 red balls and 2 blue balls.
**l** You will pick a blue ball from a bag that contains 8 red balls and 2 blue balls.

> Hint for **e**:
> In a pack of normal playing cards there are 26 red cards and 26 black cards.

**2** Put these events in the order that they might happen, starting with impossible and finishing with certain.

| A | B | C | D | E |
|---|---|---|---|---|
|  |  |  |  |  |
| Picking a red ball | Picking a red ball | Picking a red ball | Picking a red ball | Picking a red ball |

**3** Five different spinners are shown. For each spinner, state which colour is the most likely. Give a reason for your answers.

**a**     **b**     **c**     **d**

**e**

**Probability scale**

This spread will show you how to:

- Understand and use the probability scale

**Keywords**
Probability
Probability scale

You can use words to describe how likely it is that an event will happen.

more and more likely to happen

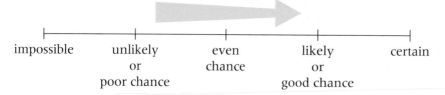

| impossible | unlikely or poor chance | even chance | likely or good chance | certain |

There are gaps in the scale.

You can use a number scale to be more accurate.

more and more likely to happen

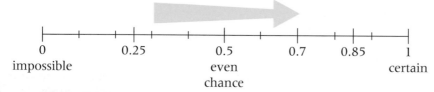

0       0.25        0.5      0.7    0.85      1
impossible              even              certain
                        chance

0 means impossible.
1 means certain.

This number is called the **probability**.
The probability measures how likely it is that an event will happen.

- All probabilities have a value between 0 and 1 and can be marked on a **probability scale**.

You can use fractions, decimals or percentages on the probability scale.

more and more likely to happen

0    $\frac{1}{10}$  $\frac{1}{5}$  $\frac{1}{4}$      $\frac{1}{2}$      $\frac{7}{10}$      1

$\frac{1}{2} = 0.5$

$\frac{7}{10} = 0.7$

Mark the position of these events on a probability scale.

a The sun setting today.
b An even number when you roll a dice.
c A glass breaking if dropped onto a stone floor.

              b              c      a
0                    0.5                    1

c is an approximate answer.

20

**1** Draw a 10 cm line. Put a mark at every centimetre.
Label the marks 0, 0.1, 0.2, ..., 0.8, 0.9, 1 as shown.

0   0.1   0.2   0.3   0.4   0.5   0.6   0.7   0.8   0.9   1

On your probability scale, mark the position of
**a** an impossible event
**b** a certain event.

**2** Draw a probability scale. Label it 0, 0.5 and 1.
Mark the points **a**, **b** and **c** on the scale to show the probability of
these events.
**a** You get a Tail when you spin a coin.
**b** Tomorrow will be Friday.
**c** You will eat tomorrow.

**3** Draw a probability scale as in question **2**.
Mark these probabilities on your scale.
**a** You roll a 7 on a dice.
**b** You roll a number 6 or less.
**c** You roll an odd number.

**4** Draw a probability scale as in question **2**.
Mark these probabilities on your scale.
**a** You will be absent from school tomorrow.
**b** You will get wet on your way home today.
**c** You will watch television tonight.

**DID YOU KNOW?**

As of 2008, the
average television
viewer in the US
watches more
than 151 hours of
television per month,
according to Nielson
Media Research.

**5** Draw a probability scale as in question **2**.
Mark these probabilities on your scale.
**a** The sun will shine in Spain this summer.
**b** The bottom card of a shuffled pack of playing cards is Red.
**c** You roll a 6 on a dice.

**6** Wayne says that the probability that he will go to school tomorrow is
1.2. Explain why the number 1.2 must be wrong.

**7** A bag contains 1 green and 2 red balls. One ball is picked out.
Draw a probability scale. Label it 0, 0.5 and 1. Mark the points **a**,
**b** and **c** on the scale to show the probability of these events.
**a** a blue ball   **b** a green ball   **c** a red ball.

# Equally likely outcomes

This spread will show you how to:

- List all outcomes for single events in a systematic way
- Understand and use estimates or measures of probability including equally likely outcomes

**Keywords**
Equally likely
Event
Outcome
Probability
Systematically

When rolling a dice, the possible **outcomes** are 1, 2, 3, 4, 5 and 6.

The six outcomes are shown in order or **systematically**.

Each outcome is **equally likely** as the faces of the dice are identical in size and shape.

- The **probability** is a number that measures how likely it is that an event will happen.

You can calculate the probability using this formula.

An event is one or more outcomes.

- Probability of an event happening $= \dfrac{\text{number of favourable outcomes}}{\text{total number of all possible outcomes}}$

p.122

All probabilities have a value between 0 and 1.

0 means impossible.
1 means certain.

---

**Example**

A counter is taken out of the bucket.

a List the possible outcomes.
b Find the probability that a blue counter is taken out.
c Find the probability that a red counter is taken out.
d Find the probability that a green counter is taken out.

..................................................

a Blue, Blue, Blue, Red, Red
b The number of blue counters is 3.
   The total number of all possible outcomes is 5.
   The probability of a blue counter is $\frac{3}{5}$.
c The number of red counters is 2.
   The total number of all possible outcomes is 5.
   Probability of a red counter is $\frac{2}{5}$.
d The number of green counters is 0.
   The total number of all possible outcomes is 5.
   Probability of a green counter is $\frac{0}{5} = 0$.

1  List all the possible outcomes when
   **a** spinning a coin
   **b** spinning this spinner
   **c** rolling an ordinary dice
   **d** trying to catch a ball
   **e** picking a letter from

2  List the three possible outcomes when a ball
   is taken from the bag.

3  List the three possible outcomes when a ball
   is taken from the bag.

4  List the three possible outcomes when a ball
   is taken from the bag.

5  List the possible outcomes when the spinner is spun.

For the questions **6–10**, the outcomes are equally likely.

6  **a** Which colour is the most likely?
   **b** Calculate the probability of spinning orange.
   **c** Calculate the probability of spinning pink.

7  Calculate the probability of spinning a Head with a coin.

8  An ordinary dice is rolled. Calculate the probability of rolling
   **a** a 3                **b** an even number                **c** a 7.

9  Some children cannot decide
   whether to go swimming,
   skating or bowling. Three
   cards are put into a tin. One
   card is taken out to decide
   the activity.
   Calculate the probability that the children go bowling.

swim   skate   bowl

10  A tetrahedron dice has only four faces.
    The four outcomes are 1, 2, 3 or 4.
    Calculate the probability that the score is
    **a** a 3          **b** an even number          **c** an odd number  **d** a 5.

**Calculating probabilities**

This spread will show you how to:
- Calculate probabilities
- Understand and use the probability scale

Keywords
Probability
Probability scale

You can measure how likely it is that an event will happen by using a number between 0 and 1 called the **probability**.

The probability can be represented on a **probability scale**.

0 means impossible.
1 means certain.

You can use decimals or fractions.

You can calculate the probability using this formula.

- Probability of an event happening = $\dfrac{\text{number of favourable outcomes}}{\text{total number of all possible outcomes}}$

The probability of an event can be written as P(event).

**Example**

The numbers 1 to 10 are put into a bag.

| 1 | 2 | 3 | 4 | 5 | 6 | 7 | 8 | 9 | 10 |

Karen picks one number out of the bag without looking.
Calculate the probability she picks

**a** the number 6
**b** a number greater than 7
**c** a multiple of 4
**d** a square number.

.........................................................................................

**a** There are 10 possible outcomes.
There is one 6.
P(6) $= \frac{1}{10}$
**b** There are three numbers greater than 7.
P(greater than 7) $= \frac{3}{10}$
**c** There are two numbers that are multiples of 4 (4, 8).
P(multiple of 4) $= \frac{2}{10} = \frac{1}{5}$
**d** There are three square numbers (1, 4, 9).
P(square number) $= \frac{3}{10}$

7 is not included in 'greater than 7'

For the following questions, the outcomes are equally likely.

**1** A bag contains one yellow ball and four red balls. One ball is taken out of the bag. Calculate the probability that the ball is
**a** red **b** yellow **c** blue.

**2** A bag contains five red balls. One ball is taken out of the bag. Calculate the probability that the ball is
**a** red **b** blue.

**3** A bag contains three red and two yellow balls. One ball is taken out of the bag. Calculate the probability that the ball is
**a** red **b** yellow **c** blue.

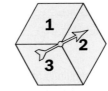

**4** This spinner is spun. Calculate the probability that the arrow lands on
**a** a 2 **b** an odd number
**c** a square number **d** a prime number
**e** a number 3 or less.

**5** If one letter is chosen at random from the word ISOSCELES, what is the probability that the letter is
**a** a C **b** an E **c** an S
**d** a vowel **e** a consonant?

**6** If one letter is chosen at random from the word PARALLELOGRAM, what is the probability that the letter is
**a** an O **b** an A **c** an L
**d** a vowel **e** a consonant?

**7** These shapes are drawn on six cards.
One card is picked at random.
What is the probability that the shape on the card
**a** is an isosceles triangle **b** is a triangle
**c** is a quadrilateral **d** is a square
**e** is an octagon **f** has more than four sides
**g** has all of its sides equal **h** is a regular shape?

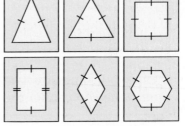

**8** There are 14 boys and 16 girls in a class.
If one student is chosen at random, what is the probability that the student is
**a** a boy **b** a girl?

This spread will show you how to:

- Identify different mutually exclusive outcomes and know the sum of the probabilities of all these outcomes is 1
- Understand and use the probability scale

A ball is picked from a box.

The possible **outcomes** are Green, Green and Red.

Probability of picking a green ball $= \frac{2}{3}$

Probability of picking a red ball $= \frac{1}{3}$

The probabilities of the events add up to 1.

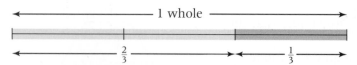

$\frac{2}{3} + \frac{1}{3} = 1$

- The probabilities of all possible outcomes of an event add up to 1.

Probability of picking a green ball $= \frac{2}{3}$.

Probability of **not** picking a green ball $= 1 - \frac{2}{3} = \frac{1}{3}$.

- Probability of an event not happening $= 1 -$ Probability of the event happening

**Example**

The probability that Emma does her homework is $\frac{7}{10}$.

Calculate the probability that she does not do her homework.

$$1 - \frac{7}{10} = \frac{3}{10}$$

Probability she does not do her homework $= \frac{3}{10}$.

These outcomes are **mutually exclusive** because if you get one outcome you cannot get the other one.

This topic is extended to calculating mutually exclusive outcomes on page 438.

- Mutually exclusive outcomes cannot occur at the same time.

**Example**

Which of these outcomes are mutually exclusive?

| A | B | C |
|---|---|---|
| Spinning a coin:<br>Head, Tail | Pressing a light switch:<br>Light on, light off | Eating breakfast:<br>Cornflakes, muesli |

**A, B.**
**C** is not mutually exclusive as you could choose both cornflakes and muesli.

**1** A bag contains one blue and four red balls. One ball is taken out.
   **a** Calculate the probability that the ball is blue.
   **b** Calculate the probability that the ball is red.
   **c** Calculate the sum of these answers.

**2** A bag contains three blue and seven green balls. One ball is taken out.
   **a** Calculate the probability that the ball is blue.
   **b** Calculate the probability that the ball is green.
   **c** Calculate the sum of these answers.

**3** An ordinary dice is rolled.
   **a** Calculate the probability of rolling
      **i** a 1    **ii** a 2    **iii** a 3    **iv** a 4    **v** a 5    **vi** a 6.
   **b** Calculate the sum of the answers.

**4** A box contains many red and blue counters.
   One counter is taken out. The probability that a red counter is taken out is 0.4.
   Calculate the probability that a blue counter is taken out.

**5** The probability of winning a raffle is 0.1.
   Calculate the probability of not winning the raffle.

**6** A spinner is made from blue, green, yellow and pink triangles.
   **a** Calculate the probability of spinning blue.
   **b** Calculate the probability of not spinning blue.

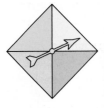

**7** A drawing pin is dropped. The probability that the pin lands point up is $\frac{4}{5}$.
   What is the probability that the pin does not land point up?

A02 | Functional Maths

**8** The probability of rain at Styhead Tarn in the Lake District is $\frac{7}{10}$.
   Calculate the probability of it not raining at Styhead Tarn.

**9** The letters of the word EQUILATERAL are put in a bag. One letter is taken out.
   **a** Calculate the probability of choosing an E.
   **b** Calculate the probability of not choosing an E.

# Two-way tables and probability

This spread will show you how to:

• Use and interpret two-way tables for discrete data

**Keywords**
Equally likely
Random
Two-way table

When someone or something is chosen at **random**, each person or item must be **equally likely** to be chosen.

For example, picking counters from a bag, provided the counters are replaced and the bag is well shaken.

• A **two-way table** links two types of information.

p.42

100 students were asked whether they preferred swimming or running for exercise.

|          | Boys | Girls |
|----------|------|-------|
| **Swimming** | 9    | 28    |
| **Running**  | 31   | 32    |

9 boys preferred swimming.

32 girls preferred running.

$9 + 28 = 37$   students preferred swimming.
$31 + 32 = 63$   students preferred running.
$9 + 31 = 40$   students were boys.
$28 + 32 = 60$   students were girls.

You can calculate the probability of randomly selecting the different groups of students using the two-way table.

**Example**

The two-way table gives the number of males/females and adults/children in a room.
One person is selected at random.

|          | Adults | Children |
|----------|--------|----------|
| **Male**   | 18     | 5        |
| **Female** | 15     | 12       |

Calculate the probability that the person selected is

**a** a female
**b** a child
**c** an adult male.

...........................................................................................

**a** $15 + 12 = 27$ female
  $P(\text{female}) = \frac{27}{50}$
**b** $5 + 12 = 17$ children
  $P(\text{child}) = \frac{17}{50}$
**c** There are 18 adult males.
  $P(\text{adult male}) = \frac{18}{50} = \frac{9}{25}$

The total number of people is $18 + 5 + 15 + 12 = 50$.

**1** The speeds of vehicles passing a school are measured.
The first 50 vehicles are shown in the table.
Calculate the probability that a vehicle passing
the school is travelling at
**a** 30 mph or under
**b** over 30 mph.
The speed limit outside the school is 30 mph.
**c** What is the probability that a vehicle passing the
school is breaking the law?

| | Number of vehicles |
|---|---|
| 30 mph or under | 15 |
| Over 30 mph | 35 |

**2** The numbers of students in a class who are
right-handed or left-handed are shown in the
two-way table.
**a** How many students are in the class altogether?
A student is chosen at random.
What is the probability that the student is
**b** a right-handed boy
**c** a right-handed girl
**d** a left-handed boy
**e** a left-handed girl?

| | Boys | Girls |
|---|---|---|
| Right-handed | 12 | 13 |
| Left-handed | 3 | 2 |

**3** A building set consists of red and yellow bricks.
Each brick is either a cube or a cuboid.
The two-way table shows the number of
each type of brick in the set.

| | Cubes | Cuboids |
|---|---|---|
| Red | 8 | 5 |
| Yellow | 1 | 6 |

**a** How many bricks are in the building set altogether?
**b** How many yellow bricks are in the building set altogether?
**c** How many cubes are in the building set altogether?
A brick is selected at random. Calculate the probability
that the brick is
**d** yellow
**e** a cube.

**4** The numbers of people in a library are
shown in the two-way table.
**a** How many people are in the library altogether?
**b** How many males are in the library?
**c** How many under 18s are in the library?
One person is selected at random. Calculate the
probability that the person is
**d** a male
**e** an under 18
**f** a female who is under 18.

| | Males | Females |
|---|---|---|
| Under 18 | 5 | 10 |
| 18 or over | 20 | 15 |

## Summary

### Check out

You should now be able to:

- Understand and use the vocabulary of probability
- Understand and use the probability scale
- List all outcomes for single events in a systematic way
- Understand and use estimates or measures of probability
- Identify mutually exclusive events and know that the sum of the probabilities of these outcomes is 1
- Use and interpret two-way tables and use them to calculate probabilities

### Worked exam question

Here is a 5-sided spinner.

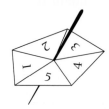

The sides of the spinner are labelled 1, 2, 3, 4 and 5
The spinner is biased.
The probability that the spinner will land on each of the numbers 1, 2, 3 and 4 is given in the table

| Number | 1 | 2 | 3 | 4 | 5 |
|---|---|---|---|---|---|
| Probability | 0.15 | 0.05 | 0.2 | 0.25 | $x$ |

Work out the value of $x$. (2)

(Edexcel Limited 2008)

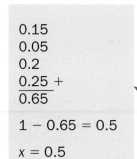

```
0.15
0.05
0.2
0.25 +
─────
0.65

1 − 0.65 = 0.5

x = 0.5
```

Show the addition and subtraction calculations.

**Examiner's tip:**
Some probability questions can include algebra.

# Exam questions

**1**

| Impossible | Unlikely | Even | Likely | Certain |

Which word from the box best describes the likelihood of each of these events?
**a** You throw an ordinary dice and get an eight. (1)
**b** You throw a coin and get a Heads. (1)
**c** December 6th 2008 is the day after December 5th 2008. (1)

(Edexcel Limited 2009)

**2 a** On a copy of the probability scale below, mark with a cross (×) the probability that you will see a rainbow in the sky at least once next year.

0    $\frac{1}{2}$    1

(1)

**b** On a copy of the probability scale below, mark with a cross (×) the probability that you will get a 7 when you roll an ordinary 6-sided dice.

0    $\frac{1}{2}$    1

(1)

**A03**

**3** The two-way table shows some information about the colours of Vauxhall cars and of BMW cars in a car park. Some of the information is missing.

|          | black | blue | red | Total |
|----------|-------|------|-----|-------|
| Vauxhall | 8     | 9    |     |       |
| BMW      |       |      |     | 22    |
| Total    | 12    |      | 14  | 40    |

One of the cars is to be picked at random.
Work out the probability that this car will be blue. (3)

31

# Introduction

In the run up to a general election, opinion polls are taken to find out which political party people are likely to vote for. The results of just a thousand people's voting intentions are taken very seriously by the media and the politicians.

## What's the point?
Surveys allow statisticians to analyse manageable amounts of data, without having to gauge the opinion of everyone in the country. The results are quicker, less costly, and still meaningful.

**Check in**

1   Put these numbers in order of size, smallest first.
    **a** 37, 42, 17, 6, 30, 19, 26, 29
    **b** 118, 135, 106, 121, 130, 115
    **c** 156, 145, 154, 165, 166, 155, 144

2   Calculate
    **a** 63 + 58          **b** 48 + 96
    **c** 73 + 95 + 84     **d** 138 + 275
    **e** 63 + 5           **f** 38 − 15
    **g** 96 − 47          **h** 136 − 54
    **i** 258 − 69         **j** 432 − 166

3   The table shows the average times of sunset and sunrise for 6 months of the year.

|           | Sunrise | Sunset |
|-----------|---------|--------|
| January   | 07:53   | 16:20  |
| March     | 06:06   | 18:17  |
| May       | 05:00   | 20:45  |
| July      | 04:58   | 21:04  |
| September | 06:35   | 19:00  |
| November  | 07:23   | 15:58  |

What time does the sun
**a** rise in July          **b** set in May?

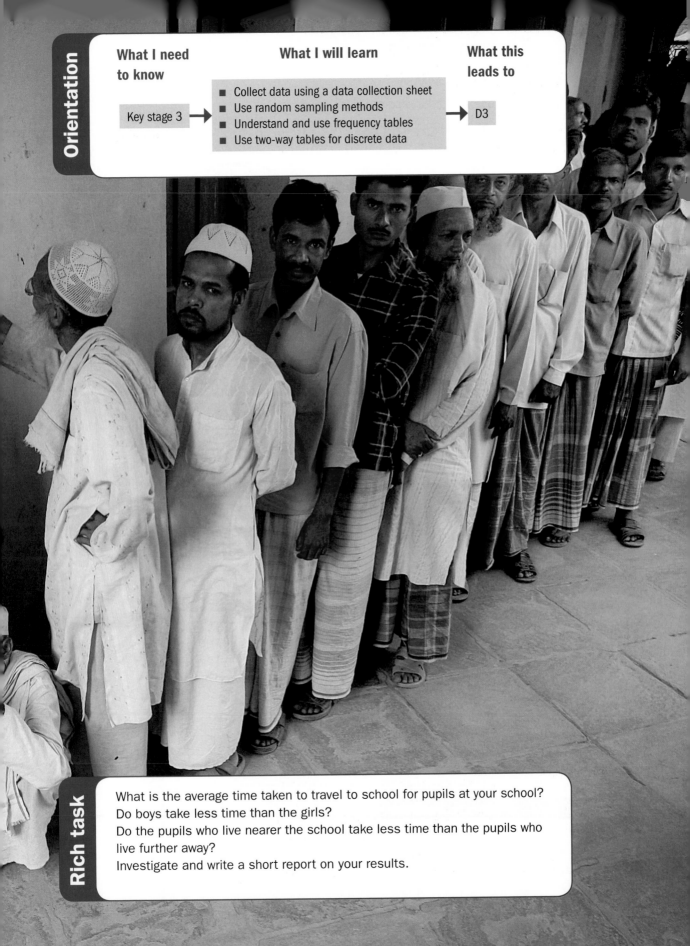

| What I need to know | What I will learn | What this leads to |
|---|---|---|
| Key stage 3 → | ■ Collect data using a data collection sheet<br>■ Use random sampling methods<br>■ Understand and use frequency tables<br>■ Use two-way tables for discrete data | → D3 |

**Rich task**

What is the average time taken to travel to school for pupils at your school?
Do boys take less time than the girls?
Do the pupils who live nearer the school take less time than the pupils who live further away?
Investigate and write a short report on your results.

# Data collection sheets

This spread will show you how to:

- Use data collection sheets for discrete data
- Understand and use frequency tables to show data

**Keywords**

Data
Data collection sheet
Frequency table
Tally chart

Before this headline could be written, information called **data** was collected.

52% of all homes have internet access.

- You can collect data using a **data collection sheet** (This one is a **tally chart**).

| Colour | Tally | Frequency |
|--------|-------|-----------|
| Red | 卌 卌 III | 13 |
| Blue | 卌 II | 7 |
| White | 卌 卌 I | 11 |

卌 = 5

- The data can also be shown using a **frequency table**.

| Colour | Frequency |
|--------|-----------|
| Red | 13 |
| Blue | 7 |
| White | 11 |

← 7 people chose Blue

**Example**

The students in a Year 10 class were asked to name their favourite season. Use the data-collection sheet to tally the data. Calculate the frequencies.

| Season | Tally | Frequency |
|--------|-------|-----------|
| Spring | | |
| Summer | | |
| Autumn | | |
| Winter | | |

| Winter | Summer | Spring | Spring | Winter | Autumn | Summer |
|--------|--------|--------|--------|--------|--------|--------|
| Spring | Autumn | Summer | Winter | Winter | Summer | Summer |
| Spring | Summer | Summer | Summer | Spring | Spring | |

| Season | Tally | Frequency |
|--------|-------|-----------|
| Spring | 卌 I | 6 |
| Summer | 卌 III | 8 |
| Autumn | II | 2 |
| Winter | IIII | 4 |

A02　Functional Maths

**1** Tickets to see an Irish band cost £5, £10, £15 or £20.
These price tickets are sold one morning:

| These values are all in pounds (£). |

| 15 | 10 | 10 | 5 | 5 | 5 | 5 | 5 | 10 | 20 |
| 20 | 5 | 5 | 5 | 5 | 10 | 5 | 10 | 5 | 15 |
| 15 | 20 | 20 | 5 | 5 | 10 | 10 | 10 | 10 | 5 |
| 5 | 5 | 10 | 5 | 10 | 15 | 20 | 20 | 20 | 20 |

**a** Copy and complete the tally chart.
**b** How many £5 tickets were sold?
**c** How many tickets were sold altogether?

| Price | Tally | Number of tickets |
|---|---|---|
| £5 | | |
| £10 | | |
| £15 | | |
| £20 | | |

**2** The vowels in a paragraph on the front page of a newspaper are

| a | e | i | a | e | o | u | e | i | a |
| e | o | a | i | e | u | e | o | i | o |
| u | o | u | i | e | e | o | i | a | e |
| a | o | e | i | o | e | e | i | o | u |
| a | a | e | e | o | i | u | e | o | e |

**a** Copy and complete the data collection sheet to show the vowels in the paragraph.
**b** Which vowel occurred the most?

| Vowel | Tally | Frequency |
|---|---|---|
| a | | |
| e | | |
| i | | |
| o | | |
| u | | |

**3** A tetrahedron dice is numbered 1, 2, 3, 4.
　**a** Copy and complete the data collection sheet to show these scores.

| 4 | 2 | 1 | 3 | 1 | 3 | 4 | 2 |
| 3 | 3 | 2 | 2 | 2 | 3 | 4 | 4 |
| 2 | 4 | 1 | 1 | 2 | 4 | 1 | 2 |
| 1 | 2 | 1 | 3 | 2 | 1 | 4 | 3 |
| 2 | 3 | 1 | 4 | 4 | 2 | 3 | 1 |

| Score | Tally | Frequency |
|---|---|---|
| 1 | | |
| 2 | | |
| 3 | | |
| 4 | | |

**b** State the number of times a 3 was rolled.

A02　Functional Maths

**4** A class of students are asked to give the month of their birthday.

| Mar | May | Apr | Jun | Sep | Mar | Jun | Feb |
| Sep | Dec | Nov | Nov | Apr | Mar | Jul | Aug |
| Aug | Mar | Apr | Feb | Jan | Sep | Jun | Jun |
| Sep | Nov | Oct | Jan | Jun | Dec | Oct | Feb |

　**a** Draw and complete a tally chart to show this information.
　**b** Calculate the number of students in the class.
　**c** In which month were most students born?

This spread will show you how to:

- Collect data using various methods including observation and controlled experiment
- Calculate total frequency from a discrete frequency table
- Use random sampling methods, taking steps to minimise bias

**Keywords**

Biased
Controlled
 experiment
Data collection
 sheet
Observation
Random sample

- You can collect data by **observation**.
 For example, to find how many people use the dodgem ride at the fair, you would have to watch and count the people on the ride.
- You can collect data by a **controlled experiment**.

This topic is extended to random sampling of databases on page 446.

**Example**

Simon throws a dice 50 times. He thinks 'lucky' 6 will happen more often than the other numbers. The results are shown.

| 3 | 1 | 4 | 3 | 5 | 2 | 6 | 2 | 1 | 3 |
| 4 | 2 | 2 | 6 | 3 | 1 | 1 | 2 | 3 | 4 |
| 5 | 6 | 1 | 2 | 1 | 4 | 3 | 5 | 6 | 2 |
| 1 | 4 | 6 | 3 | 2 | 2 | 1 | 5 | 5 | 6 |
| 2 | 4 | 3 | 2 | 5 | 6 | 4 | 4 | 6 | 3 |

Complete the **data collection sheet** to show the dice scores for this controlled experiment.

| Score | Tally | Freq. |
|-------|-------|-------|
| 1 | | |
| 2 | | |
| 3 | | |
| 4 | | |
| 5 | | |
| 6 | | |

| Score | Tally | Freq. |
|-------|-------|-------|
| 1 | IIII III | 8 |
| 2 | IIII IIII I | 11 |
| 3 | IIII IIII | 9 |
| 4 | IIII III | 8 |
| 5 | IIII I | 6 |
| 6 | IIII III | 8 |
| | | 50 |

Check the frequencies add to 50.

Sometimes it is impossible to collect data from all the population and so a **random sample** is used.

Instead of asking every student in your school, you could choose a random sample of 50 students. The students are chosen so that the sample is not **biased**.

- The larger the sample, the more accurate the data will be.

1 Decide whether each of these data collections is an observation or a controlled experiment.
   **a** Rolling a dice
   **b** Spinning a coin
   **c** Whether people walk under a ladder
   **d** The colour of vehicles
   **e** Spinning a spinner
   **f** The number of birds in a garden
   **g** The punctuality of trains
   **h** The choices of a school meal
   **i** Choosing chocolates out of a selection box
   **j** The ages of teachers at a school

**A02 Functional Maths**

2 The number of passengers in passing cars are counted.
   The results are shown.

   | 1 | 0 | 2 | 0 | 1 | 0 | 1 | 3 | 1 | 0 | 3 | 2 |
   | 0 | 1 | 0 | 0 | 2 | 1 | 0 | 0 | 0 | 1 | 2 | |

   **a** Is this data collection an observation or a controlled experiment?
   **b** Copy and complete the data collection sheet to show this information.
   **c** Calculate the total number of cars that passed.

   | Number of passengers | Tally | Number of cars |
   |---|---|---|
   | 0 | | |
   | 1 | | |
   | 2 | | |
   | 3 | | |

3 A spinner, labelled A to E, is spun and the letter is recorded.
   The results are shown.

   | C | B | E | D | E | A | B | D | A | E |
   | B | C | D | A | E | B | C | B | A | E |
   | A | E | D | E | B | C | B | A | D | E |
   | E | C | B | D | A | B | A | C | D | C |

   **a** Is this data collection an observation or a controlled experiment?
   **b** Copy and complete the frequency table to show the results.
   **c** How many times was the spinner spun altogether?
   **d** Do you think the spinner is biased? Explain your answer.
   **e** How could you improve the reliability of your answer?

   | Letter | Tally | Frequency |
   |---|---|---|
   | A | | |
   | B | | |
   | C | | |
   | D | | |
   | E | | |

**Surveys**

This spread will show you how to:

- Collect data using various methods including questionnaires and surveys

**Surveys** are used to find people's views and opinions.

> 2 out of 3
> boys like
> chocolate
> but only

- You can collect data with a survey using
  - a data collection sheet
  - a questionnaire.

You can collect all the data on one **data collection sheet**.

| Age group under 16/16 + | M/F | Like chocolate? |
|---|---|---|
| 16+ | F | no |
| under 16 | F | yes |
| 16+ | M | yes |
| | | |
| | | |

You will need one **questionnaire** for each person in your survey.

**Chocolate questionnaire**

Age group

Under 16 ☐     16 or more ☐

Gender                    Do you like chocolate?

M ☐   F ☐            Y ☐   N ☐

Any other comments?

- You must be careful what questions you ask in a survey.
  - Never ask a personal question.    For example, did you brush your teeth yesterday? What is your age?
  - Never ask a leading question.     For example, what do you think of this beautiful wood being chopped down to build a noisy road?
  - Never ask a vague question.       For example, how often do you eat meat?
  - Never ask a question that will    For example, what did you eat yesterday?
    give too many answers.

**Example**

One question in a questionnaire is

**How often do you do homework?**

Sometimes ☐    Occasionally ☐    Regularly ☐

Explain why the suggested answers are not satisfactory.

1 Always/never are not given.
2 Sometimes/occasionally mean the same.
3 Regularly could mean every day, every week or every month.

**1** James uses a data collection sheet for a survey to find his class's favourite soup.
He limits the choice to Tomato (T), Vegetable (V), Fish (F) or Other (O).
His completed sheet is

| | | | | | | | | | |
|---|---|---|---|---|---|---|---|---|---|
| T | T | T | V | F | V | V | T | T | V |
| F | O | T | V | O | O | T | V | T | F |
| O | T | V | O | T | V | O | O | O | O |

**a** Copy and complete the tally chart to show the data.

**b** Calculate the number of students in James's class.

**c** State the most favourite soup.

| Type of soup | Tally | Number of students |
|---|---|---|
| Tomato (T) | | |
| Vegetable (V) | | |
| Fish (F) | | |
| Other (O) | | |

**2** Andrew uses a questionnaire for a survey about eating habits.
His questionnaire is shown.
He stops people in the street and asks them to answer the questions.

Name:

Age:

What is your favourite meal?

The first response from an elderly lady is shown.
Write three criticisms of Andrew's questionnaire.

Name:　Anonymous

Age:　Older than you!

What is your favourite meal?

Prawn cocktail, soup, meat and two veg, dumplings, gravy, chocolate gateau with ice cream, cheese and
PTO

**3** These questions appeared on a questionnaire.
Write one criticism of each question.
**a** What is your favourite sweet?
**b** How often do you use a computer?
**c** How much pocket money/allowance are you given?
**d** Did you have a shower this morning?
**e** These buses are always late. What do you think of the bus service?
**f** How much do you spend on clothes?
**g** How tall are you?
**h** Do you like shopping?
**i** Where do you live?
**j** How many DVDs do you own?　　loads　　a lot　　many

This spread will show you how to:

- Understand the difference between primary and secondary data
- Understand and use frequency tables to show data
- Identify which primary data you need to collect and in what format, including grouped data, considering equal class intervals

- **Primary data** is data you collect yourself, for example, you count the number of heads when spinning a coin.
- **Secondary data** is data someone else has already collected, for example, National Census, information from newspapers or the internet.

Some surveys produce data with too many different values. For example, 36, 44, 18, 27, 23, 6, 73, 25, 19, 31, 80, 46, 51, 55, 65 could be the exam marks for 15 students.

A data collection sheet or a frequency table would have too many categories.

- You can **group** the data into **class intervals** to avoid this.

**Example**

The number of cars in a car park was recorded every day for one month. The results are shown.

| 8 | 34 | 10 | 15 | 24 | 49 | 0 | 13 | 25 | 19 |
|---|----|----|----|----|----|---|----|----|----|
| 23 | 31 | 45 | 0 | 15 | 3 | 21 | 22 | 27 | 47 |
| 0 | 9 | 24 | 36 | 17 | 19 | 45 | 0 | 18 | 5 |

Complete the grouped frequency table.

| Number of cars | Tally | Freq. |
|----------------|-------|-------|
| 0 to 9 | | |
| 10 to 19 | | |
| 20 to 29 | | |
| 30 to 39 | | |
| 40 to 49 | | |

class intervals

| Number of cars | Tally | Freq. |
|----------------|-------|-------|
| 0 to 9 | ⵏ⊞ III | 8 |
| 10 to 19 | ⵏ⊞ III | 8 |
| 20 to 29 | ⵏ⊞ II | 7 |
| 30 to 39 | III | 3 |
| 40 to 49 | IIII | 4 |
| | | 30 |

⟵ Check that the frequencies add to 30.

卌 = 5

**1** Decide whether these data collection methods give primary data or secondary data.
　**a** The times of the goals in football matches from a newspaper
　**b** Measuring heights of students in your class
　**c** The rainfall each month in Paris from the internet
　**d** The number of Heads when spinning a coin
　**e** The results of an experiment you do in a science lesson
　**f** The number of telephone calls your class made yesterday evening
　**g** The number of people who went to the theatre in 2005 from information on the internet
　**h** The population of Switzerland from a book
　**i** The reaction times of students in your class by an experiment
　**j** The times of low and high tides from a leaflet.

**2 a** Copy and complete the frequency table using these weights of people, in kilograms.

| 67 | 40 | 56 | 65 | 57 | 42 | 45 |
|----|----|----|----|----|----|----|
| 56 | 66 | 69 | 42 | 51 | 58 | 63 |
| 65 | 69 | 61 | 44 | 67 | 55 | 43 |
| 58 | 63 | 68 | 54 | 57 | 49 | 48 |
| 47 | 42 |    |    |    |    |    |

| Weight (kg) | Tally | Number of people |
|-------------|-------|------------------|
| 40 to 44 | | |
| 45 to 49 | | |
| 50 to 54 | | |
| 55 to 59 | | |
| 60 to 64 | | |
| 65 to 69 | | |

　**b** Calculate the number of people shown in the frequency table.

**3 a** Copy and complete the frequency table using these exam marks.

| 45 | 36 | 34 | 56 | 71 | 38 | 55 |
|----|----|----|----|----|----|----|
| 63 | 72 | 80 | 14 | 25 | 44 | 37 |
| 51 | 58 | 35 | 47 | 22 | 10 | 33 |
| 37 | 54 | 61 | 77 | 24 | 27 | 29 |
| 31 | 35 | 27 | 28 | 32 | 36 | 52 |
| 58 | 59 | 60 | 50 | 35 | 29 | 18 |
| 66 | 55 | 32 | 35 | 21 | 53 | 67 |
| 79 |    |    |    |    |    |    |

| Exam mark | Tally | Frequency |
|-----------|-------|-----------|
| 1 to 10 | | |
| 11 to 20 | | |
| 21 to 30 | | |
| 31 to 40 | | |
| 41 to 50 | | |
| 51 to 60 | | |
| 61 to 70 | | |
| 71 to 80 | | |

　**b** Calculate the number of people who took the exam.

**4** The heights, in centimetres, of students are shown.

| 148 | 143 | 148 | 152 | 155 | 160 | 171 | 144 |
|-----|-----|-----|-----|-----|-----|-----|-----|
| 132 | 133 | 161 | 172 | 133 | 149 | 150 | 164 |
| 168 | 170 | 153 | 150 | 138 | 139 | 144 | 151 |
| 163 | 165 | 180 | 180 | 155 | 160 | 165 | 155 |
| 145 | 133 | 138 | 161 | 168 | 136 | 147 | 145 |

　**a** Draw and complete a frequency table, using suitable class intervals.
　**b** Calculate the total number of students in the frequency table.

# Two-way tables and surveys

This spread will show you how to:

- Use two-way tables for discrete and grouped data
- Collect data using various methods

**Keywords**
Column
Frequency table
Row
Total
Two-way table

You can summarise data in a **frequency table**.
This table shows the preferred takeway food of a sample of people.

| Food | Number of people |
|------|------------------|
| Pizza | 8 |
| Burger | 7 |
| Curry | 5 |

7 people prefer a burger.

You can show more detail in a **two-way table**.

A two-way table links two types of information, for example, food and gender.

| | Men | Women |
|------|-----|-------|
| Pizza | 3 | 5 |
| Burger | 4 | 3 |
| Curry | 5 | 2 |

3 women prefer a burger.

You can extend the two-way table by adding
– an extra **row** to give the total of men, women and people
– an extra **column** to give the total of each food.
The extra row and column headings are **totals**.

| | Men | Women | Totals |
|------|-----|-------|--------|
| Pizza | 3 | 5 | 8 |
| Burger | 4 | 3 | 7 |
| Curry | 3 | 2 | 5 |
| Totals | 10 | 10 | 20 |

3 + 5 = 8
10 + 10 = 20
3 + 4 + 3 = 10

**Example**

Some children are asked, 'Do you ever eat fruit?'
The results of a survey are shown in the two-way table.
**a** How many girls never eat fruit?
**b** How many boys eat fruit?
**c** How many children answered the survey?

**Do you ever eat fruit?**

| | Yes | No |
|-------|-----|----|
| Boys | 6 | 8 |
| Girls | 9 | 7 |

**a** 7 girls
**b** 6 boys
**c** 6 + 8 + 9 + 7 = 30 children

**A02 Functional Maths**

**1** The results of an eye colour survey are shown.
Use the two-way table to find the number of
 **a** blue-eyed boys
 **b** brown-eyed girls
 **c** boys
 **d** girls
 **e** blue-eyed children
 **f** brown-eyed children.

| | Eye colour | | |
|---|---|---|---|
| | **Blue** | **Brown** | **Other** |
| **Boys** | 35 | 24 | 14 |
| **Girls** | 47 | 36 | 4 |

**2** At a local school, students have the opportunity
to study French and Spanish.
The table shows the choice for all Year 10 students.
Find the number of students that study
 **a** French and Spanish
 **b** French but not Spanish
 **c** neither French nor Spanish
 **d** Spanish
 **e** French.

| | **Spanish** | **Not Spanish** |
|---|---|---|
| **French** | 16 | 55 |
| **Not French** | 51 | 14 |

**3** There are two cinemas in a Cinecomplex.
The number of people in each cinema is shown
in the two-way table.
Calculate the number of
 **a** adults in the Cinecomplex
 **b** children in the Cinecomplex
 **c** people in Cinema 1
 **d** people in Cinema 2
 **e** people in the whole Cinecomplex.

| | Cinema | |
|---|---|---|
| | **1** | **2** |
| **Adult** | 31 | 47 |
| **Child** | 12 | 8 |

**4** In a traffic survey, the colour and speed of 100 cars are recorded.
The results are summarised in the two-way table.
 **a** State the number of cars that are
  **i** red and over the speed limit
  **ii** not speeding and not red.
 **b** Calculate the number of cars that are
  **i** red    **ii** over the speed limit.
 **c** Calculate, as a simplified fraction, the number of cars that are
  **i** not speeding    **ii** not red.
 **d** Maria claims that drivers of red cars tend to break speed limits.
  Use the two-way table to decide whether you agree with Maria.

| | **Not speeding** | **Over the speed limit** |
|---|---|---|
| **Red** | 5 | 55 |
| **Not red** | 10 | 30 |

## Summary

### Check out
You should now be able to:

- Use data collection sheets for discrete and grouped data
- Understand and use frequency tables
- Collect data using a variety of methods
- Collect data from a variety of sources
- Identify possible sources of bias
- Use two-way tables for discrete data

### Worked exam question
Heather carried out a survey about her friends' pets.
Here are her results.

| | | | | |
|---|---|---|---|---|
| Cat | Cat | Dog | Hamster | Cat |
| Dog | Hamster | Cat | Cat | Dog |
| Hamster | Dog | Hamster | Dog | Fish |
| Cat | Dog | Fish | Cat | Cat |

Complete the table to show Heather's results.

| Pet | Tally | Frequency |
|---|---|---|
| Cat | | |
| Dog | | |
| Fish | | |
| Hamster | | |

(3)

(Edexcel Limited 2007)

| | | | | |
|---|---|---|---|---|
| ~~Cat~~ | ~~Cat~~ | ~~Dog~~ | ~~Hamster~~ | Cat |
| Dog | Hamster | Cat | Cat | Dog |
| Hamster | Dog | Hamster | Dog | Fish |
| Cat | Dog | Fish | Cat | Cat |

Cross out each pet in turn to create the tally.

| Pet | Tally | Frequency |
|---|---|---|
| Cat | ЖН ||| | 8 |
| Dog | ЖН | | 6 |
| Fish | || | 2 |
| Hamster | |||| | 4 |

There are 8 cats.

Use ЖН to represent 5

Check:
8 + 6 + 2 + 4 = 20
There are 20 pets.

# Exam questions

**1** The two-way table shows some information about students in Years 7, 8 and 9.

| | Year 7 | Year 8 | Year 9 | Total |
|---|---|---|---|---|
| **Can swim** | | 61 | 74 | |
| **Cannot swim** | 33 | | | 60 |
| **Total** | | | 84 | 250 |

Copy and complete the two-way table. (3)

(Edexcel Limited 2007)

**2** A student wanted to find out how many pizzas adults ate. He used this question on a questionnaire.

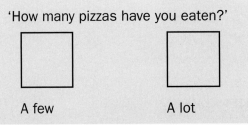

'How many pizzas have you eaten?'

☐ A few    ☐ A lot

**a** Write down two things that are wrong with this question. (2)

He gave his questionnaire to 10 of his teachers.

**b** Give two reasons why this is not a good way to find out how many pizzas adults ate. (2)

(Edexcel Limited 2006)

**3** The table gives information about the number of goals scored by a football team in each match during a season.

| Number of goals | Number of matches |
|---|---|
| 0 | 9 |
| 1 | 8 |
| 2 | 12 |
| 3 | 5 |

Work out the total number of goals scored by the football team during the season. (2)

(Edexcel Limited 2005)

# Functional Maths 1: Weather

Before creating a weather forecast, data is collected from all over the world to give information about the current conditions. A supercomputer and knowledge about the atmosphere, the Earth's surface and the oceans are then used to create the forecast.

Write down the temperature shown on each of these thermometers:

Each day, the Met Office receives and uses around half a million observations.

This chart shows the average mean temperature for January in the UK over the 30 year period from 1971 to 2000:

Write down an approximate value for the average temperature at
a) each of the cities labelled
b) your home town

Average value (°C)
- 7.5 – 10.5
- 7 – 7.5
- 6 – 7
- 5 – 6
- 4 – 5
- 2.5 – 4
- -2 – 2.5

EDINBURGH
NEWCASTLE
BELFAST
BIRMINGHAM
CARDIFF
LONDON

How do these average temperatures compare to the temperatures in the UK this January?

Which area(s) had the
c) highest
d) lowest average temperature?

What is the difference (approximate, in °C) between these temperatures?

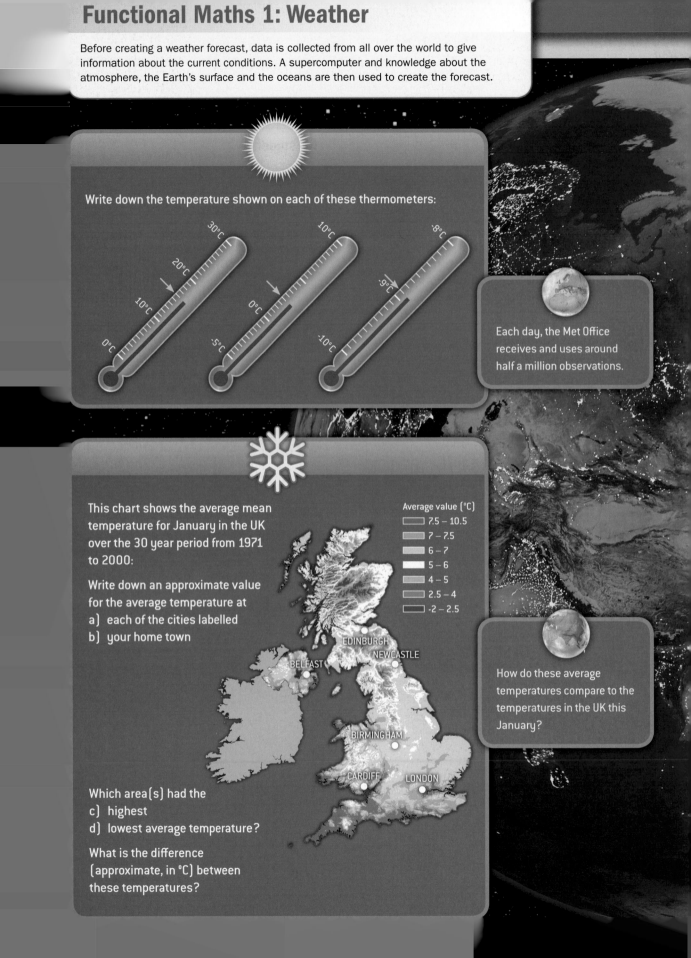

Wind direction is measured in tens of degrees relative to true North and is always given from where the wind is blowing. In the UK, wind speed is measured in knots, where 1knot = 1.15mph, or in terms of the Beaufort Scale.

Research the Beaufort Scale using the internet.

Easterly wind, 090°

Describe the wind speed (in knots) and direction (in tens of degrees and in words) shown by each of these arrows:

| 15 knots | 30 knots | 13.5 mph |
|---|---|---|

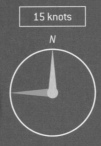  

Observed data can be used to make predictions, but there is always some level of uncertainty. This graph shows the range of uncertainty in temperature in Exeter with some indication of the most probable values:

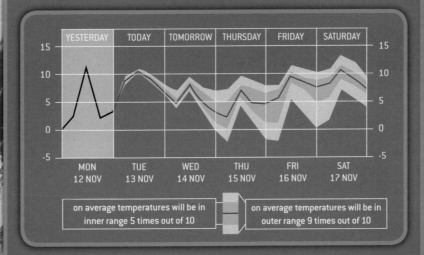

on average temperatures will be in inner range 5 times out of 10

on average temperatures will be in outer range 9 times out of 10

What predictions do you think a weather forecaster would have made about the temperature in Exeter during the week shown?

Justify your response by referring to the graph.

# Introduction

In many professions it is vital to perform mental checks on answers that have been calculated. These include doctors working out the dose of medicine to give a patient, pilots checking the fuel required for a flight, or civil engineers calculating the amount of material required to construct a building.

## What's the point?
If doctors, pilots and engineers don't check that their answers are sensible, things could go badly wrong and it will affect other people.

**Check in**

1   Round 2916 to the nearest
   **a**  1000          **b**  100          **c**  10

2   Calculate
   **a**  95 − 47          **b**  76 + 29
   **c**  576 + 239       **d**  914 − 685

3   Calculate
   **a**  5 × 6           **b**  48 ÷ 8
   **c**  12 × 6          **d**  282 ÷ 2
   **e**  12 × 14         **f**  91 ÷ 7

**Orientation**

| What I need to know | What I will learn | What this leads to |
|---|---|---|
| N1 → | ■ Use mental and written methods for addition and subtraction<br>■ Use mental and written methods for multiplication and division | → N7 |

**Rich task**

The numbers 3 and 6 are multiplied together and then the answer is doubled. This gives 36 (a 2-digit number made from the two original numbers).

Find two 2-digit numbers that when multiplied together and doubled give a 4-digit number.

This spread will show you how to:

- Use a range of mental methods for addition and subtraction of whole numbers

**Keywords**
Compensation
Mental methods
Partitioning

### Partitioning

Split the numbers into parts (hundreds, tens and units).
Then add or subtract the parts.

> Strategies to help you work out additions and subtractions in your head are called **mental methods**.

**Example**

Calculate   **a** $37 + 78$   **b** $95 - 43$

**a** $37 + 78 = 30 + 7 + 70 + 8$
$= 70 + 30 + 15$
$= 100 + 15$
$= 115$

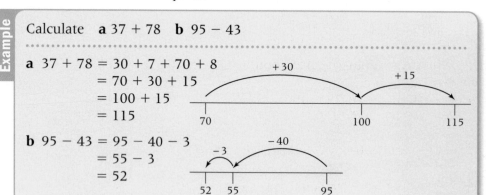

**b** $95 - 43 = 95 - 40 - 3$
$= 55 - 3$
$= 52$

p.340

### Compensation

When the number you are adding or subtracting is nearly a multiple of 10 or a multiple of 100, round the number up or down.

**Example**

Calculate   **a** $63 + 29$   **b** $174 - 39$

**a** $63 + 29 = 63 + 30 - 1$
$= 93 - 1$
$= 92$

**b** $174 - 39 = 174 - 40 + 1$
$= 134 + 1$
$= 135$

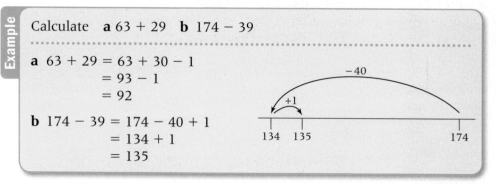

> Remember to add or subtract to finish your calculation.

You can also count up from the smallest number to the largest number.

> This is called shopkeeper's subtraction. Use a number line to help you.

**Example**

Gerta earns £408 a week. She spends £187 a week on her mortgage. How much money does she have left?

£408 − £187

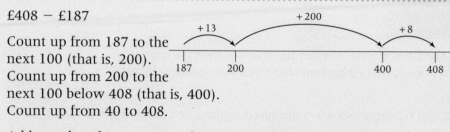

Count up from 187 to the next 100 (that is, 200).
Count up from 200 to the next 100 below 408 (that is, 400).
Count up from 40 to 408.

Add together the counts you have made (that is, $13 + 200 + 8$).

$£408 - £187 = 13 + 200 + 8 = £221$

1 Write the answers to each of these calculations.
   **a** 17 + 13    **b** 17 − 8    **c** 16 + 17
   **d** 18 − 9    **e** 19 + 19    **f** 27 − 14

2 Find the missing number in each of these calculations.
   **a** 63 + ? = 100    **b** ? + 43 = 100
   **c** 31 + ? = 100    **d** 53 + ? = 100

3 Use a mental method for each of these calculations.
   **a** 27 + 43    **b** 48 + 12    **c** 27 + 23
   **d** 26 + 52    **e** 34 + 23    **f** 61 + 28

4 Use a mental method for each of these calculations.
   Write the method you have used.
   **a** 25 + 36    **b** 46 + 31    **c** 72 − 19
   **d** 48 + 49    **e** 56 + 38    **f** 123 + 39

**A02 Functional Maths**

**5** Use a mental method of calculation to solve each of these
   problems.
   **a** Liam spends 43p on a can of cola and 39p on a packet of
   crisps. How much money has he spent?
   **b** Brad scores 29 points in a game of rugby. In the next game he
   scores 23 points. What is his total score of points for the two
   games?
   **c** Laura looks after 29 horses. Emma looks after 37 horses.
   How many horses do the girls look after altogether?
   **d** Thomas owns 56 CDs. He sells 39 of his CDs. How many CDs
   does he have left?

6 Use a mental method to calculate
   **a** 134 + 29    **b** 245 + 85    **c** 313 + 63
   **d** 278 + 75    **e** 378 + 208    **f** 512 − 369

**A03 Problem**

**7 a** Using each of the digits 1, 2, 3, 4 and 5 only once, what is the
   largest answer for an addition calculation that you can make?

   **b** Using each of the digits 1, 2, 3, 4 and 5 only once, what is the
   smallest answer for a subtraction calculation that you can make?

8 Use a mental method for each of these calculations.
   Write the method you have used.

   **a** Decrease 132 by 64.
   **b** How many less than 156 is 79?
   **c** 234 + □ = 507. What is the value of □?
   **d** 638 subtract 199.
   **e** What is the total of 259 and 325?

# Written addition and subtraction

This spread will show you how to:
- Use a range of written methods for addition and subtraction of whole numbers
- Estimate the answers to problems

**Keywords**
Addition
Subtraction
Written method

- There is a standard **written method** for addition.

  p.174

To calculate 3518 + 765:

Set out the calculation in columns:

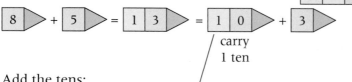

3 5 1 8
7 6 5

Add the units:

8 + 5 = 1 3 = 1 0 + 3

carry
1 ten

This is based on the **partitioning** mental method.

Add the tens:

1 0 + 6 0 + 1 0 = 8 0

Add the hundreds:

5 0 0 + 7 0 0 = 1 2 0 0

= 1 0 0 0 + 2 0 0

carry
1 thousand

You should always estimate the answer.
3518 + 765
≈ 3500 + 800
= 4300

Add the thousands:

3 0 0 0 + 1 0 0 0 = 4 0 0 0

So 3518 + 765 = 4000 + 200 + 80 + 3.

You could set out the calculation like this:

```
    3  5  1  8
 +     7  6  5
    4  2  8  3
    1     1
```

- There is a standard written method for subtraction that is based upon the partitioning mental method.

**Example**

Calculate 3518 − 765.

| | | | | | | | |
|---|---|---|---|---|---|---|---|
| ²3̶ ¹⁴5̶ ¹1 8 | | | Set out the calculation in columns | | | | |
| −   7 6 5 | | | | | | | |
| 2 7 5 3 | | | Subtract the units | | | | 8 − 5 = **3** |
| | | | | | | | |
| | | | Subtract the tens | | | | 10 − 60 is not possible! |
| | | | Move 1 hundred into the tens column | | | | 110 − 60 = **50** |
| | | | | | | | |
| | | | Subtract the hundreds | | | | 400 − 700 is not possible! |
| | | | Move 1 thousand into the hundreds column | | | 1400 − 700 = **700** | |
| | | | | | | | |
| | | | Subtract the thousands | | | | 2000 − 0 = **2000** |

1 Use a written method to work out these calculations.
   **a** 234 + 133   **b** 342 + 445   **c** 437 + 261   **d** 487 + 311

2 Use a written method to work out these calculations.
   **a** 356 − 234   **b** 769 − 436   **c** 786 − 472   **d** 167 − 35

3 Use a written method to work out these additions.
   **a** 432 + 549   **b** 537 + 249   **c** 345 + 273
   **d** 487 + 432   **e** 472 + 715   **f** 654 + 533

In questions 3–6, you may need to carry.

4 Use a written method for each of these additions.
   **a** 368 + 725   **b** 793 + 432   **c** 527 + 395
   **d** 438 + 287   **e** 383 + 769   **f** 783 + 978

5 Use a written method for each of these subtractions.
   **a** 562 − 417   **b** 837 − 618   **c** 748 − 563   **d** 865 − 472

6 Use a written method for each of these subtractions.
   **a** 584 − 378   **b** 738 − 568   **c** 483 − 277   **d** 407 − 321

7 Use a written method for each of these calculations.
   **a** 265 + 846   **b** 371 + 686   **c** 831 − 488
   **d** 1345 + 874   **e** 2576 − 784   **f** 4762 − 1875

A02 Functional Maths

8 A battery costs 83p.
   Saima has £5. She buys as many batteries as she can.
   Work out the amount of change Saima should get from £5.

9 Yvonne is planning a holiday. She has a maximum budget of £1800.
   There are three parts to her holiday: transport, accommodation and
   spending money. She can choose various options for each part of
   her holiday:

| Transport | | Accommodation | | Spending money |
|---|---|---|---|---|
| Flights | £378 | Villa | £637 | £800 |
| Train | £289 | Hotel | £892 | £700 |
| Car | £278 | Camping | £278 | £600 |

For example    car + villa + spending money
                £278 + £637 + £800 = £1715

Write three choices she could make which would
be within her budget of £1800.

This spread will show you how to:

- Use a range of mental methods for multiplication and division of whole numbers

**Keywords**

Divisibility
Factor
Mental method
Multiple
Partitioning

There are lots of strategies you can use to help you work out multiplications and divisions in your head.

### Partitioning

Split the numbers into parts (hundreds, tens and units).
Then multiply or divide each part separately.

**Example**

Calculate     **a** $16 \times 7$     **b** $342 \div 3$

**a**   $16 = 10 + 6$

$16 \times 7 = (10 \times 7) + (6 \times 7)$

$= 70 + 42$

$= 112$

**b**   $342 = 300 + 42$

$342 \div 3 = (300 \div 3) \div (42 \div 3)$

$= 100 + 14$

$= 114$

**Remember**
To multiply a number by 10, all the digits move one place to the left of the decimal point, for example, $10 \times 7 = 70$.

### Compensation

Use this method when the number you are multiplying by is nearly a **multiple** of 10 or a multiple of 100.

**Example**

Calculate $14 \times 9$.

$9 = 10 - 1$

$14 \times 9 = (14 \times 10) - (14 \times 1)$

$= 140 - 14$

$= 126$

Here are some other methods you can use.

**1**   $23 \times 20 = 23 \times 2 \times 10$

$23 \times 2 = 46$
$46 \times 10 = 460$

$23 \times 20 = 460$

Think of multiply by 20 as multiply by 2, followed by multiply by 10

**2**   $84 \div 6 = 84 \div 2 \div 3$

$84 \div 2 = 42$
$42 \div 3 = 14$

$84 \div 6 = 14$

$6 = 2 \times 3$ so $84 \div 6$ is the same as $84 \div (2 \times 3)$. This means you can divide by 2 and then by 3.

### Doubling and halving

Double one of the numbers and halve the other before you multiply.

$12 \times 15 = 6 \times 30$
$\phantom{12 \times 15} = 180$

### Doubling

Double both of the numbers before you divide.

$80 \div 5 = 160 \div 10$
$\phantom{80 \div 5} = 16$

**1** Calculate
    **a** $4 \times 7$      **b** $120 \div 10$      **c** $2 \times 34$      **d** $78 \div 2$
    **e** $5 \times 6$      **f** $340 \div 10$      **g** $93 \times 2$      **h** $5 \times 9$

**2** Use the mental method of partitioning to calculate these.
Show the method you have used.
    **a** $6 \times 11$      **b** $13 \times 6$      **c** $7 \times 13$      **d** $11 \times 9$
    **e** $16 \times 6$      **f** $12 \times 6$

**3** Use the mental method of partitioning to calculate these.
Show the method you have used.
    **a** $36 \div 3$      **b** $48 \div 4$      **c** $88 \div 8$      **d** $69 \div 3$
    **e** $65 \div 5$      **f** $48 \div 3$

**4** Use the mental method of compensation to calculate each of these.
Show the method you have used.
    **a** $7 \times 9$      **b** $12 \times 9$      **c** $13 \times 11$      **d** $11 \times 19$
    **e** $14 \times 11$      **f** $21 \times 6$

**5** Use the mental method of factors to calculate each of these.
Show the method you have used.
    **a** $13 \times 20$      **b** $48 \div 6$      **c** $23 \times 4$      **d** $7 \times 8$
    **e** $132 \div 6$      **f** $17 \times 4$

**6** Use the mental method of halving and doubling to calculate each
of these. Show the method you have used.
    **a** $4 \times 27$      **b** $3 \times 14$      **c** $33 \times 4$      **d** $14 \times 15$

**7** Use an appropriate mental method to calculate each of these.
    **a** $7 \times 12$      **b** $8 \times 9$      **c** $54 \div 6$      **d** $11 \times 16$
    **e** $12 \times 12$      **f** $124 \div 4$

**A02** **Functional Maths**

**8** Use an appropriate mental method to solve
each of these problems.
    **a** Harry buys 13 CDs at £9 each.
      How much does he spend?
    **b** Kelvin shares £76 between his four
      grandchildren.
      How much does each child receive?
    **c** Hope runs every 20 metres in six seconds.
      How long will it take her to run 400 metres?
    **d** Pens are packed into boxes of six.
      How many boxes will be needed for 78 pens?
    **e** Trent pays for nine bars of chocolate.
      Each bar of chocolate costs 26p.
      How much money does he spend?

**DID YOU KNOW?**

The world's first music CD went on sale in 1982. It was an album called The Visitors by the Swedish pop group Abba. Since then, more than 200 billion CDs have been sold worldwide.

This spread will show you how to:

- Use a range of written methods for multiplication and division of whole numbers
- Estimate the answers to problems

**Keywords**
Dividend
Divisor
Estimate
Grid method
Standard
  method
Whole number

You can use the **grid method** to multiply whole numbers.

**Example**

Calculate $312 \times 42$

$42 \times 312 \approx 40 \times 300$
$\qquad = 12\,000$

| × | 300 | 10 | 2 |
|---|---|---|---|
| **40** | $40 \times 300 = 12\,000$ | $40 \times 10 = 400$ | $40 \times 2 = 80$ |
| **2** | $2 \times 300 = 600$ | $2 \times 10 = 20$ | $2 \times 2 = 4$ |

You should always **estimate** the answer first.

The calculation is split into four simpler calculations.

You can use written methods for multiplication and division to solve problems.

 p.176

**Example**

Ali buys 16 chocolate bars. Each bar costs 14 p.
How much does he spend?

Estimate:   $16 \times 14 \approx 20 \times 10 = 200$ pence

$$\begin{array}{r} 16 \\ \times\ 14 \\ \hline 160 \\ +64 \\ \hline 224 \end{array}$$

$16 \times 10$
$16 \times 4$

Ali spends $16 \times 14$ pence = 224 pence
$\qquad\qquad\qquad\qquad = £2.24.$

This is the **standard method** for multiplication.

**Example**

Karen shares £85 between her five children. How much will each child get?

Estimate:   $85 \div 5 \approx 100 \div 5 = £20$

$$\begin{array}{r} 5)\overline{85} \\ -50 \\ \hline 35 \\ -25 \\ \hline 10 \\ -10 \\ \hline 0 \end{array}$$

$5 \times 10$

$5 \times 5$

$5 \times \dfrac{2}{17}$

$85 \div 5 = 17$                 So each child receives £17.

This is the informal 'chunking' method for division.

You subtract 5 (the **divisor**) a total of 17 times from 85 (the **dividend**).

**1** Copy and complete these multiplications. Use the same method with parts **c** and **d**.

**a** $14 \times 8$

| × | 8 |
|---|---|
| 10 | $10 \times 8 = 80$ |
| 4 | $4 \times 8 =$ |

$14 \times 8 = 80 + \underline{\quad}$
$= $

**b** $12 \times 9$

| × | 9 |
|---|---|
| 10 | = |
| 2 | = |

$12 \times 9 = \underline{\quad} + \underline{\quad}$
$= $

**c** $14 \times 9$     **d** $17 \times 8$

**2** Copy and complete these multiplications using the grid method. Remember to do a mental approximation first.

**a** $12 \times 13$

| × | 10 | 3 |
|---|---|---|
| 10 | $10 \times 10 = 100$ | $10 \times 3 = 30$ |
| 2 | $2 \times 10 =$ | $2 \times 3 =$ |

$12 \times 13 = 100 + 30 + \underline{\quad} + \underline{\quad}$
$= $

**b** $15 \times 16$

| × | 10 | 6 |
|---|---|---|
| 10 | $10 \times 10 =$ | $10 \times 6 =$ |
| 5 | = | = |

$15 \times 16 = \underline{\quad} + \underline{\quad} + \underline{\quad} + \underline{\quad}$
$= $

**c** $15 \times 18$

| × | 10 | 8 |
|---|---|---|
| 10 | = | = |
| 5 | = | = |

$15 \times 18 = \underline{\quad} + \underline{\quad} + \underline{\quad} + \underline{\quad}$
$= $

**3** Use an appropriate method of calculation to work out each of these multiplications.

  **a** $13 \times 124$    **b** $17 \times 183$    **c** $13 \times 167$    **d** $23 \times 143$    **e** $62 \times 158$
  **f** $83 \times 176$    **g** $36 \times 254$    **h** $53 \times 271$    **i** $83 \times 512$

**4** Use an appropriate method of calculation to work out each of these divisions.

  **a** $138 \div 6$    **b** $176 \div 8$    **c** $140 \div 5$    **d** $217 \div 7$
  **e** $297 \div 9$    **f** $448 \div 8$    **g** $112 \div 8$    **h** $126 \div 7$

**5** Use an appropriate method to solve each of these problems.

  **a** Ian uses 19 text messages. Each message costs 7p.
    What is the total cost of the text messages?

  **b** Samira buys 17 fruit bushes at a cost of £7 per bush.
    What is the total cost of the 17 fruit bushes?

  **c** Mika has 14 packets of sweets. Each packet contains 14 sweets.
    How many sweets does he have altogether?

  **d** Albert buys 13 chocolate bars. Each bar costs 16 pence.
    How much does he spend?

This spread will show you how to:

● Know and use the order of operations, including brackets

Eve and Sarah are working out this calculation.

$2 + 3 \times 4$

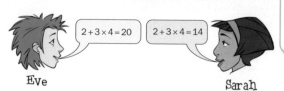

Eve    $2 + 3 \times 4 = 20$    $2 + 3 \times 4 = 14$    Sarah

To find out who is correct, use the **order of operations**.

**Brackets**
First work out the contents of any brackets.

**Powers or indices**
Then work out any powers or roots.

**Multiplication and division**
Then work out any multiplications and divisions.

**Addition and subtraction**
Finally work out any additions and subtractions.

$2 + 3 \times 4$

$= 2 + 12$
$= 14$

Sarah is correct because she has followed the order of operations.

**Example**

Put brackets into this expression to make the answer correct.

$2 \times 3 + 4 - 5 = 9$

By inserting a pair of brackets

$2 \times (3 + 4) - 5 = 2 \times 7 - 5$     (work out the multiplication)
$= 14 - 5$     (work out the subtraction)
$= 9$     ✓ the correct answer

For lots of additions and subtractions (or multiplications and divisions), work them out from left to right.

Calculations involving brackets need to be interpreted carefully.

**Example**

Calculate each of these amounts.

**a** $\dfrac{160}{5 + 11}$

**b** $21 + 2(8 + 7)$

**a** $\dfrac{160}{5 + 11} = \dfrac{160}{(5 + 11)}$
$= 160 \div (5 + 11)$
$= 160 \div 16$
$= 10$

**b** $21 + 2(8 + 7) = 21 + 2 \times 5$
$= 21 + 30$
$= 51$

Rewrite division calculations using brackets, like part **a**.

**A03 Problem**

**1** Match each of these calculations with one that gives the same answer.

| | | | |
|---|---|---|---|
| **A** | $7 + 3$ | **1** | $7 - 4$ |
| **B** | $2 + 3 \times 4$ | **2** | $33 - 9$ |
| **C** | $18 \div 6$ | **3** | $6 \times 3 - 4$ |
| **D** | $6 \times 4$ | **4** | $15 - 5$ |

**2** Calculate these using the order of operations.

**a** $2 + 6 \times 3$    **b** $2 \times 12 - 7$    **c** $8 + 20 \div 4$    **d** $2 \times 3 + 4 \times 2$

**e** $14 \div 2 + 3$   **f** $2 + 7 \times 5$    **g** $2 + 3 \times 3 - 4$    **h** $4 \times 3 + 2 \times 6$

**3** Calculate these using the order of operations.

**a** $(2 + 6) \times 3$           **b** $2 \times (12 - 7)$

**c** $(8 + 20) \div 4$         **d** $2 \times (3 + 4) \times 2$

**e** $15 \div (2 + 3)$         **f** $(2 + 7) \times 5$

**g** $(2 + 3) \times 3 - 4$     **h** $4 \times (3 + 2) \times 6$

**4** Calculate these using the order of operations.

**a** $2 + 3^2 \times 4$         **b** $2^2 \times 3 - 7$

**c** $4^2 + 20 \div 4$       **d** $2 \times 3^2 + 4 \times 2$

**e** $16 \div 2^2 + 3$       **f** $2 + 7 \times 5^2$

**5** Calculate these using the order of operations.

**a** $(2 + 6) \times 3^2$       **b** $2^2 \times (12 - 7)$

**c** $(8^2 - 20) \div 4$     **d** $2 \times (3^2 + 4)$

**e** $33 \div (2 + 3^2)$     **f** $(2^2 + 7) \times 5$

**6** Copy these calculations. Insert brackets where necessary to make each of them correct.

**a** $3 \times 2 + 1 = 9$         **b** $5 \times 3 - 1 = 10$

**c** $3 + 5 \div 2 = 4$         **d** $2 + 3^2 \times 4 = 44$

**e** $4^2 \div 5 + 3 = 2$      **f** $4 \times 5 + 5 \times 6 = 240$

**7** Calculate each of these amounts.

**a** $\dfrac{3 + 7}{5}$      **b** $\dfrac{14 - 8}{2 + 1}$      **c** $\dfrac{5 \times 4}{2 \times 5}$

**d** $\dfrac{2 \times 3 + 4}{5}$      **e** $\dfrac{24}{2 + 3 \times 5}$

**8** Calculate these amounts.

**a** $3(2 + 5)$    **b** $4(2 + 6)$     **c** $5 + 4(7 - 3)$    **d** $3^2 + 2(7 - 4)$

**A03 Problem**

**9** Use the numbers 3, 4, 5, 7 and 8 to make as many of the numbers as you can from 10 to 40.

You may use each digit only once in each calculation.

| Number | Calculation | | Number | Calculation |
|---|---|---|---|---|
| 10 | $= 3 + 7$ | | 26 | $=$ |
| 11 | $= 4 + 7$ | | 27 | $= (4 + 5) \times 3$ |
| 12 | $=$ | | 28 | $=$ |
| 13 | $= 8 - 7 + 3 \times 4$ | | 29 | $= 3 \times 7 + 8$ |

Use the correct order of operations for each calculation.

Copy and complete this table to show all your results.

## Check out

You should now be able to:

- Use mental and written methods for addition and subtraction of whole numbers
- Use mental and written methods for multiplication and division of whole numbers
- Know and use the order of operations, including brackets

## Worked exam question

**a** Work out $500 - 107$       (2)

**b** Work out $327 \times 4$       (2)

(Edexcel Limited 2007)

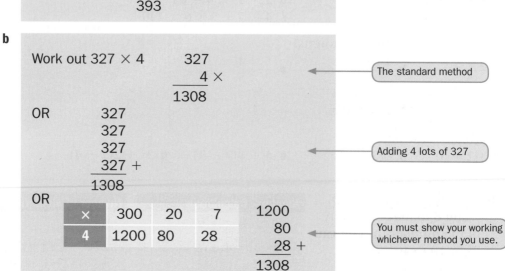

**a**

$$500 - 107$$

$$500 - 100 = 400$$
$$400 - 7 = 393$$ ← Subtracting 100 then 7

OR
$$\begin{array}{r} {}^{4}\cancel{5}{}^{9}\cancel{0}{}^{1}0 \\ 107 - \\ \hline 393 \end{array}$$ ← The standard method

OR
$$107 + \quad 3 = 110$$
$$110 + \quad 90 = 200$$
$$200 + \underline{300} = 500$$
$$\qquad\quad 393$$ ← The counting on method

**b**

Work out $327 \times 4$

$$\begin{array}{r} 327 \\ 4 \times \\ \hline 1308 \end{array}$$ ← The standard method

OR
$$\begin{array}{r} 327 \\ 327 \\ 327 \\ 327 + \\ \hline 1308 \end{array}$$ ← Adding 4 lots of 327

OR

| ×   | 300  | 20 | 7  |
|-----|------|----|----|
| 4   | 1200 | 80 | 28 |

$$\begin{array}{r} 1200 \\ 80 \\ 28 + \\ \hline 1308 \end{array}$$ ← You must show your working whichever method you use.

# Exam questions

**1** 33 people were on a bus.

19 people got off.
15 people got on.

How many people are now on the bus?  (2)

(Edexcel Limited 2006)

**2**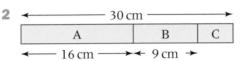

Diagram NOT accurately drawn

Here is a picture of a stick.
The stick is in three parts, A, B and C.

The total length of the stick is 30 cm.
The length of part A is 16 cm.
The length of part B is 9 cm.

Find the length of part C.  (2)

(Edexcel Limited 2009)

**3** Work out $46 \times 14$  (2)

**4** 600 football supporters are going to a match by bus.
Each bus can carry 35 students.
Work out the smallest number of buses needed to carry
all the supporters.  (2)

**5** Work out
**a** $3 \times 3 - 5$
**b** $20 \div (12 - 2)$
**c** $7 + 8 \div 4$  (3)

(Edexcel Limited 2008)

**A02**

**6**

## Waxworks

Adult ticket: £8.50
Child ticket: £4.50

Mr and Mrs Jones take their three children to the Waxworks.
Mrs Jones pays for 2 adult tickets and 3 child tickets.
She pays with a £50 note.

How much change should she receive from £50?  (3)

(Edexcel Limited 2007)

# Introduction

Over 30% of the numbers in everyday use begin with the digit 1.
'Benford's law', as it is called, makes it possible to detect when a list of numbers has been falsified. This is particularly useful in fraud investigations for detecting 'made-up' entries on claim forms and expense accounts, and it was also used in investigating the 2009 Iranian elections.

## What's the point?

Recognising patterns in numbers and measures helps us to understand them, and also helps us to make sense of a world that is increasingly swamped with data.

**1** Calculate each of these divisions.
   **a** 360 ÷ 2        **b** 360 ÷ 4        **c** 360 ÷ 10        **d** 360 ÷ 5
   **e** 360 ÷ 6        **f** 360 ÷ 12        **g** 360 ÷ 180        **h** 360 ÷ 90

**2** Put these numbers in order of size, smallest first.
   **a** 31, 43, 25, 29, 36, 41, 49, 30
   **b** 243, 342, 324, 234, 432, 423
   **c** 21.3, 23.1, 31.2, 13.2, 12.3, 32.1

**3** Find the value of the angle $x$.

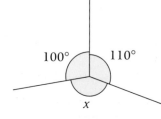

**Orientation**

| What I need to know | What I will learn | What this leads to |
|---|---|---|
| D2 → | ■ Use pictograms, bar charts and pie charts to display data in categories<br>■ Use stem-and-leaf diagrams to display numerical data<br>■ Draw line graphs for numerical data | → D4 |

**Rich task**

Here are some statements about young people:

'They eat too many sweets'

'They've all got mobile phones and iPods'

'They stay up too late'

'They don't do any homework'

Investigate if these statements are true.

This spread will show you how to:
● Draw and produce pictograms for data in **categories**

**Keywords**
Category
Pictogram
Represents

● You can use a **pictogram** to display data.

Pictograms use symbols to give an eye-catching picture of the size of each category.

A pictogram shows
– how each **category** compares with the others
– all the data, but in categories.

You may have to use part of a symbol to **represent** some quantities.

**Number of bottles of milk sold**

| Monday | 🍼🍼 |
| Tuesday | 🍼🍼 |
| Wednesday | |
| Thursday | 🍼🍼 |
| Friday | 🍼🍼🍼🍼🍼 |

Key: 🍼 represents 2 bottles

🍼 represents 2 bottles

🍼 represents 1 bottle

Always give a key.

**Example**

The number of cars that a car salesman sells is given in the table.

| Week | Cars sold |
|------|-----------|
| 1 | 4 |
| 2 | 6 |
| 3 | 12 |
| 4 | 10 |

**a** Draw a pictogram to illustrate this information.
Use 🚗 to represent 4 cars.

**b** In which week did he sell most cars?

...........................................................................................

**a** So 🚗 represents 2 cars.

| Week 1 | 🚗 |
| Week 2 | 🚗🚗 |
| Week 3 | 🚗🚗🚗 |
| Week 4 | 🚗🚗🚗 |

Key: 🚗 represents 4 cars

**b** In week 3.

4 + 2 = 6

4 + 4 + 2 = 10

Don't forget the key.

**1** The number of people who eat different take-away food is shown in the pictogram.
Copy and complete the pictogram to show six people eating Chinese and five people eating Indian.

Key:

represents one person

| Italian | |
|---|---|
| English | |
| Chinese | |
| Indian | |

**2** The colours of flowers in a garden are shown in the pictogram.
Copy and complete the pictogram with this information.

Key:

represents 5 flowers

| Red | Yellow | Blue | White | Other |
|---|---|---|---|---|
| 5 | 20 | 10 | 15 | 25 |

| Red | |
|---|---|
| Yellow | |
| Blue | |
| White | |
| Other | |

**3** The pictogram shows where people use the internet the most.
Copy the pictogram and represent this information on your diagram:

Library 6    School 9    Work 17

Key:

represents 2 people

| Home | |
|---|---|
| Internet cafe | |
| Library | |
| School | |
| Work | |

**4** This data is from a newspaper survey.

Draw a pictogram using to represent 10 people.

| Daily paper A | 40 |
|---|---|
| Daily paper B | 50 |
| Daily paper C | 35 |
| Daily paper D | 25 |
| Other | 15 |

**5** The results of a survey about people's favourite hot drink are given in the table.

Letting represent 20 people, draw a pictogram for this data.

| Tea | 80 |
|---|---|
| Coffee | 60 |
| Hot chocolate | 50 |
| Soup | 30 |
| Other | 20 |

This spread will show you how to:
- Draw and produce bar charts for data in categories
- Draw bar-line charts

You can use a **bar chart** to display data.

Bar charts use bars to give a visual picture of the size of each category.

- A bar chart shows
  - how each category compares with the others
  - all the data, but in categories.

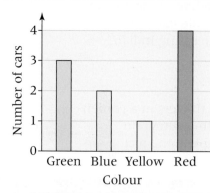

**Vertical** bars

Note the equal gaps between the bars.

The bars can be horizontal or vertical.

**Horizontal** bars

- **Bar-line charts** are a good way to display (discrete) numerical data.

Lines are drawn instead of bars.

**Example**

A class are asked to name one favourite pet. The results are shown.

| Pet | Dog | Cat | Guinea pig | Other |
|---|---|---|---|---|
| Frequency | 16 | 9 | 12 | 3 |

Draw a bar chart to show this information.

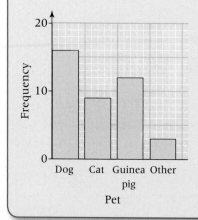

**1** The cost of renting a car for a day in different countries is shown.
Copy and complete the bar chart.

| Country | Cost |
|---------|------|
| UK | £15 |
| Portugal | £16 |
| Ireland | £21 |
| Germany | £19 |
| France | £17 |
| USA | £16 |

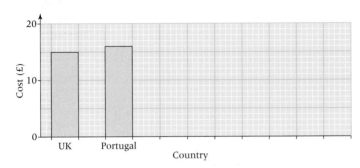

**2** The number of concerts held at various venues is given.
Copy and complete the bar chart.

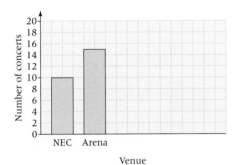

| Venue | Number of concerts |
|-------|--------------------|
| NEC | 10 |
| Arena | 15 |
| MEN | 20 |
| NIA | 18 |
| Wembley | 9 |

| Flavour | Number of packets |
|---------|--------------------|
| Plain | 5 |
| Salt'n'Vinegar | 3 |
| Cheese & Onion | 4 |
| Smokey Bacon | 1 |
| Other | 8 |

**3** The numbers of packets of crisps in a shop are shown in the frequency table.
Draw a vertical bar chart to show this information.

**4** The number of Bank Holidays in different countries is shown.
Draw a bar chart to show this information.

| Country | Number of Bank Holidays |
|---------|--------------------------|
| UK | 8 |
| Italy | 16 |
| Iceland | 15 |
| Spain | 14 |

**5** The cost to fly to certain resorts is given in the frequency table.
Draw a bar chart to show this information.

| Resort | Cost (£) |
|--------|----------|
| Lisbon | 90 |
| Crete | 100 |
| Malta | 80 |
| Menorca | 70 |
| Cyprus | 110 |

# Interpreting pictograms and bar charts

This spread will show you how to:

- Understand the difference between discrete and continuous data
- Interpret data from pictograms and bar charts
- Calculate the modal category of a data set

**Keywords**
Bar chart
Category
Discrete
Modal
Pictogram

- **Discrete** data can only take exact values (usually collected by counting). For example, the number of pets in a home.
- You can interpret information on **categories** and discrete data from a **pictogram** or a **bar chart**.

Continuous data can have any value, for example, your height.

The size of each category gives the frequency.

---

**Example**

The pictogram shows the number of students attending school in a week.
The class has 20 students.

| Monday | ◯ ◯ ◯ ◯ |
|---|---|
| Tuesday | ◯ ◯ ◖ |
| Wednesday | ◯ ◯ ◯ |
| Thursday | ◯ ◖ |
| Friday | ◯ ◯ ◿ |

Key: ◯ represents 4 students

Calculate
**a** the number of students that attended on Tuesday
**b** the number of students that were absent on Thursday.

.........................................................................

**a** 4 + 4 + 2 = 10 students
**b** 20 − (4 + 3) = 20 − 7 = 13 students

---

**Example**

The bar chart shows the types of sweets in an assorted box.
Calculate
**a** the number of chocolate sweets
**b** the total number of sweets in the box.
**c** Find the **modal** type of sweet.

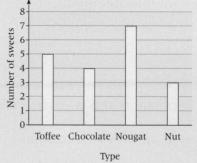

Modal means the most frequent type.

.........................................................................

**a** 4
**b** 5 + 4 + 7 + 3 = 19 sweets
**c** Nougat

**1** The numbers of buses that stop at a village through the week are shown on the bar chart.
  **a** How many buses stop at the village on Thursday?
  **b** On which days is there no bus service?
  **c** Calculate the total number of buses that stop at the village throughout the week.

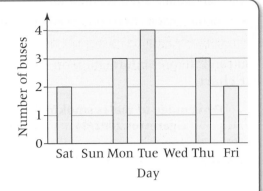

**2** The number of foreign language teachers at a school is shown in the pictogram.
  **a** Which subject has only one teacher?
  **b** How many French teachers teach at the school?
  **c** Calculate the total number of foreign language teachers at the school.

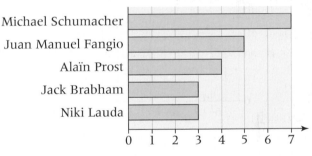

Key: 🗙 represents 2 teachers

**3** The number of times each racing driver has been the Formula 1 World Champion is shown on the bar chart.
  **a** Who has been the F1 World Champion the most times?
  **b** How many times has Alaïn Prost been the F1 World Champion?

Michael Schumacher
Juan Manuel Fangio
Alaïn Prost
Jack Brabham
Niki Lauda

0  1  2  3  4  5  6  7
Number of times World Champion

**4** Four friends played a series of games. The number of wins for each person is shown in the pictogram.
  Angela won six games.
  **a** What does ⊞ represent?
  **b** How many games did Robert win?
  **c** Who won the most games and how many did that person win?
  **d** Who won the least games and how many did that person win?
  **e** Calculate the total number of games played.

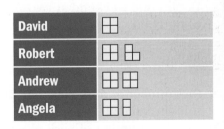

Key: ⊞ represents ?

69

# Comparative bar charts

This spread will show you how to:
● Use the shape of comparative bar charts to compare two data sets

**Keywords**
Bar chart
Comparative bar
  chart

You can interpret information on categories and discrete data from a **bar chart**.

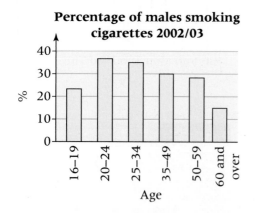

Percentage of males smoking cigarettes 2002/03

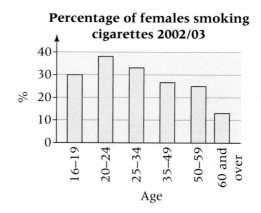

Percentage of females smoking cigarettes 2002/03

● You can combine two bar charts to create a **comparative bar chart**, which helps you to compare two sets of data.

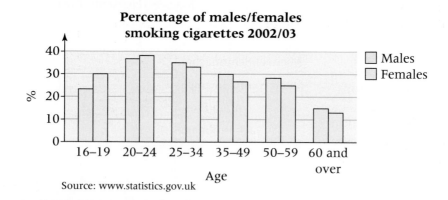

Percentage of males/females smoking cigarettes 2002/03

Source: www.statistics.gov.uk

The sets of data you compare must be the same type, for example Boy/Girl.

**Example**

The chart shows the sales of pork pies one weekend at two rival butchers.

Calculate

**a** the number of pork pies that Billy sold on Sunday
**b** the total number of pork pies that were sold by both butchers.

**a** 7 pork pies
**b** 5 + 7 + 6 + 5 = 23 pork pies

**A02 Functional Maths**

**1** The number of letters delivered one week to No 10 and No 12 on the same street is shown on the bar chart.

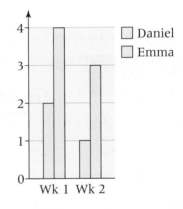

  **a** State the number of letters that were delivered to
   **i** No 10 on Tuesday
   **ii** No 12 on Friday.
  **b** Which day did
   **i** No 12 receive no letters
   **ii** No 10 receive 2 letters?
  **c** Which was the only day that No 12 received more post than No 10?
  **d** Calculate the total number of letters delivered in the week to
   **i** No 10    **ii** No 12.
  **e** Which day did the postman deliver the most letters to No 10 and No 12 combined?

**2** The number of visits to the swimming baths over two weeks for Daniel and Emma is shown on the bar chart.
  **a** State the number of visits for
   **i** Emma in Week 1
   **ii** Daniel in Week 2.
  **b** Calculate the total number of visits for
   **i** Daniel
   **ii** Emma.

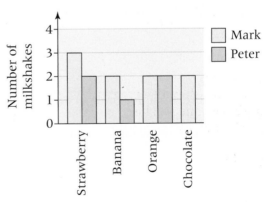

**3** The bar chart shows the number and flavour of milkshakes that Mark and Peter drank.
  **a** State the number of
   **i** banana milkshakes drunk by Mark
   **ii** orange milkshakes drunk by Peter.
  **b** Which flavour milkshake was not drunk by Mark?
  **c** Which flavour milkshake did Mark and Peter drink the same number of?
  **d** Calculate the total number of milkshakes drunk by
   **i** Mark
   **ii** Peter.

71

This spread will show you how to:
- Draw and produce pie charts for data in categories

**Keywords**
Angle
Category
Pie chart
Proportion
Sector

You can use a **pie chart** to display data.

Pie charts use a circle to give a quick visual picture of all the data.
The size of each **angle** shows the size of each **category**.

- A pie chart shows
  - the **proportion** or fraction of each category compared to the whole circle
  - all the data, but in categories.

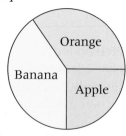

Apple is a quarter of all the data.

Banana is the biggest **sector**.

All the data must be included.

**Example**

A group of 12 students were asked how they travelled to school that day.
The results are shown.

| Method of travel | Walked | Bus | Car | Other |
|---|---|---|---|---|
| Frequency | 6 | 2 | 3 | 1 |

Draw a pie chart to illustrate this information.

**Method 1**
Calculate the angle for one person:
$360° ÷ 12 = 30°$
Divide the circle into sectors of 30°.
Colour and label the sectors.

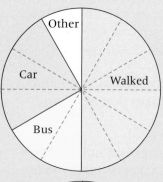

The angles at a point add to 360°.

**Method 2**
Calculate the angle for one person:
$360° ÷ 12 = 30°$
Calculate the angles for each category

| | | |
|---|---|---|
| Walked | $6 × 30°$ | $= 180°$ |
| Bus | $2 × 30°$ | $= 60°$ |
| Car | $3 × 30°$ | $= 90°$ |
| Other | $1 × 30°$ | $= 30°$ |
| | Add to check: | $360°$ |

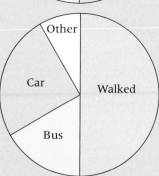

Measure, colour and label the sectors.

Check by adding the angles of the sectors.

In the above example, Method 1 is time-consuming and inaccurate.
It is better to use Method 2.

**A02 Functional Maths**

**1** Alvin makes eight sandwiches
   1 tuna
   2 cheese and tomato
   3 chicken
   2 corned beef

Draw a pie chart to show this information.

**2** Sophie spends £6 on her hobby of painting.
   £1 on paper
   £2 on paint brushes
   £3 on paint

Draw a pie chart to show this information.

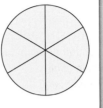

**3** A survey question asks 'Do you think smoking should be banned in public places?'
The results are:

| Yes | 5 |
|-----|---|
| No  | 4 |

  **a** Calculate the number of people who were asked the question.
  **b** Calculate the angle one person represents in a pie chart.
  **c** Calculate the angles to represent Yes and No.
  **d** Draw a pie chart to show the results of the survey.

**4** Seven boys and five girls attend an after-school homework club.
  **a** Calculate the total number of students.
  **b** Calculate the angle one student represents in a pie chart.
  **c** Calculate the angles to represent boys and girls.
  **d** Draw a pie chart to show the information.

**5** A school fete is open from 10 am to 4 pm.
  **a** Calculate the number of minutes the school fete is open.

A teacher has offered to help.
She spends these times on each stall.

  **b** Draw a pie chart to show this information.

| Stall | Time |
|-------|------|
| Bat the Rat | 30 mins |
| Hook a Duck | 25 mins |
| Smash a Plate | 35 mins |
| Roll a Coin | 80 mins |
| Tombola | 70 mins |
| Break 1 | 60 mins |
| Break 2 | 60 mins |

**6** In one week, 180 letters were delivered to a business.
The letters were delivered in this pattern.

Draw a pie chart to show this information.

| Mon | 45 |
|-----|----|
| Tues | 30 |
| Wed | 25 |
| Thurs | 20 |
| Fri | 50 |
| Sat | 10 |
| Sun | 0 |

**DID YOU KNOW?**

In 2007, the proportion of smokers in the UK fell to 21%, down from 45% in 1974.

**Interpreting pie charts**

This spread will show you how to:

- Interpret data from a pie chart
- Calculate the modal category of a data set

**Keywords**
Category
Modal
Pie chart
Proportion
Sector

- You can interpret data from a **pie chart**.

A pie chart does not show the actual number of items in each **category**.

A pie chart does show the size of each category compared to the total number of items.

**Drinks sold at a machine**

Cappuccino is the biggest **sector**.

The pie chart shows the **proportion** of drinks bought at a vending machine.
More cappuccinos were sold compared to the other categories, but we do not know how many drinks were sold.

**Example**

60 vehicles are shown on the pie chart.

**a** Calculate the numbers of cars, vans, buses and lorries.

**b** State the modal type of vehicle.

**Vehicles parked in the High St.**

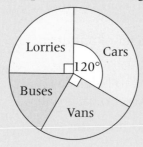

. . . . . . . . . . . . . . . . . . . . . . . . . . . . . . . . . . . . . . . . . . . . . . . . . . . . . . . . . . . . . . . . . . . . . .

**a** 60 vehicles = 360°
1 vehicle = 6°
The angle for Buses is 360° − (90° + 90° + 120°) = 60°
  Cars    120 ÷ 6 = 20 cars
  Vans     90 ÷ 6 = 15 vans
  Buses    60 ÷ 6 = 10 buses
  Lorries  90 ÷ 6 = 15 lorries
Check:   20 + 15 + 10 + 15 = 60 vehicles

**b** The modal type of vehicle is Car.

The angles at a point add to 360°.

**Modal** means the most frequent type.

**A02 Functional Maths**

**1** The survey results for the favourite band of
100 people are shown.
 **a** What fraction of the circle represents
 **i** Kasabian      **ii** The Prodigy      **iii** Glasvegas?
 **b** Calculate the number of people who voted for
 **i** Kasabian      **ii** The Prodigy      **iii** Glasvegas.
 **c** State the modal band.

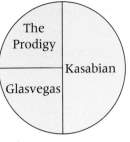

**2** Six drinks of soup are represented on the pie chart.
 **a** Copy and complete      6 drinks = 360°
               1 drink = ___°

 **b** Calculate the number of drinks that are
 **i** tomato      **ii** chicken      **iii** beef.
 **c** State the modal type of drink.

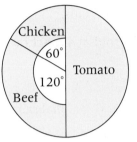

**3** A shop sells 12 loaves of three different types: organic,
wholegrain and white.
 **a** Copy and complete      12 loaves = 360°
               1 loaf = ___°

 **b** Calculate the number of loaves that are
 **i** organic      **ii** wholegrain      **iii** white.
 **c** State the modal type of loaf.

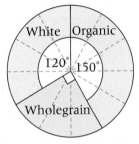

**4** Nine newspapers delivered on a street are shown on
the pie chart.
 **a** Copy and complete      9 newspapers = 360°
               1 newspaper = ___°

 **b** Calculate the number of newspapers delivered that are
 **i** the Planet      **ii** the News      **iii** the Daily Rag.
 **c** State the modal newspaper.

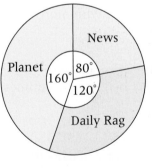

**5** A car dealer sells 18 cars in one week of three different
types: diesel, petrol and electric.
 **a** Calculate the angle that represents one car.
 **b** Calculate the number of cars sold that are
 **i** diesel      **ii** petrol      **iii** electric.
 **c** State the modal type of car sold.

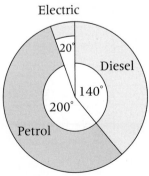

# Stem-and-leaf diagrams 1

This spread will show you how to:

● Draw and produce stem-and-leaf diagrams

**Keywords**
Ordered
Stem-and-leaf
diagram

You can use a **stem-and-leaf diagram** to display numerical data.

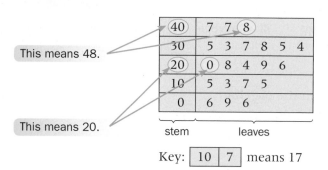

This means 48.

This means 20.

stem          leaves

Key:  | 10 | 7 |  means 17

This stem-and-leaf diagram is **unordered**.

It works by partitioning each number into two parts.

A stem-and-leaf diagram is quick and easy to construct.

● A stem-and-leaf diagram shows
  – the shape of the distribution
  – each individual value of the data.

Gives a 'feel' for the data.

No loss of detail of the data.

This stem-and-leaf diagram is **ordered**, as the data is in numerical order.

A stem-and-leaf diagram is like a bar chart, but with more detail.

| 40 | 7 7 8 |
| 30 | 3 4 5 5 7 8 |
| 20 | 0 4 6 8 9 |
| 10 | 3 5 5 7 |
| 0 | 6 6 9 |

stem          leaves

Key:  | 10 | 7 |  means 17

---

**Example**

The heights, in centimetres, of 10 students are shown.

168   154   172   167   156
154   163   160   165   158

Show the heights in an ordered stem-and-leaf diagram.

p.94

| 150 | |
| 160 | |
| 170 | |

| 150 | 4 6 4 8 |
| 160 | 8 7 3 0 5 |
| 170 | 2 |

order →

| 150 | 4 4 6 8 |
| 160 | 0 3 5 7 8 |
| 170 | 2 |

Key:  | 150 | 4 |  means 154 cm

Key:  | 150 | 4 |  means 154 cm

You can order the data before you draw the diagram if you want.

**1** The numbers of houses on each street of a town are shown.

| 12 | 5 | 25 | 27 | 7 | 35 | 15 | 10 | 22 | 18 |
| 34 | 30 | 14 | 19 | 20 | 28 | 32 | 4 | 25 | 36 |

**a** Copy and complete the stem-and-leaf diagram.

| 0 | |
|---|---|
| 10 | |
| 20 | |
| 30 | |

Key: | 10 | 8 | means 18 houses

**b** Redraw the table to give an ordered stem-and-leaf diagram.

**2** The weights, in kilograms, of 30 students are shown.

| 48 | 47 | 48 | 53 | 61 | 70 | 45 | 56 | 57 | 60 |
| 42 | 46 | 44 | 55 | 63 | 65 | 49 | 50 | 55 | 65 |
| 70 | 53 | 64 | 61 | 46 | 47 | 56 | 40 | 41 | 54 |

Draw an ordered stem-and-leaf diagram using stems of 40, 50, 60, 70.
Remember to give the key.

**3** The exam marks of 40 students are shown.

| 33 | 48 | 18 | 63 | 51 | 66 | 52 | 19 | 55 | 43 |
| 50 | 35 | 52 | 66 | 43 | 48 | 32 | 18 | 17 | 26 |
| 5 | 15 | 10 | 25 | 36 | 51 | 61 | 48 | 58 | 68 |
| 38 | 67 | 11 | 18 | 27 | 30 | 40 | 60 | 46 | 55 |

Draw an ordered stem-and-leaf diagram using stems of 0, 10, 20, 30, 40, 50, 60.
Remember to give the key.

**4** The attempted heights, in centimetres, during a High Jump event are shown.

| 214 | 204 | 225 | 230 | 244 |
| 210 | 207 | 209 | 240 | 232 |
| 230 | 216 | 242 | 233 | 238 |
| 206 | 217 | 236 | 216 | 211 |
| 208 | 230 | 209 | 237 | 241 |

Draw an ordered stem-and-leaf diagram using stems of 200, 210, 220, 230, 240.

**5** The times, in seconds, taken for 24 athletes to run 200 metres are given.

| 24.5 | 20.1 | 20.3 | 21.4 | 22.1 | 22.0 | 24.8 | 21.0 |
| 25.1 | 21.5 | 22.6 | 23.5 | 20.9 | 21.6 | 23.5 | 24.0 |
| 25.0 | 21.8 | 21.8 | 22.1 | 21.0 | 23.5 | 24.6 | 21.5 |

Copy and complete an ordered stem-and-leaf diagram to show this data.

| 20 | |
|---|---|
| 21 | |
| 22 | |
| 23 | |
| 24 | |
| 25 | |

Key: | 20 | 9 | means 20.9 seconds

This spread will show you how to:

• Draw and produce line graphs for time series data

**Keywords**
Horizontal
Line graph
Time series
  graph
Trend

You can use a **line graph** to show how data changes as time passes.

The temperature in Belfast is measured every hour from 8 am to 4 pm.

The graph shows the data.

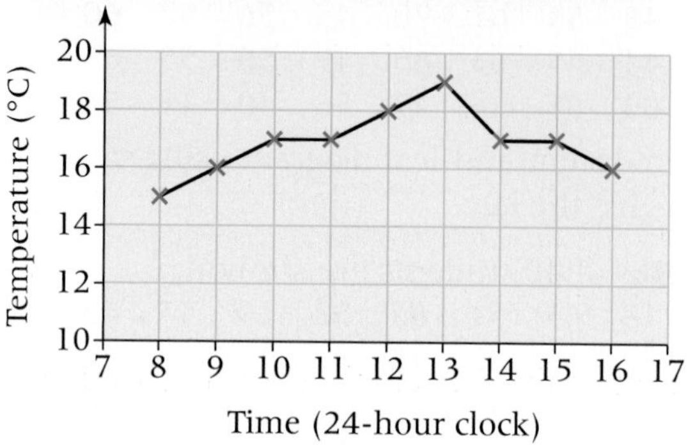

Time is always the **horizontal** axis.

These line graphs are called **time series graphs**.

Time series graph will not be assessed in your exams.

• A time series graph shows
  - how the data changes, or the **trend**
  - each individual value of the data.

**Example**

The number of Christmas cards Britney received are shown in the table.

| Date in December | 12 | 13 | 14 | 15 | 16 | 17 | 18 | 19 | 20 | 21 | 22 | 23 | 24 |
|---|---|---|---|---|---|---|---|---|---|---|---|---|---|
| Number of cards | 1 | 2 | 4 | 0 | 3 | 3 | 4 | 3 | 2 | 4 | 7 | 8 | 5 |

Draw a line graph to show this information.

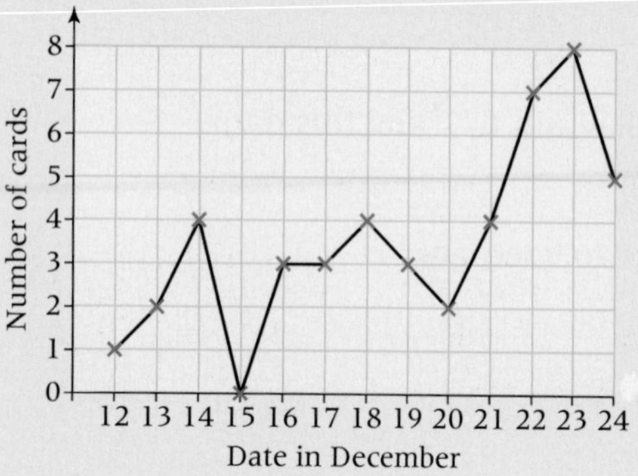

**1** The number of photographs taken each day during a 7-day holiday is given.

| Sunday | Monday | Tuesday | Wednesday | Thursday | Friday | Saturday |
|--------|--------|---------|-----------|----------|--------|----------|
| 8 | 12 | 11 | 16 | 19 | 2 | 13 |

Copy and complete the line graph to show this information.

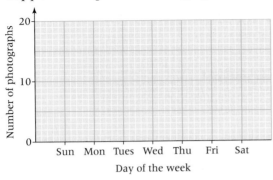

**2** The number of sunny days in each month is given.

| Jan | Feb | Mar | Apr | May | Jun | Jul | Aug | Sep | Oct | Nov | Dec |
|-----|-----|-----|-----|-----|-----|-----|-----|-----|-----|-----|-----|
| 9 | 8 | 10 | 15 | 19 | 20 | 21 | 25 | 24 | 18 | 17 | 11 |

Copy and complete the line graph, choosing a suitable vertical scale.

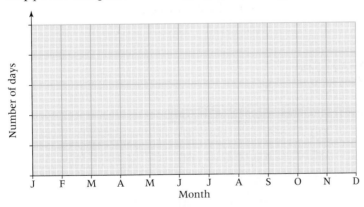

**3** The number of points gained by the winners of the football Premiership is shown from 1993–2005.

| Year | 1993 | 1994 | 1995 | 1996 | 1997 | 1998 |
|------|------|------|------|------|------|------|
| Points | 84 | 92 | 89 | 82 | 75 | 78 |
| Winner | Man Utd | Man Utd | Blackburn | Man Utd | Man Utd | Arsenal |

| Year | 1999 | 2000 | 2001 | 2002 | 2003 | 2004 | 2005 |
|------|------|------|------|------|------|------|------|
| Points | 79 | 91 | 80 | 87 | 83 | 90 | 95 |
| Winner | Man Utd | Man Utd | Man Utd | Arsenal | Man Utd | Arsenal | Chelsea |

Draw a line graph to show this information.

## Summary

### Check out

You should now be able to:

- Produce pictograms, vertical and horizontal bar charts, bar-line charts and pie charts to display data
- Draw and use stem-and-leaf diagrams
- Interpret graphs and charts
- Look at data to find patterns and exceptions

### Worked exam question

The table gives information about the drinks sold in a café one day.

| Drink | Frequency | Size of angle |
|---|---|---|
| Hot chocolate | 20 | 80° |
| Soup | 15 | |
| Coffee | 25 | |
| Tea | 30 | |

Complete the pie chart to show the information. (3)

(Edexcel Limited 2008)

20 drinks is represented by 80°
1 drink is represented by 80° ÷ 20 = 4°

| Drink | Frequency | Size of angle |
|---|---|---|
| Hot chocolate | 20 | 80° |
| Soup | 15 | 15 × 4 = 60° |
| Coffee | 25 | 25 × 4 = 100° |
| Tea | 30 | 30 × 4 = 120° |

Write down the angles in the table.

Check
80°
60°
100°
120° +
360°

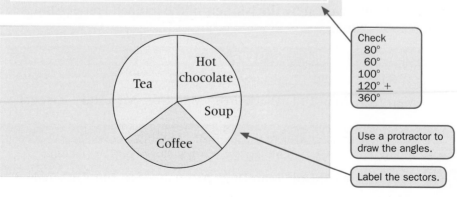

Use a protractor to draw the angles.

Label the sectors.

# Exam questions

1  Jessica asked some students to tell her their favourite pet.
   She used the information to draw this bar chart.

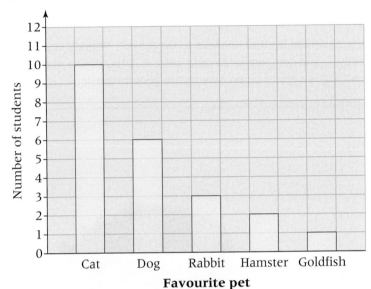

a How many students said a rabbit? (1)
b Which pet did most students say? (1)
c Work out the number of students that Jessica asked. (1)

(Edexcel Limited 2008)

2  José is in hospital.
   Here is his temperature chart during one day.

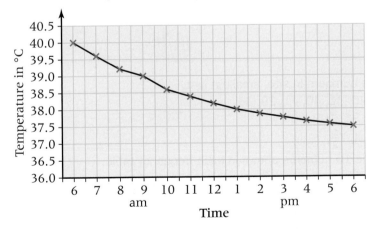

a At what time was José's temperature 39.0°C? (1)
b What can you say about José's temperature from 6 am to 6 pm? (1)

(Edexcel Limited 2007)

# Introduction

Statistics are vital in medicine as they are used to test the safety and performance of new drugs. Tests are performed on large groups of people and the analysis of the results is used to evaluate the safety and reliability of the new drug.

## What's the point?

When data is analysed it is essential for that analysis to be correct. Statisticians use a range of techniques to analyse and compare large data sets. It is the use of statistical techniques that ensures a drug is safe to be on sale to the general public.

1 Order these numbers in size, smallest first.
   **a** 35, 48, 26, 31, 40, 41, 29, 36
   **b** 101, 92, 91, 102, 98
   **c** 6, $4\frac{1}{2}$, 8, 4, $7\frac{1}{2}$

2 Write out the 10 numbers shown in each frequency table.

**a**

| Number | Frequency |
|--------|-----------|
| 80 | 3 |
| 81 | 0 |
| 82 | 1 |
| 83 | 2 |
| 84 | 4 |

**b**

| Number | Frequency |
|--------|-----------|
| 45 | 2 |
| 46 | 1 |
| 47 | 0 |
| 48 | 4 |
| 49 | 3 |

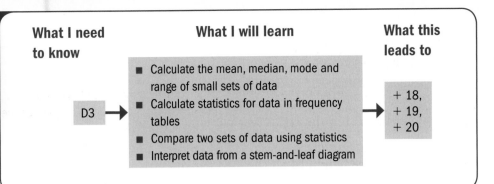

| What I need to know | What I will learn | What this leads to |
|---|---|---|
| D3 | ■ Calculate the mean, median, mode and range of small sets of data <br> ■ Calculate statistics for data in frequency tables <br> ■ Compare two sets of data using statistics <br> ■ Interpret data from a stem-and-leaf diagram | + 18, <br> + 19, <br> + 20 |

**Rich task**

What is the most likely time during a football game for a team to score a goal?

It is frequently stated by football commentators that teams are most likely to concede a goal within five minutes of scoring a goal themselves. Is this true?

Investigate and write a report on your results.

**The mean**

This spread will show you how to:
- Calculate the mean of small sets of data

The **average** 15-year-old girl in the UK is 164 cm tall.

This does not suggest that every girl's height is 164 cm, but that 164 cm can be used to represent the height of all the 15-year-old girls in the UK.

You can use one value to represent a set of data.
One **representative value** is called the **mean**.

- Mean $= \dfrac{\text{total sum of the values}}{\text{number of values}}$

**Example**

Five students measured their pulse rates.
The beats per minute for the students were

64   73   75   78   68

Calculate the mean pulse rate.

........................................................

Mean $= \dfrac{\text{total sum of the values}}{\text{number of values}}$

$= \dfrac{64 + 73 + 75 + 78 + 68}{5}$

$= \dfrac{358}{5}$

$= 71.6$ beats per minute

Notice that the mean does not have to be one of the values.

71.6 is between the lowest value (64) and the highest value (78).

**1  a** Calculate the mean of these five numbers
    1, 1, 2, 4, 7
 **b** Copy the diagram to illustrate the five numbers.
 **c** Mark the mean on your diagram with a horizontal line.
 **d** Show how the parts of bars above the mean can be
    moved to give five equal numbers.

**2  a** Calculate the mean of these six numbers
    1, 2, 2, 6, 6, 7
 **b** Draw a diagram to illustrate the six numbers.
 **c** Mark the mean on your diagram.
 **d** Show how seven parts of bars can be moved to give
    six equal numbers.

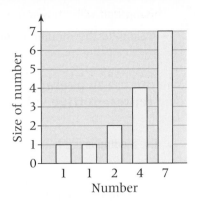

**A02  Functional Maths**

**3** The times taken for Pete to travel to work are

| Monday | Tuesday | Wednesday | Thursday | Friday |
|--------|---------|-----------|----------|--------|
| 24 mins | 18 mins | 21 mins | 17 mins | 15 mins |

Calculate his mean time taken.

**4** Calculate the mean for each set of numbers.
 **a** 4, 9, 7, 12           **b** 8, 11, 8
 **c** 3, 2, 2, 3, 0          **d** 1, 9, 8, 6
 **e** 2, 2, 4, 1, 0, 3        **f** 23, 22, 25, 26
 **g** 17, 19, 19, 20, 18, 17, 16   **h** 103, 104, 105
 **i** 14, 10, 24, 12         **j** 4, 6, 7, 6, 4, 4, 3, 7, 3, 6

**5** Calculate the mean for each set of numbers.
 **a** 3, 2, 1, 4, 2          **b** 8, 7, 6, 5
 **c** 3, 2, 2, 5, 1, 2         **d** 14, 15, 15, 13, 18, 15, 16, 18
 **e** 108, 107, 110, 101

**6** The numbers of matches in five different matchboxes are
  shown on the diagram.
  Calculate the mean number of matches in a box.

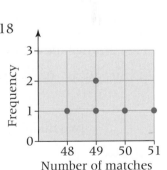

**A03  Problem**

**7** The mean of these three numbers is 8.
  Calculate the missing number.

**8** Find two numbers with a mean of 3.5.

# The median

This spread will show you how to:
- Calculate the median of small sets of data

**Keywords**
Event
Expected
  number
Mutually
  exclusive
Outcome

You can use an **average** to represent a set of data.
One **representative value** is called the median.

- The **median** is the middle value when the data are arranged in order of size.

The data must be in numerical order.

**Example**

Lisa catches a bus each day.
The number of minutes that the bus is late is shown.

1, 3, 1, 4, 0, 2, 2

Calculate the median number of minutes late.

First arrange the data in numerical order.

0, 1, 1, 2, 2, 3, 4

middle value

Median = 2 minutes

- When there are two middle numbers, the median is the number that is halfway between these two middle numbers.

**Example**

The numbers of passengers in 10 cars were counted. The results were

2  0  1  0  3  2  0  0  4  0

Calculate the median number of passengers.

First arrange the data in numerical order.

0  0  0  0  ⓪ ①  2  2  3  4

two middle values

Median = (0 + 1) ÷ 2

= 0.5 passengers

For an even number of data items, there will be two middle values.

**1 a** Write these numbers in order, smallest first.

**i** 7, 8, 8, 5, 4, 3, 3  **ii** 11, 12, 10, 9, 9

**iii** 38, 35, 30, 37, 34  **iv** 101, 98, 103, 97, 99, 97, 95

**v** 3, 2, 0, 0, 1, 2, 1, 2, 3

**b** Use your answers to find the median of each set of numbers.

**2** The weights of five boys are given on the right.

**a** Arrange the weights in order, smallest first.

**b** Find the median weight.

**c** Which boy has the median weight?

| Tony | 71 kg |
| Tom | 64 kg |
| Tim | 61 kg |
| Tariq | 70 kg |
| Thomas | 66 kg |

**3** Eleven students were asked how many hours of television they had watched yesterday. The results were

$4, 3\frac{1}{2}, 0, 1, \frac{1}{2}, 5, 2, 2\frac{1}{2}, 10, 1, 1\frac{1}{2}$

Find the median number of hours of television watched.

**4** The numbers of tomatoes on each of seven plants in a greenhouse are

12, 6, 9, 15, 10, 9, 7

Find the median number of tomatoes on the plants.

**5** The ages, in years, of eight children in a creche are:

2, 4, 2, 3, 5, 1, 3, 4

Find the median age for the children.

**6** Ten students were asked to estimate a minute.

Their attempts, in seconds, were

65, 71, 57, 41, 56, 68, 85, 42, 58, 60

Calculate the median time in seconds.

**7** The numbers of passengers in 20 cars are recorded.

The numbers are

1, 0, 0, 1, 2, 3, 5, 0, 1, 2, 1, 1, 2, 0, 0, 0, 4, 2, 1, 1

Calculate the median number of passengers.

**8** Explain why these statements are wrong.

**a** The median of 3, 2, 1, 5, 6 is 1.

**b** The median of 1, 1, 2, 3 is 1 or 2.

**c** You cannot find the median of 8, 8, 9, 10 because there is no middle number.

This spread will show you how to:

● Calculate the mode and range of small sets of data

**Keywords**

Average
Modal
Mode
Range
Representative
  value
Spread

You can use an **average** to represent a set of data.
One **representative value** is called the mode.

● The **mode** is the value that occurs most often.

**Example**

In the last ten football matches,
Matlock Town scored
2, 5, 2, 3, 4, 1, 3, 1, 1, 1 goals.
Calculate the modal number
of goals.

1 goal occurred most often.
Mode = 1 goal
You can represent the goals
on a diagram.

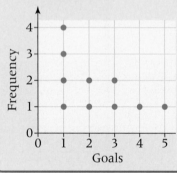

The mode is also
called the **modal**
value.

The modal number
of goals scored
is 1.

● You can measure the **spread** of the numbers by calculating the range.

● The **range** is the highest value minus the lowest value.

The range
measures the
spread of the
data.

**Example**

Find

**a** the range
**b** the mode of these numbers of goals.

1, 1, 1, 1, 2, 2, 3, 3, 4, 5, 3, 3

**a** Range = highest value − lowest value
        = 5 − 1
        = 4 goals
**b** There are 2 modes: 1 and 3

Unit 1

**A02 | Functional Maths**

**1** The shop Tops4U sells 25 tops in one day.
The sizes sold are

L   M   L   M   XL   L   M   M   XL   M
M   XL   XL   L   M   M   L   L   M   L
L   L   XL   M   M

M = Medium
L = Large
XL = Extra large

**a** Copy and complete the frequency table for the tops.

| Size | Tally | Frequency |
|---|---|---|
| Medium (M) | | |
| Large (L) | | |
| Extra large (XL) | | |

**b** State the modal size.

**2** Calculate the mode and range of each set of numbers.

**a** 0, 0, 1, 1, 1, 1, 2, 2, 2, 3, 3, 4, 4        **b** 5, 5, 6, 6, 6, 7, 7, 7, 7, 8, 8, 8, 8, 8

**c** 10, 11, 11, 11, 12, 12, 13, 14        **d** 21, 22, 23, 24, 24, 25, 25, 25, 26

**e** 8, 8, 8, 9, 9, 10, 11        **f** 4, 3, 5, 5, 6, 6, 4, 3, 4, 5, 6, 5, 3

**3** Calculate the mode and range of these sets of numbers.

**a**
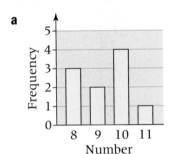

**b**
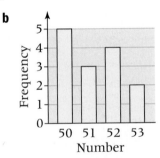

**c**
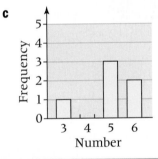

**A02 | Functional Maths**

**4** The mean monthly temperature, in °F, is shown for Leeds.

**Average temperature**

| | Jan | Feb | Mar | Apr | May | Jun | Jul | Aug | Sep | Oct | Nov | Dec |
|---|---|---|---|---|---|---|---|---|---|---|---|---|
| °F | 41 | 41 | 44 | 46 | 54 | 58 | 62 | 61 | 56 | 52 | 45 | 44 |

Source: www.weatherbase.com

Calculate the range of the temperatures.

**A03 | Problem**

**5** The range of five weights is 18 kg.
The five weights in order are 35 kg, 42 kg, 43 kg, 51 kg, ? kg.
Calculate the value of the unknown weight.

**6** The mode of these five numbers is 4.
Find the missing number and calculate the range.

| 6 | 4 | 6 | 4 | ? |

89

This spread will show you how to:

• Calculate the mean, mode, median and range of sets of data

**Keywords**
Frequency table
Mean
Median
Mode
Range
Spread

• You can calculate
  – the **mean**
  – the **mode**
  – the **median**
  – the **range**
  from a **frequency table**.

**Example**

A dice was thrown ten times. The scores were

6, 1, 4, 1, 1, 5, 5, 1, 1, 6

Complete the frequency table and calculate the mean, mode, median and range of the ten scores.

| Score | Tally | Frequency |
|-------|-------|-----------|
| 1     |       |           |
| 2     |       |           |

This topic is extended to finding the mean from a frequency table on page 442.

| Score | Tally | Frequency |
|-------|-------|-----------|
| 1     | IIII  | 5         |
| 2     |       | 0         |
| 3     |       | 0         |
| 4     | I     | 1         |
| 5     | II    | 2         |
| 6     | II    | 2         |
|       |       | 10        |

1 was thrown on five occasions.

6 was thrown on two occasions.

The results can be written in numerical order

1, 1, 1, 1, 1, 4, 5, 5, 6, 6

Mean = total of scores ÷ number of throws
     = $\frac{31}{10}$
     = 3.1
Mode = 1 as 1 occurs the most often.
Median = (1 + 4) ÷ 2
       = 2.5 as there are two middle scores.
Range = highest value − lowest value
      = 6 − 1
      = 5

The mean, mode and median must be between 1 and 6 inclusive.

The range measures the **spread** of the results.

**1** The numbers of days that 20 students
were absent from school in a week were

1  2  1  0  5  0  5  3  3  1
2  1  1  5  1  2  4  0  0  1

**a** Copy and complete the frequency table.
**b** Calculate the mean, mode, median and
range of the 20 numbers.

| Number of days | Tally | Frequency |
|---|---|---|
| 0 | | |
| 1 | | |
| 2 | | |
| 3 | | |
| 4 | | |
| 5 | | |

**2** The numbers of shots taken for each hole
for a round of golf were

3  4  3  2  3  4  3  4  3
4  3  2  4  6  3  4  4  4

**a** Copy and complete the frequency table.

| Number of shorts | Tally | Frequency |
|---|---|---|
| 2 | | |
| 3 | | |
| 4 | | |
| 5 | | |
| 6 | | |

**b** Calculate the mean, mode, median and
range of the 18 scores.

**3** Twenty people are asked 'How many
televisions do you have in your home?'
The results are

1  2  0  2  3  2  1  1  1  2
1  3  3  1  4  2  1  2  1  1

**a** Copy and complete the frequency table.
**b** Calculate the mean, mode, median and
range of the 20 numbers.

| Number of TVs | Tally | Frequency |
|---|---|---|
| 0 | | |
| 1 | | |
| 2 | | |
| 3 | | |
| 4 | | |

**4** Ten people are asked to choose a number from

| 1 | or | 2 | or | 3 | or | 4 |

The results are shown in the bar chart.
**a** Write the ten numbers in order of size,
smallest first.
**b** Calculate the mean, mode, median and
range of the ten numbers.

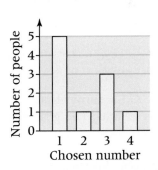

**Comparing data**

This spread will show you how to:

- Compare two sets of data using mean, mode, median and range
- Draw and interpret diagrams to represent data

**Keywords**
Compare
Mean
Median
Mode
Range
Spread

The **mean**, **mode** and **median** each give one typical value to represent the data. The **range** is a number that measures the **spread** of the data.

- You can **compare** two sets of data using
  - any of the mean, mode and median
  - the range.

**Example**

The results of a test are shown in the diagrams.

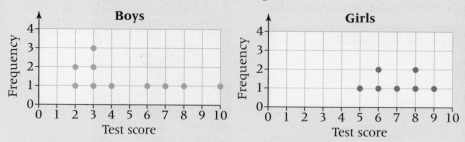

**a** Calculate the mean and median for each set of data.
**b** Compare the sets of data using the mean and median.
**c** Calculate the range for each set of data.
**d** Compare the sets of data using the range.

. . . . . . . . . . . . . . . . . . . . . . . . . . . . . . . . . . . . . . . . . . . . . . . . . . . . . . . .

**a** Boys' mean   $= (2 + 2 + 3 + 3 + 3 + 4 + 6 + 7 + 8 + 10) \div 10$
$= 48 \div 10 = 4.8$
Boys' median $= (3 + 4) \div 2 = 3.5$ (the mean of the 5th and 6th test scores)
Girls' mean   $= (5 + 6 + 6 + 7 + 8 + 8 + 9) \div 7$
$= 49 \div 7 = 7$
Girls' median $= 7$                    (the 4th test score)

**b** The mean and median show on average the girls did better in the test than the boys.

Use the words 'on average'.

**c** Boys' range $= 10 - 2 = 8$
Girls' range $= 9 - 5 = 4$

**d** The range shows that the boys' results are more spread out than the girls' results. The girls' results are more consistent.

- When you compare data, you should use
  - a measure of average
  - a measure of spread.

**1** The numbers of people who live in each house in Windermere
Street are
1, 1, 1, 1, 2, 2, 2, 4, 4
**a** Calculate the mean, mode and median of these numbers.
The numbers of people who live in each house in Coniston
Road are
3, 3, 3, 3, 4, 6, 6
**b** Calculate the mean, mode and median of these numbers.
**c** Use your answers to compare the average number of people in
each house for the two streets.

**2** John throws three darts. He scores 40, 20, 20.
Jim throws three darts. He scores 1, 5, 60.
**a** Calculate the range of the scores for John
and Jim.
**b** Who is more consistent?

**3** The ages of ten teachers are
25, 22, 51, 34, 28, 45, 37, 28, 33, 50.
**a** Calculate the range of these ages.
**b** All the Year 11 students are either 15 or 16 years old.
Calculate the range of the Year 11 ages.
**c** Explain the meaning of these two answers.

**4** The highest recorded monthly temperatures for St Tropez in
France and for Wick in Scotland are shown.

**Highest recorded temperature (°C)**

|  | Jan | Feb | Mar | Apr | May | Jun | Jul | Aug | Sep | Oct | Nov | Dec |
|---|---|---|---|---|---|---|---|---|---|---|---|---|
| St Tropez | 17 | 22 | 22 | 24 | 27 | 30 | 34 | 33 | 29 | 26 | 20 | 19 |
| Wick | 13 | 13 | 16 | 19 | 22 | 24 | 23 | 23 | 21 | 19 | 15 | 13 |

**a** List the temperatures for St Tropez and for Wick in order, smallest first.
**b** Calculate the median temperature for St Tropez and for Wick.
**c** Using the answers for the median, compare the two sets of data.
**d** Calculate the range of the temperatures for St Tropez and for Wick.
**e** Using the answers for the range, compare the two sets of data.

This spread will show you how to:

- Interpret data from a stem-and-leaf diagram
- Calculate the mean, mode, median and range from a stem-and-leaf diagram

**Keywords**

Ordered
Stem-and-leaf diagram

p.76

- You can interpret numerical data from a **stem-and-leaf diagram**.

Hannah recorded the lengths in mm of the leaves that fell off an oak tree one October day.

The numbers in her stem-and-leaf diagram are

104, 105, 108, 112, 112, 114, 115, 120, 124, 127, 132, 138, 141, 142, 147.

| (140) | 1 2 (7) | ← This means 147. |
|---|---|---|
| 130 | 2 8 | |
| (120) | (0) 4 7 | ← This means 120. |
| 110 | 2 2 4 5 | |
| 100 | 4 5 8 | |

stem        leaf

Key: | 110 | 4 | means 114 mm        Always give the key.

Her stem-and-leaf diagram is **ordered** as the data is in numerical order.

- You can calculate the mean, mode, median and range from the stem-and-leaf diagram.

**Example**

The ages of nine people in a judo club are shown in the diagram.

| 40 | 6 |
|---|---|
| 30 | 2 4 5 5 |
| 20 | 7 8 |
| 10 | 1 3 |

Calculate

**a** the mean
**b** the mode
**c** the median
**d** the range.

Key: | 20 | 7 | means 27

..........

**a** Mean = (11 + 13 + 27 + 28 + 32 + 34 + 35 + 35 + 46) ÷ 9
= 261 ÷ 9 = 29
**b** Mode = 35, the most common age
**c** Median = 32, the middle age when arranged in order
**d** Range = 46 − 11 = 35 years (highest age minus lowest age)

**1** Emma takes a spelling test every week. Her marks are shown in the stem-and-leaf diagram.

| 0 | 9 |
|----|-------------------------|
| 10 | 1  2  3  3  4  4  5  7  7 |
| 20 | 0  0  0 |

Key:  | 10 | 5 |  means 15 marks

  **a** Write out her 13 scores in numerical order, smallest first.
  **b** Calculate
    **i** the mean        **ii** the mode
    **iii** the median     **iv** the range.

**2** The cost, in pence, of various types of sweets are
  38   44   48   20   29   37   29   39   40
  **a** Copy and complete the stem-and-leaf diagram.

| 20 | |
|----|----|
| 30 | |
| 40 | |

Key:  | 20 | 9 |  means 29p

  **b** Redraw your table to give an ordered stem-and-leaf diagram.
  **c** Calculate
    **i** the mean        **ii** the mode
    **iii** the median     **iv** the range.

**3** The weights, in kilograms, of seven students are shown in the stem-and-leaf diagram.

| 40 | 3  5  5 |
|----|----------|
| 50 | 0  6 |
| 60 | 3  9 |

Key:  | 40 | 3 |  means 43 kg

  Calculate
  **a** the mean        **b** the mode
  **c** the median       **d** the range.

**4** The reaction times, in seconds, for 15 people are shown in the stem-and-leaf diagram.

| 9  | 9 |
|----|-------------------------|
| 10 | 0  1  1  1  2  3  5  7 |
| 11 | 8  9 |
| 12 | 0  7  7 |

Key:  | 10 | 5 |  means 10.5 seconds

  Calculate
  **a** the mean        **b** the mode
  **c** the median       **d** the range.

## Summary

### Check out
You should now be able to:

- Calculate the mean, mode, median, range and modal class
- Compare sets of data using mean, mode, median and range
- Interpret diagrams and draw conclusions

### Worked exam question
Ali found out the number of rooms in each of 40 houses in a town.
He used the information to complete the frequency table.

| Number of rooms | Frequency | |
|---|---|---|
| 4 | 4 | |
| 5 | 7 | |
| 6 | 10 | |
| 7 | 12 | |
| 8 | 5 | |
| 9 | 2 | |

Ali said that the mode is 9.
Ali is wrong.
**a** Explain why. (1)
**b** Calculate the mean of the rooms. (3)

(Edexcel Limited 2007)

· · · · · · · · · · · · · · · · · · · · · · · · · · · · · · · · · · · · · · · · · · · · · · · · · · · · · · · · · · · · · · · · · · · · · · · · · · · · · · · · · · · · ·

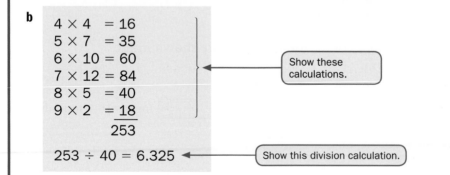

**a**  The mode is 7 because 7 has the highest frequency. ◄——— ( Give a reason. )

**b**
```
4 × 4  = 16
5 × 7  = 35          ◄——— ( Show these
6 × 10 = 60                  calculations. )
7 × 12 = 84
8 × 5  = 40
9 × 2  = 18
          253
```

253 ÷ 40 = 6.325 ◄——— ( Show this division calculation. )

# Exam questions

1 Sarah works in a post office.
She recorded the number of parcels on each of 16 days.
Here are her results.

| 2 | 2 | 5 | 3 | 2 | 4 | 2 | 2 |
|---|---|---|---|---|---|---|---|
| 3 | 6 | 4 | 6 | 2 | 2 | 3 | 3 |

a Complete the frequency table to show Sarah's results.

| Number of parcels | Tally | Frequency |
|---|---|---|
| 2 | | |
| 3 | | |
| 4 | | |
| 5 | | |
| 6 | | |

(2)

b Write down the mode. (1)
c Work out the range. (2)

(Edexcel Limited 2009)

2 Jason collected some information about the heights of 19 plants.
This information is shown in the stem and leaf diagram.

| 1 | 1  2  3  3 |
|---|---|
| 2 | 3  3  5  9  9 |
| 3 | 0  2  2  6  6  7 |
| 4 | 1  1  4  8 |

Key: 4|8 means 48 mm

Find the median. (2)

(Edexcel Limited 2008)

A02

3 Mr. Jones kept a record of the number of absences in his class for
two weeks.
Here are his results.

| 3 | 0 | 5 | 4 | 9 | 2 | 0 | 1 | 0 | 3 |
|---|---|---|---|---|---|---|---|---|---|

Using measures of average and the range, comment on the absences
in Mr. Jones's class. (4)

The manager of a catering company can use data about customer numbers in order to spot trends in customer behaviour and to plan for the future.

## Simply Sandwiches

### Simply Sandwiches

ches, paninis, baguettes and salads

### Simply Sandwiches

Customer numbers at 'Simply sandwiches' takeaway over a given two-week period were:

| Day | Number of Customers | |
|---|---|---|
| | Week 1 | Week 2 |
| Monday | 50 | 54 |
| Tuesday | 68 | 60 |
| Wednesday | 47 | 53 |
| Thursday | 58 | 57 |
| Friday | 52 | 56 |
| Saturday | 76 | 70 |
| Total | | |

### Simply Sandwiches

Use the data in the table to construct a bar chart to show how many customers visit the sandwich shop on each day during this two-week period.

Copy and complete the table.

During this two-week period,

a) which is the busiest day at the sandwich shop

b) what is the range of daily customer numbers?

This bar chart shows customer behaviour over a different two-week period. Compare the two sets of data, including reference to the quietest/busiest days and the spread of the data. Give possible explanations and justify your response with reference to the data.

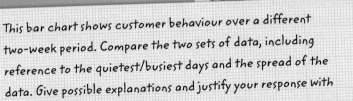

Is data collected over a two-week period enough to be able to estimate customer numbers for any given week? Justify your answer referring to the information.

A manager can use data about customer numbers to help estimate how much stock to order each week. In reality, limitations due to space and the shelf life of products also apply.

In the second week of the two-week period at 'Simply sandwiches', sales of the different varieties of sandwiches were:

| Variety | Mon | Tues | Weds | Thurs | Fri | Sat | Total | Average |
|---------|-----|------|------|-------|-----|-----|-------|---------|
| Ham | 14 | 16 | 13 | 14 | 17 | 18 | | |
| Cheese | 9 | 11 | 12 | 10 | 8 | 12 | | |
| Hummous | 6 | 5 | 7 | 4 | 6 | 8 | | |
| Tuna | 7 | 6 | 6 | 8 | 6 | 9 | | |
| Chicken | 18 | 22 | 15 | 21 | 19 | 23 | | |
| Total | | | | | | | | |

Copy the table and fill in the missing values.

The manager does a weekly stocktake every Sunday before placing the order for the following week.

The stocktake figures for this week were:

| Product | Stock (packs) | Portions per pack | Portions left | Stock needed | Amount to order |
|---------|---------------|-------------------|---------------|--------------|-----------------|
| Bread | 6 | 20 | | | |
| Ham | 2.5 | 10 | | | |
| Cheese | 3 | 10 | | | |
| Hummous | 2 | 14 | | | |
| Tuna | 1.5 | 8 | | | |
| Chicken | 1 | 10 | | | |

Copy and complete the table to show an estimate of how much of each product the manager should order to last for the following week.

The stock will be delivered on Wednesday morning.

Estimate how much (if any) of each product the manager will have in stock when the order arrives.

Comment on how well the manager estimated the order for the previous week.

Justify your answers by referring to the data.

Simply Sandwiches

sandwiches, paninis, baguettes and salads

# Introduction

In modern society, people often want to buy their own house, own a new car or go to university. To do these things they often need to borrow money from a bank or building society. These organisations lend the money but charge a fee (called 'interest') that is calculated as a percentage or fraction of the amount borrowed.

## What's the point?

Being able to solve problems involving percentages gives people greater control of their finances. It allows them to budget properly and be aware of the risks involved in borrowing too much money, which can lead to debt and bankruptcy.

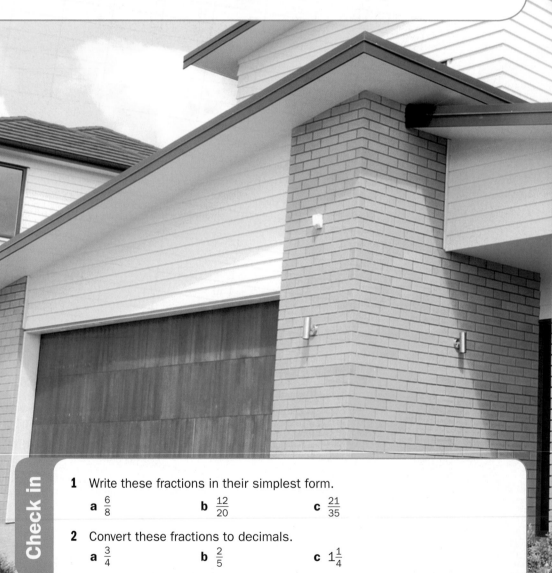

## Check in

1  Write these fractions in their simplest form.

   **a** $\frac{6}{8}$         **b** $\frac{12}{20}$         **c** $\frac{21}{35}$

2  Convert these fractions to decimals.

   **a** $\frac{3}{4}$         **b** $\frac{2}{5}$         **c** $1\frac{1}{4}$

3  Convert these decimals to fractions in their simplest form.

   **a** 0.6         **b** 0.25         **c** 0.2

**Rich task**

A pair of trainers cost £80.
They are increased in price by 10%.

By what percentage do they need to be reduced to get back to the original cost of £80?

This spread will show you how to:

- Use fraction notation and vocabulary
- Calculate a given fraction of a given quantity
- Express a given number as a fraction of another

**Keywords**
Denominator
Equal
Fraction
Numerator

In real life you don't just use whole numbers.

When a pizza is divided into 8 equal slices

Each slice is part of the whole pizza.
One slice is $\frac{1}{8}$ of the whole pizza.

When you measure someone's height

$1\frac{1}{2}$ m

This person is one whole metre and half of another metre.

When you read the petrol gauge in a car

This car is about $\frac{3}{4}$ full with petrol.

- You can use a **fraction** to describe a part of a whole. To use a fraction the whole must be divided into **equal** sized parts.

5 out of the 9 equal sections are shaded.

Fraction shaded $= \frac{5}{9}$

**Numerator:** the top number shows how many parts you have.

**Denominator:** the bottom number shows how many equal sized parts the whole has been divided into.

> **Example**
>
> In a class there are 30 students. 19 of the students are girls. What fraction of the class are girls?
>
> ..........................................................................
>
> 19 out of the 30 students are girls.
> Fraction of girls $= \frac{19}{30}$

The whole is the entire class of 30.

> **Example**
>
> Here is a fuel gauge from a car. How full is the petrol tank? Give your answer as a fraction.
>
> Empty                                                  Full
>
> .......................................................................................
>
> The fuel gauge is divided into five equal sections.
> Three of the sections are coloured, and showing fuel.
> The car is $\frac{3}{5}$ full.

1  Write the fraction of each of these shapes that is shaded.

a   b   c

d   e  f

**A02 Functional Maths**

2 a There are 28 students in a class. 15 are boys and 13 are girls.
     What fraction of the class are
     **i** boys                    **ii** girls?
   b Tyrone has eight pairs of brown shoes and seven pairs of
     black shoes. What fraction of his shoes are
     **i** brown                   **ii** black?
   c Wesley earns £300 a week. He pays £91 of his money each
     week in tax. He saves £60 each week. What fraction of his
     weekly wage does Wesley
     **i** pay in tax              **ii** save?
   d A teacher works for eight hours at school and three hours at
     home. What fraction of the day does the teacher work
     **i** at school               **ii** at home?
   e Rory has a collection of 13 CDs, 15 DVDs and nine computer
     games. What fraction of his collection is
     **i** CDs        **ii** DVDs          **iii** computer games?
   f Irene has 38 hardback books and 77 paperback books.
     What fraction of her books are
     **i** hardbacks               **ii** paperbacks?

3  Write the fraction indicated by each of the pointers.

a

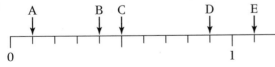

b

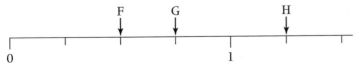

c

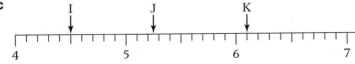

Some of these
fractions are
greater than 1.
You write $1\frac{1}{4}$.

**Equivalent fractions**

This spread will show you how to:

- Simplify fractions by cancelling common factors
- Recognise and find equivalent fractions
- Add and subtract simple fractions

**Keywords**

Cancel
Common factor
Equivalent
Fraction
Simplest form

The same fraction of each rectangle is shaded.

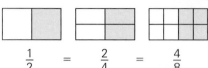

$$\frac{1}{2} = \frac{2}{4} = \frac{4}{8}$$

These fractions are called **equivalent** fractions.

Equivalent fractions are assessed in Unit 2.

- You can find equivalent fractions by multiplying the numerator and denominator by the same number.

This topic is extended to adding and subtracting fractions on page 410.

**Example**

Find two equivalent fractions for $\frac{4}{7}$.

$$\overset{\times 3}{\overbrace{\frac{4}{7} = \frac{12}{21}}}_{\times 3} \qquad \overset{\times 5}{\overbrace{\frac{4}{7} = \frac{20}{35}}}_{\times 5}$$

So $\frac{12}{21} = \frac{4}{7}$ and $\frac{20}{35} = \frac{4}{7}$

- You can simplify a fraction by dividing the numerator and denominator by the same number. This process is called **cancelling**.

**Example**

Write each of these fractions in its **simplest form.**

**a** $\frac{15}{20}$   **b** $\frac{24}{30}$

**a** $$\overset{\div 5}{\overbrace{\frac{15}{20} = \frac{3}{4}}}_{\div 5}$$   **b** $$\overset{\div 2}{\overbrace{\frac{24}{30} = \frac{12}{15}}} \overset{\div 3}{\overbrace{= \frac{4}{5}}}_{\div 2 \qquad \div 3}$$

- You can add or subtract fractions with the same denominator.

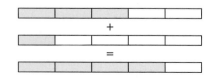

$$\frac{3}{5} + \frac{1}{5} = \frac{4}{5}$$

When the denominators are the same, you can add or subtract fractions by simply adding or subtracting the numerators.

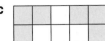
**1** Write the fraction of each of these shapes that is shaded.
Give your answer in its simplest form.

a

b

c

d

e

**2** Copy and complete each of these equivalent fraction families.

a $\frac{1}{2} = \frac{2}{4} = \frac{?}{10} = \frac{?}{16}$

b $\frac{3}{10} = \frac{6}{20} = \frac{?}{30} = \frac{15}{?} = \frac{30}{?}$

c $\frac{4}{5} = \frac{?}{10} = \frac{12}{?} = \frac{?}{25} = \frac{?}{100}$

d $\frac{5}{8} = \frac{10}{?} = \frac{?}{24} = \frac{?}{80} = \frac{75}{?}$

e $\frac{2}{9} = \frac{?}{18} = \frac{6}{?} = \frac{10}{?} = \frac{?}{81}$

f $\frac{7}{4} = \frac{?}{8} = \frac{?}{12} = \frac{?}{40} = \frac{77}{?}$

**3** Find the missing number in each of these pairs of equivalent fractions.

a $\frac{2}{3} = \frac{?}{9}$

b $\frac{4}{5} = \frac{12}{?}$

c $\frac{3}{4} = \frac{?}{20}$

d $\frac{1}{8} = \frac{?}{40}$

e $\frac{5}{7} = \frac{30}{?}$

f $\frac{4}{9} = \frac{?}{63}$

g $\frac{7}{8} = \frac{?}{48}$

h $\frac{7}{10} = \frac{?}{100}$

i $\frac{12}{15} = \frac{?}{5}$

j $\frac{18}{24} = \frac{3}{?}$

k $\frac{30}{35} = \frac{?}{7}$

l $\frac{14}{35} = \frac{2}{?}$

m $\frac{?}{3} = \frac{16}{24}$

n $\frac{4}{?} = \frac{20}{55}$

o $\frac{?}{10} = \frac{56}{80}$

p $\frac{9}{13} = \frac{?}{65}$

**4** Cancel down each of these fractions into their simplest form.

a $\frac{4}{8}$

b $\frac{3}{9}$

c $\frac{4}{6}$

d $\frac{8}{10}$

e $\frac{9}{12}$

f $\frac{10}{15}$

g $\frac{3}{15}$

h $\frac{12}{16}$

i $\frac{14}{16}$

j $\frac{13}{16}$

k $\frac{12}{18}$

l $\frac{8}{20}$

m $\frac{16}{24}$

n $\frac{21}{28}$

o $\frac{20}{25}$

p $\frac{18}{30}$

q $\frac{12}{36}$

r $\frac{24}{40}$

s $\frac{14}{42}$

t $\frac{27}{63}$

**5** Find an equivalent fraction for each fraction. Both of your fractions
should have the same denominator.

a $\frac{1}{2}$ and $\frac{1}{3}$

b $\frac{1}{5}$ and $\frac{1}{3}$

c $\frac{1}{2}$ and $\frac{1}{5}$

d $\frac{2}{3}$ and $\frac{1}{4}$

e $\frac{3}{10}$ and $\frac{1}{3}$

f $\frac{4}{5}$ and $\frac{1}{4}$

g $\frac{1}{3}$ and $\frac{3}{7}$

h $\frac{5}{6}$ and $\frac{3}{4}$

**6** Calculate each of these. Give your answer in its simplest form.

a $\frac{1}{3} + \frac{1}{3}$

b $\frac{2}{5} + \frac{1}{5}$

c $\frac{3}{10} + \frac{7}{10}$

d $\frac{4}{9} + \frac{2}{9}$

e $\frac{7}{8} + \frac{5}{8}$

f $\frac{13}{7} - \frac{6}{7}$

g $\frac{5}{16} - \frac{1}{16}$

h $\frac{13}{18} - \frac{5}{18}$

i $\frac{12}{15} + \frac{8}{15}$

j $\frac{19}{16} - \frac{7}{16}$

k $\frac{12}{35} + \frac{8}{35}$

l $\frac{23}{30} - \frac{7}{30}$

This spread will show you how to:

- Understand and interpret percentages
- Convert fractions into percentages
- Convert percentages into fractions

**Keywords**

Equivalent
Fraction
Percentage

- A **percentage** is a fraction of something. It is written as the number of parts per hundred.

$40\%$ is the fraction $\frac{40}{100}$.

$40\%$ of this line is shaded. The line is divided into 100 parts and 40 of them are shaded.

- To change a percentage into a **fraction** you write it as a fraction out of a 100 and then simplify.

Some useful equivalents to remember.

$10\% = \frac{10}{100} = \frac{1}{10}$

$20\% = \frac{20}{100} = \frac{1}{5}$

$25\% = \frac{25}{100} = \frac{1}{4}$

$50\% = \frac{50}{100} = \frac{1}{2}$

$75\% = \frac{75}{100} = \frac{3}{4}$

**Example**

Write these percentages as fractions in their simplest form.

**a** $60\%$ **b** $45\%$

**a** $60\% = \frac{60}{100}$

$$\overset{\div 10}{\overset{\frown}{\frac{60}{100}}} = \overset{\div 2}{\overset{\frown}{\frac{6}{10}}} = \frac{3}{5} \quad 60\% = \frac{3}{5}$$
$$\underset{\div 10}{\underset{\smile}{}} \quad \underset{\div 2}{\underset{\smile}{}}$$

**b** $45\% = \frac{45}{100}$

$$\overset{\div 5}{\overset{\frown}{\frac{45}{100}}} = \frac{9}{20} \quad 45\% = \frac{9}{20}$$
$$\underset{\div 5}{\underset{\smile}{}}$$

To simplify a fraction, divide the numerator and denominator by the same number. Equivalent fractions are assessed in Unit 2.

- To change a fraction into a percentage you write it as an equivalent fraction out of 100 and then change it into a percentage.

**Example**

Change these fractions into percentages.

**a** $\frac{7}{10}$ **b** $\frac{7}{25}$

**a**
$$\overset{\times 10}{\overset{\frown}{\frac{7}{10}}} = \frac{70}{100} \quad \frac{70}{100} = 70\%$$
$$\underset{\times 10}{\underset{\smile}{}}$$

**b**
$$\overset{\times 4}{\overset{\frown}{\frac{7}{25}}} = \frac{28}{100} \quad \frac{28}{100} = 28\%$$
$$\underset{\times 4}{\underset{\smile}{}}$$

You can express something as the percentage of a whole by first finding the fraction of the whole.

**Example**

What percentage of this shape is shaded?

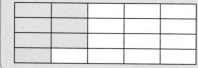

There are 20 equal parts. 7 of the parts are shaded. The fraction shaded is $\frac{7}{20}$.
Converting to a percentage:
% shaded $= \frac{7}{20} = \frac{35}{100} = 35\%$

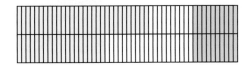
1 This rectangle has been divided into 100 parts.

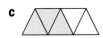

   **a** What percentage of the rectangle is shaded yellow?
   **b** What percentage of the rectangle is shaded green?
   **c** What percentage of the rectangle is not shaded green?

2 Write these percentages as fractions out of 100.
   **a** 35%      **b** 10%      **c** 67%      **d** 43%
   **e** 95%      **f** 56%      **g** 140%    **h** 135%

3 Write the value of each of the letters on these number lines.

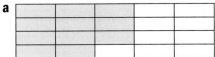

0 5%    20%       A  B     75%    C   100%

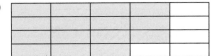

0  D     E       $\frac{1}{2}$  $\frac{11}{20}$     F    $\frac{9}{10}$  1

4 Write these percentages as fractions in their simplest form.
   **a** 50%      **b** 80%      **c** 15%      **d** 85%
   **e** 28%      **f** 6%       **g** 150%    **h** 115%

5 Write each of these fractions as a percentage.
   **a** $\frac{27}{100}$     **b** $\frac{1}{2}$     **c** $\frac{7}{10}$     **d** $\frac{11}{25}$     **e** $\frac{3}{4}$
   **f** $\frac{34}{200}$     **g** $\frac{6}{5}$     **h** $\frac{21}{20}$     **i** $\frac{26}{40}$     **j** $\frac{33}{75}$

6 What percentage of each of these shapes is shaded?

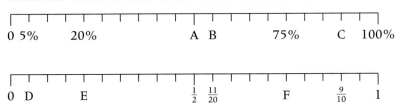

   **c**                   **d**

7 **a** A shirt is 65% polyester and 35% cotton.
     Write 35% as a fraction.
     Give your answer in its simplest form.

   **b** How would you write $17\frac{1}{2}$% as a fraction in
     its simplest form?
     Show all your working out.

This spread will show you how to:
- Convert between fractions, decimals and percentages
- Order fractions, decimals and percentages

**Keywords**
Decimal
Equivalent
Fraction
Order
Percentage

You can change between fractions, decimals and percentages.

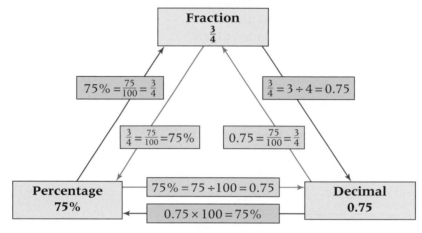

p.170

p.294

You can compare the size of fractions by placing them on a number line.

**Example**

Which is bigger, $\frac{3}{5}$ or $\frac{5}{8}$?

Divide a line into five equal pieces and shade three of them.
This is $\frac{3}{5}$ of the line.

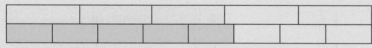

Divide a second line of the same length into eight equal pieces and shade five of them. This is $\frac{5}{8}$ of the line.

$\frac{5}{8}$ is greater than $\frac{3}{5}$.

This topic is extended to comparing fractions on page 410.

- You can **order fractions**, decimals and percentages by converting them into decimals.

**Example**

Write these numbers in order of size. Start with the smallest number.

   0.85      72%      $\frac{7}{8}$      $\frac{4}{5}$

$72\% = \frac{72}{100} \div 100 = 0.72$

$\frac{7}{8} = 7 \div 8 = 0.875$

$\frac{4}{5} = 4 \div 5 = 0.8$

Placing the decimals in order      0.72    0.8    0.85    0.875

So the order is            72%    $\frac{4}{5}$    0.85    $\frac{7}{8}$

1 Write these percentages as decimals.
   **a** 67%      **b** 78%      **c** 99%      **d** 70%      **e** 39%
   **f** 88%      **g** 150%     **h** 125%     **i** 99.9%    **j** 110%

2 Write these decimals as percentages.
   **a** 0.32     **b** 0.22     **c** 0.85     **d** 0.03     **e** 0.54
   **f** 0.63     **g** 0.38     **h** 0.375    **i** 0.333    **j** 1.25

3 Write these decimals as fractions in their simplest form.
   **a** 0.8      **b** 0.28     **c** 0.325    **d** 0.05     **e** 0.12

4 Change these fractions to decimals. Give your answers to two
   decimal places as appropriate.

   **a** $\frac{3}{10}$      **b** $\frac{7}{25}$      **c** $\frac{7}{12}$      **d** $\frac{9}{15}$      **e** $\frac{15}{7}$

5 Write these percentages as fractions in their simplest form.
   **a** 25%      **b** 40%      **c** 65%      **d** 15%      **e** 145%

6 A shirt is 65% polyester and 35% cotton.
   Write 65% as a decimal.

7 Write each of these fractions as percentages.
   Give your answers to one decimal place as appropriate.

   **a** $\frac{48}{100}$      **b** $\frac{6}{25}$      **c** $\frac{17}{10}$      **d** $\frac{8}{15}$      **e** $\frac{11}{16}$

   > Try converting the
   > fraction into a
   > decimal first.

8 Copy and complete this table. Use the most effective method to
   convert between fractions, decimals and percentages.

| Fraction (in its simplest form) | | $\frac{5}{9}$ | | $\frac{13}{5}$ | |
|---|---|---|---|---|---|
| Decimal (to 3 dp) | 0.76 | | | 0.125 | |
| Percentage (to 1 dp) | | 85% | | | 17.5 |

   > dp means
   > decimal places.

9 For each pair of fractions, write which is the larger fraction.

   **a** $\frac{3}{4}$ and $\frac{2}{3}$ (draw a number line 12 cm long)

   **b** $\frac{4}{5}$ and $\frac{3}{4}$ (draw a number line 20 cm long)

   **c** $\frac{4}{5}$ and $\frac{5}{6}$ (draw a number line 30 cm long)

   **d** $\frac{2}{3}$ and $\frac{3}{5}$ (draw a number line 15 cm long)

   **e** $\frac{4}{7}$ and $\frac{2}{5}$ (draw a number line 35 cm long)

   > Draw a number
   > line and mark
   > each fraction on
   > the number line.

10 Put these lists of numbers in order, starting with the smallest.

   **a** 0.4        43%        $\frac{3}{8}$        0.35

   **b** $\frac{3}{5}$        0.56        61%        $\frac{4}{7}$

   **c** $\frac{3}{4}$        $\frac{2}{3}$        70%        0.715

This spread will show you how to:

- Express one number as a fraction of another number
- Calculate a given fraction of an amount
- Use mental, written and calculator methods to calculate with fractions

**Keywords**
Fraction

You can express one number as a **fraction** of another number.

**Example**

In a class there are 30 students. 18 of the students are boys. What fraction of the class are boys? Give your answer in its simplest form.

 p.344

There are 30 students in the class altogether (the **whole**).
18 of the students are boys.
Fraction of the class who are boys $= \frac{18}{30} = \frac{3}{5}$

You can calculate a fraction of a number or quantity in several ways.

**Example**

Calculate using a mental method.

**a** $\frac{1}{4}$ of £20     **b** $\frac{3}{5}$ of €200

**a**

$\frac{1}{4}$ of £20 = 20 ÷ 4 = £5

**b**

$\frac{1}{5}$ of €200 = 200 ÷ 5 = €40

$\frac{3}{5}$ of €200 = 3 × 40 = €120

Finding $\frac{1}{5}$ of something is the same as dividing by 5.

**Example**

Calculate $\frac{3}{8}$ of 56 kg using a written method.

$\frac{3}{8}$ of 56 kg $= \frac{3}{8} \times 56$ kg

To work out a fraction of an amount, multiply the fraction by the amount.

$= 3 \times \frac{1}{8} \times 56$ kg

$= \frac{3 \times 56}{8}$

$= \frac{168}{8} = 21$ kg

Multiplying by $\frac{1}{8}$ is the same as dividing by 8.

You could also work out
$3 \times (56 \div 8) = 3 \times 7$
$= 21$

**Example**

Calculate $\frac{7}{8}$ of £93 using a calculator.

Decimal equivalent for $\frac{7}{8} = 7 \div 8 = 0.875$

$\frac{7}{8}$ of £93 $= \frac{7}{8} \times$ £93 $= 0.875 \times 93$
$= 81.375 = $ £81.38

1  Write the fraction of each of these shapes that is shaded, leaving your answer as a fraction in its simplest form.

a      b      c 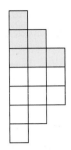     d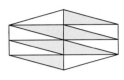

2  Use a mental method to calculate each of these amounts.

   **a** $\frac{1}{2}$ of 40 sheep   **b** $\frac{1}{3}$ of 15 apples   **c** $\frac{1}{5}$ of 25 shops   **d** $\frac{1}{4}$ of 48 marks

**3** For each answer state the fraction in its simplest form.
   **a** There are 30 students in a class. 20 are boys and 10 are girls. What fraction of the class are
      **i** boys          **ii** girls?
   **b** Horace earns £500 a week. He pays £150 of his money each week in tax. He saves £120 each week. What fraction of his weekly wage does Horace
      **i** pay in tax      **ii** save?
   **c** Michael and Shafique share £200. Michael has £80 and Shafique has £120. What fraction of the £200 belongs
      **i** to Michael      **ii** to Shafique?

4  Use a mental or written method to work out these.

   **a** $\frac{8}{10}$ of €200

   $\frac{1}{10}$ of €200 = 200 ÷ 10 = _____

   $\frac{8}{10}$ of €200 = 8 × _____ = _____

   **b** $\frac{2}{5}$ of £40      **c** $\frac{3}{4}$ of 60 minutes      **d** $\frac{4}{7}$ of 77 pencils

   **e** $\frac{3}{10}$ of £84      **f** $\frac{5}{6}$ of 42 apples      **g** $\frac{7}{12}$ of 36p

5  Use a suitable method to calculate each of these. Where appropriate round your answer to two decimal places.

   **a** $\frac{7}{15}$ of 375      **b** $\frac{9}{10}$ of $450      **c** $\frac{4}{7}$ of 800 kg

   **d** $\frac{5}{9}$ of 234 m      **e** $\frac{17}{18}$ of 400 tonnes      **f** $\frac{4}{5}$ of 360°

   **g** $\frac{12}{25}$ of 750 marbles      **h** $\frac{11}{15}$ of £255      **i** $\frac{4}{15}$ of £345

   **j** $\frac{1}{6}$ of 546 hours

This spread will show you how to:

- Use percentage as an operator
- Calculate a percentage of an amount using mental and written methods

**Percentages**, fractions and decimals are ways of writing the same thing.

$$25\% = \frac{25}{100} = \frac{1}{4} = 0.25$$

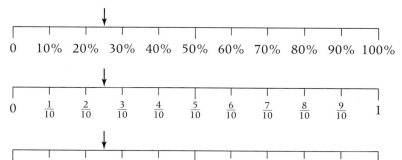

Some useful equivalents to remember.

$$1\% = \frac{1}{100} = 0.01$$
$$10\% = \frac{10}{100} = \frac{1}{10} = 0.1$$
$$20\% = \frac{20}{100} = \frac{1}{5} = 0.2$$
$$25\% = \frac{25}{100} = \frac{1}{4} = 0.25$$
$$50\% = \frac{50}{100} = \frac{1}{2} = 0.5$$

You can calculate simple percentages of amounts in your head using equivalent fractions.

**Example**

Calculate
**a** 10% of £41                    **b** 50% of 84 m

....................................................................................................

**a** $\frac{1}{10}$ of £41    $\left(10\% = \frac{1}{10}\right)$

$= \frac{1}{10} \times £41$

$= £41 \div 10$

$= £4.10$

**b** $\frac{1}{2}$ of 84 m    $\left(50\% = \frac{1}{2}\right)$

$= \frac{1}{2} \times 84$ m

$= 84$ m $\div 2$

$= 42$ m

- To calculate a percentage of an amount using a written method, change the percentage to its equivalent fraction and multiply by the amount.

**Example**

Calculate 15% of £80.

....................................................................................................

$15\%$ of £80 $= \frac{15}{100} \times £80$

$= 15 \times £80 \times \frac{1}{100}$

$= \frac{15 \times £80}{100}$

$= \frac{£1200}{100}$

$= £12$

Alternatively you could use a mental method:

$10\%$ of £80 $= \frac{1}{10}$ of 80

$= 80 \div 10 = 8$

So  5% of 80 $= 8 \div 2 = 4$

So 15% of 80 $= 8 + 4 = 12$

15% of £80 is £12.

$15\% = 10\% + 5\%$

**1** **a** What fraction of this shape is shaded?

**b** What percentage of the shape is shaded?
**c** Copy the shape and shade in more squares so that 70% of the shape is shaded.

**2** Calculate these percentages without using a calculator.
  **a** 50% of £60  **b** 50% of 40      **c** 50% of 272p     **d** 10% of 40
  **e** 10% of 370p **f** 1% of £700     **g** 50% of 12 kg    **h** 50% of £31
  **i** 1% of 200   **j** 1% of 420 m

**3** Calculate these percentages using a mental method.
  **a** 10% of £40  **b** 10% of £340    **c** 5% of £120      **d** 20% of 210 km
  **e** 20% of $530 **f** 25% of £300    **g** 20% of £32      **h** 5% of 28 m

**4** Calculate these percentages using a mental method.
  The first one is started for you.
  **a** 60% of 40

$$50\% \text{ of } 40 = \tfrac{1}{2} \text{ of } 40 = 20$$
$$10\% \text{ of } 40 = \tfrac{1}{10} \text{ of } 40 = ?$$
$$\overline{60\% \text{ of } 40 \qquad\qquad = ?}$$

> Use percentages which you can work out quickly in your head:

  **b** 60% of £70       **c** 40% of £30       **d** 40% of 45 m
  **e** 2.5% of £80      **f** 70% of 150 m     **g** 15% of 120 kg
  **h** 35% of 400 mm    **i** 7.5% of 300 km

**5** Write how you would use a mental method to calculate
  **a** 15% of anything  **b** 5% of anything   **c** 20% of anything
  **d** 90% of anything  **e** 11% of anything  **f** 17.5% of anything.

**6** Calculate these percentages using a mental or written method. Show all the steps of your working out.
  **a** 11% of £18       **b** 60% of 7300 km   **c** 8% of £30
  **d** 2% of €3000      **e** 7% of 60 m       **f** 13% of 40 cm
  **g** 75% of 48 m      **h** 3% of £70

**7** Rearrange these cards to make three correct statements.

| 25% of | £450 | = £128 |
| 30% of | £640 | = £130 |
| 20% of | £520 | = £135 |

A03 Problem

**Percentage increase and decrease**

This spread will show you how to:

- Calculate a percentage of an amount
- Calculate percentage increase and decrease

**Keywords**

Decrease
Increase
Percentage

You can already calculate a **percentage** of an amount.

> **Example**
>
> Calculate
> **a** 12% of £50
> **b** 12.6% of 320 m
>
> **a** 12% of £50 $= \frac{12}{100} \times £50$
> $= \frac{12 \times £50}{100}$
> $= \frac{£600}{100}$
> $= £6$
>
> **b** 12.6% of 320 m $= \frac{12.6}{100} \times 320$
> $= 0.126 \times 320$
> $= 40.32$ m

This topic is extended to harder percentage increase and decrease on page 414.

Percentages are used in real life to show how much an amount has increased or decreased.

- To calculate a percentage **increase**, work out the increase and add it to the original amount.
- To calculate a percentage **decrease**, work out the decrease and subtract it from the original amount.

> **Example**
>
> **a** Karen is paid £800 a month. Her employer increases her wage by 6%. Calculate the new wage Karen is paid each month.
> **b** In January a car costs £3400. In February the price is reduced by 17%. What is the new price of the car?
>
> **a** Increase in wage $= 6\%$ of £800 $= \frac{6}{100} \times £800$
> $= \frac{6 \times £800}{100}$
> $= \frac{£4800}{100}$
>
> Increase in wage $= £48$
> Karen's new wage $= £800 + £48$
> $= £848$
>
> **b** Price reduction $= 17\%$ of £3400 $= \frac{17}{100} \times £3400$
> $= 0.17 \times £3400$
> Price reduction $= £578$
> New price of car $= £3400 - £578$
> $= £2822$

- Calculate 6% of Karen's monthly wage.
- Add this to her monthly wage.

**Unit 1**

**1** Calculate these amounts without using a calculator.
- **a** 10% of £400
- **b** 10% of 2600 cm
- **c** 5% of 64 kg
- **d** 25% of 80 m
- **e** 50% of 380p
- **f** 5% of £700
- **g** 25% of 12 kg
- **h** 20% of £31
- **i** 15% of 360
- **j** 1% of 720 m
- **k** 30% of £25
- **l** 25% of 444

**2** Calculate these percentages, giving your answer to two decimal places where appropriate.
- **a** 45% of 723 kg
- **b** 25% of $480
- **c** 23% of 45 kg
- **d** 21% of 28 kg
- **e** 17.5% of £124
- **f** 34% of 230 m

**3** Calculate these percentages, giving your answer to two decimal places where appropriate.
- **a** 4.5% of £320
- **b** 2.5% of $4300
- **c** 3.6% of 54 kg
- **d** 13.2% of 220 m$^2$
- **e** 4.8% of 245 litres
- **f** 5.1% of 2050 hectares

**Functional Maths A02**

**4 a** There are 62 million people living in the UK. 23% of the population are under 18. How many people are under 18?
  **b** The price of a pair of trainers is normally £85. In a sale the price is reduced by 30%. How much cheaper are the trainers in the sale?
  **c** The recommended daily allowance (RDA) of iron is 14 mg. A bowl of cereal provides 45% of the RDA of iron. How much iron is there in a bowl of cereal?
  **d** Joanne earns £78 450 a year. She pays 36% of her earnings in tax. How much money does she pay in tax?

**DID YOU KNOW?**

The population of the UK is predicted to reach 71.6 million by 2033.

**5** Calculate these percentage changes.
- **a** Increase £450 by 10%
- **b** Decrease 840 kg by 20%
- **c** Increase £720 by 5%
- **d** Decrease 560 km by 30%
- **e** Increase £560 by 17.5%
- **f** Decrease 320 m by 20%

**Functional Maths A02**

**6 a** A drink can contains 330 ml. The size is increased by 15%. How much drink does it now contain?
  **b** The price of a coat was £95. The price is reduced by 20% in a sale. What is the sale price of the coat?
  **c** A holiday package is advertised in the brochure at a price of £2400. The travel agent reduces the price by 8%. What is the new price of the holiday package?
  **d** A house is bought for £190 000. During the next two years the house increases in price by 23%. What is the new value of the house?

This spread will show you how to:

- Calculate a fraction or a percentage of an amount using a variety of methods

**Keywords**

Fraction
Percentage

You can calculate a **fraction** or a **percentage** of something using different methods.

### Mental methods

> **Example**
>
> Calculate **a** $\frac{2}{3}$ of £240 **b** 20% of €104
>
> **a** Find $\frac{1}{3}$ of £240 = 240 ÷ 3 = £80
>
> Calculate $\frac{2}{3}$ of £240 = 2 × 80 = £160
>
> **b** 20% of €104
>
> Find 10% of €104 = $\frac{1}{10}$ of €104
>
> $= \frac{1}{10} \times €104$
>
> $= €104 ÷ 10 = €10.4$
>
> Calculate 20% of €104 = 2 × 10.4 = €20.8

### Written methods

> **Example**
>
> Calculate **a** $\frac{4}{7}$ of £63 **b** 45% of 320 kg
>
> **a** $\frac{4}{7}$ of £63 = $\frac{4}{7} \times$ £63
>
> $= 4 \times \frac{1}{7} \times$ £63    Multiplying by $\frac{1}{7}$ is the same as dividing by 7.
>
> $= \frac{4 \times 63}{7}$
>
> $= \frac{252}{7}$
>
> $= £36$
>
> **b** 45% of 320 kg = $\frac{45}{100} \times 320$
>
> $= \frac{45 \times 1 \times 320}{100}$
>
> $= \frac{45 \times 320}{100}$
>
> $= \frac{14\,400}{100}$
>
> $= 144$ kg
>
> This is the same as multiplying the amount by 45 and dividing by 100, that is, you work out 45 × 320 ÷ 100

### Calculator methods

> **Example**
>
> Calculate
>
> **a** $\frac{7}{16}$ of 130 m (to one decimal place) **b** 43% of £75
>
> **a** Decimal equivalent of $\frac{7}{16}$ = 7 ÷ 16 = 0.4375
>
> $\frac{7}{16}$ of 130 m = $\frac{7}{16} \times 130$ m
>
> $= 0.4375 \times 130$ m
>
> $= 56.875$ m = 56.9 m (1 dp)
>
> **b** Decimal equivalent of 43% = 43 ÷ 100 = 0.43
>
> 43% of £75 = 0.43 × £75 = £32.25
>
> Another method of finding a percentage of an amount is to find 1%, and then multiply by the percentage. To find 12% of 3500 m
>
> 1% of 3500 = 3500 ÷ 100 = 35
>
> 12% of 3500 = 12 × 35 = 420 m

1. Use a mental method to calculate each of these amounts.

   **a** $\frac{1}{4}$ of 60 carrots     **b** $\frac{1}{3}$ of 24 rulers     **c** $\frac{1}{8}$ of 32 windows

2. Use a mental method to calculate each of these amounts.

   **a** 50% of £90     **b** 1% of 600 m$^2$     **c** 10% of 48 kg
   **d** 25% of 60 kg     **e** 20% of 70p     **f** 1% of £65

   > Try to use the equivalent fractions.

3. Calculate these fractions of amounts without using a calculator.

   **a** $\frac{3}{4}$ of €40     **b** $\frac{2}{3}$ of 60p     **c** $\frac{5}{8}$ of 48 g

   **d** $\frac{3}{10}$ of 80p     **e** $\frac{1}{7}$ of £84     **f** $\frac{5}{9}$ of $45

4. Calculate these percentages without using a calculator.

   **a** 25% of £60     **b** 5% of 40     **c** 10% of 272p
   **d** 75% of 40     **e** 70% of £40     **f** 30% of £50
   **g** 15% of 35 m     **h** 2.5% of £26     **i** 45% of 400 mm

---

**A02 Functional Maths**

5. Calculate these fractions of amounts without using a calculator.

   **a** A jacket normally costs £130. In a sale the jacket is priced at $\frac{4}{5}$ of its normal selling price. What is the new price of the jacket?

   **b** Hector rents out a holiday flat. His flat is available for 45 weeks of the year. He rents the flat out to tourists for $\frac{7}{9}$ of the time it is available. For how many weeks is Hector's flat occupied by tourists?

6. Calculate these percentages without using a calculator.

   **a** Kelvin collects models. He owns 170 models. He has painted 20% of the models. How many of the models has he painted?

   **b** A barrel can hold 70 litres. Water is poured into the barrel until it is 80% full. How much water is there in the barrel?

---

7. Use a suitable method to calculate each of these quantities. Where appropriate round your answer to two decimal places.

   **a** $\frac{7}{12}$ of 450     **b** $\frac{9}{10}$ of 360 m     **c** $\frac{2}{7}$ of 400 kg     **d** $\frac{7}{9}$ of 250 mm

   **e** $\frac{3}{4}$ of 9 tonnes **f** $\frac{4}{11}$ of 2365 m     **g** $\frac{7}{25}$ of 43 000     **h** $\frac{3}{7}$ of £345

8. Calculate these using an appropriate method.

   **a** Increase £450 by 10%.     **b** Decrease 76 kg by 5%.

   **c** Increase $990 by $\frac{1}{3}$.     **d** Decrease 620 km by $\frac{1}{100}$.

## Summary

### Check out

You should now be able to:

- Understand and interpret percentages
- Recognize the equivalence of fractions, decimals and percentages
- Convert between fractions, decimals and percentages
- Order fractions, decimals and percentages
- Express a number as a fraction of another number
- Calculate a fraction and a percentage of an amount

### Worked exam question

The table shows the percentage of each of the materials used in making a car tyre.

| Material | Percentage |
|---|---|
| Natural rubber | 12% |
| Synthetic polymers | 25% |
| Carbon black | 26% |
| Oil | 17% |
| Fabric | 4% |
| Wire | 10% |
| Other | 6% |

**a** Write down the name of the material with the largest percentage. (1)

**b** Write 10% as a decimal. (1)

**c** Write 4% as a decimal. (1)

**d** Write 26% as a fraction.

Give your answer in its simplest form. (2)

(Edexcel Limited 2007)

**a**

> Only the name of the material is needed.

Carbon black

**b**

$$10\% = \frac{10}{100}$$
$$= \frac{1}{10}$$
$$= 0.1$$

> Each answer must be a decimal.

**c**

> Each answer must be a decimal.

$$4\% = \frac{4}{100}$$
$$= 0.04$$

**d**

$$26\% = \frac{26}{100}$$
$$= \frac{13}{50}$$

> Write $\frac{26}{100}$ as well as the simplified answer.

# Exam questions

**1** **a** Copy and shade $\frac{3}{5}$ of this shape.

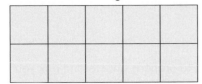

(1)

**b** Copy and shade 0.2 of this shape.

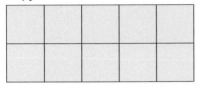

(1)

**2** A television reporter did a survey.
She asked people to name their favourite sport.
The table gives some information about the answers she got.

| Favouite sport | Percentage |
|----------------|------------|
| Football | 30% |
| Cricket | 14% |
| Hockey | 9% |
| Snooker | 8% |
| Tennis | 4% |
| Other | ...... |

**a** Copy and complete the table. (1)
**b** Write down the percentage of people who said snooker. (1)
**c** Write 30% as a fraction.
Give your answer in its simplest form. (2)

**d** Write 9% as a decimal. (1)

2000 people took part in the survey.
**e** Work out the number of people who said cricket. (2)

40 people said golf.
**f** Work out 40 out of 2000 as a percentage. (2)

(Edexcel Limited 2008)

**3** Calculate 36% of €2500. (2)

# Introduction

Car insurance companies keep data on past road accidents and are able to use this to work out the probability (risk) of a person having a car accident. They then work out the cost of your insurance premium based on your age, type of vehicle, driving experience and other factors.

## What's the point?
All forms of insurance rely on risk assessment, and to properly understand risk you need to have a good grasp of probability.

1 Choose a number from the rectangle that is
   **a** prime          **b** square
   **c** triangular      **d** a multiple of 4
   **e** a factor of 10.

2 Cancel these fractions to their simplest form.
   **a** $\frac{12}{15}$          **b** $\frac{8}{10}$          **c** $\frac{5}{20}$
   **d** $\frac{15}{25}$          **e** $\frac{10}{10}$

3 Work out each of these subtractions.
   **a** $1 - \frac{1}{4}$          **b** $1 - \frac{7}{10}$          **c** $1 - \frac{3}{5}$

4 Work out each of these multiplications.
   **a** $\frac{1}{5} \times 50$          **b** $\frac{2}{5} \times 100$          **c** $\frac{2}{3} \times 300$

Key stage 3 →

- Understand and use the probability scale
- Calculate probabilities of outcomes
- List all outcomes for single events and two events
- Calculate the expected frequency of an event
- Understand and use relative frequency

D1 →

→ +16, +17

**Rich task**

Inside a bag are three cards with the names Anna, Neve and Davma written on them.
You are allowed to pick one card from the bag and then replace the card in the bag.
What is the probability you pick the same name twice?

This spread will show you how to:

- Understand and use the probability scale
- Calculate probabilities of outcomes, including equally likely outcomes, giving answers in their simplest form
- List all outcomes for single events

An **event** is an activity, for example, spinning a spinner.

The possible **outcomes** are Blue, Yellow, Green, Red.

The **probability** is a number that measures how likely it is that an outcome will happen.

All probabilities have a value between 0 and 1.

- You can show a probability on a **probability scale**.

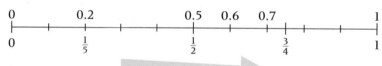

more and more likely to happen

0 means impossible.
1 means certain.

You can use decimals, fractions or percentages.

- You can calculate the probability using these formulae:

p.22

$$\text{Probability of an outcome happening} = \frac{\text{number of ways the outcome can happen}}{\text{total number of all possible outcomes}}$$

Probability of an outcome not happening = 1 − probability of the outcome happening

Probability of an outcome can be written as P(outcome).

**Example**

20 counters are put into a bag. There are 1 red, 3 blue, 4 yellow and 12 green counters. Edward takes out a counter without looking. Calculate, giving your answers in simplest form, the probability that Edward takes out
a a red counter
b any colour that is not red
c a green or yellow counter
d a purple counter.

'Simplest form' means cancel the fraction.

a There is one red counter. There are 20 possible outcomes.
P(red) $= \frac{1}{20}$

b $1 - \frac{1}{20} = \frac{19}{20}$   P(not red) $= \frac{19}{20}$

c There are 16 green or yellow counters. P(green or yellow) $= \frac{16}{20} = \frac{4}{5}$

d There are 0 purple counters.   P(purple) $= \frac{0}{20} = 0$

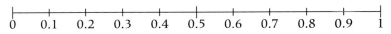
For all these questions, the outcomes are equally likely.

**1** A bag contains four red and six blue balls. One
   ball is taken out of the bag.
   **a** Calculate the probability that the ball is red.
   **b** Calculate the probability that the ball is blue.
   **c** Draw a probability scale as shown.

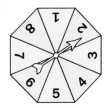

```
├──┬──┬──┬──┬──┬──┬──┬──┬──┬──┤
0  0.1 0.2 0.3 0.4 0.5 0.6 0.7 0.8 0.9  1
```

   On your scale mark the positions of P(red) and P(blue).
   **d** Which colour ball is most likely to be taken out?
   **e** Which colour ball is least likely to be taken out?

**2** This spinner is spun. Calculate the probability that
   the spinner lands on
   **a** a 3
   **b** an even number
   **c** a number greater than 6
   **d** a number less than 6
   **e** a square number
   **f** a multiple of 3
   **g** a multiple of 4
   **h** a prime number.

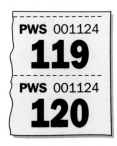

**Functional Maths**

**A02**

**3** A raffle has only one prize. 200 raffle tickets
   are sold. Calculate the probability of winning
   the prize if you buy
   **a** one ticket
   **b** two tickets.

PWS 001124
**119**

PWS 001124
**120**

**4** There are 25 students in a class. Each student is given a different
   number from 1 to 25. The 25 numbers are put into a bag, and one is
   taken out. Calculate the probability that the number is
   **a** odd                          **b** not odd
   **c** a multiple of 5               **d** a multiple of 10
   **e** a square number              **f** a prime number
   **g** greater than 18              **h** less than 10
   **i** not less than 10.

**Expected frequency**

This spread will show you how to:
- Calculate the expected frequency of an event

**Keywords**
Expect
Expected
 frequency
Trial

The probability is a number that measures how likely it is that an event will happen.

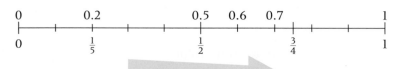

more and more likely to happen

0 means impossible.
1 means certain.

If you know the probability of an event, you can calculate how many times you **expect** the outcomes to happen.

**Example**

The probability of getting a Tail when you spin a coin is $\frac{1}{2}$.
How many Tails would you expect if the coin was spun 100 times?

••••••••••••••••••••••••••••••••••••••••••••••••••••••••••••••••••

$\frac{1}{2}$ of 100 = 50 Tails

- The **expected frequency** is the number of times you expect the outcomes to happen.

- Expected frequency = probability × number of trials

Each spin of the coin is called a **trial**.

**Example**

Red and yellow counters are put in a bag.
The probability of taking out a red counter is $\frac{3}{5}$.

**a** Calculate the probability of taking out a yellow counter.
**b** If a counter is taken out and replaced 20 times, how many yellow counters would you expect to be taken out?

••••••••••••••••••••••••••••••••••••••••••••••••••••••••••••••••••

**a** $1 - \frac{3}{5} = \frac{2}{5}$
 P(yellow counter) = $\frac{2}{5}$
**b** Expected frequency = probability × number of trials
 $= \frac{2}{5} \times 20$
 $= 8$ yellow counters

The expected frequency does not guarantee the outcomes.
For example, if you spin a coin 100 times you may not always get the outcomes of 50 Tails.

**1** A coin is spun.
  **a** State the probability of spinning a Head.
  **b** If the coin is spun 50 times, how many Heads would you expect?

**2** An ordinary dice is rolled.
  **a** Find the probability of rolling a 3.
  **b** If the dice is rolled 60 times, how many 3s would you expect?

**3** The spinner is made from a regular pentagon.
  **a** Calculate the probability of spinning an even number.
  **b** If the spinner is spun 100 times, how many even numbers would you expect?

**4** A bag contains 3 red balls and 7 green balls. One ball is taken out and then replaced back in the bag.
  **a** Calculate the probability that the ball is red.
  **b** Calculate the probability that the ball is green.
    If a ball is taken out and replaced 100 times, how many of the balls would you expect to be
  **c** red
  **d** green?

**5** The probability of sun on a day in June on the Costa del Sunny is $\frac{2}{3}$. Calculate the number of days in June on which you would expect sun on the Costa del Sunny.

**6** The probability that a fuchsia plant will survive after a severe ground frost is $\frac{4}{5}$.
  **a** Calculate the probability that the fuchsia will not survive after a severe ground frost.
    A gardener has 50 of these fuchsia plants.
  **b** How many of the plants should he expect to die after a severe ground frost?

**7** The probability of seeing a red car is $\frac{7}{20}$.
  **a** Calculate the probability of not seeing a red car.
  **b** If 100 cars go past you, how many of these would you expect not to be red?

**8** The probability that a seed germinates is $\frac{9}{10}$.
  If 60 seeds are planted, how many seeds would you expect to germinate?

30 days has September, April, June and November.

125

This spread will show you how to:
- Understand and use relative frequency

You can calculate a **theoretical** probability for objects such as coins and dice.

It is not always possible to calculate the theoretical probability, for example the probability of a car accident on a stretch of road.

You can, however, **estimate** the probability from experiments.

- The estimated probability is called the **relative frequency**.

This topic is extended on page 440.

**Example**

James spins a square spinner 50 times.
The results are shown in the data collection sheet.

| Colour | Tally | Frequency |
|--------|-------|-----------|
| Red | ЖЖ ЖЖ | 10 |
| Blue | ЖЖ ЖЖ IIII | 14 |
| Yellow | ЖЖ IIII | 9 |
| Green | ЖЖ ЖЖ ЖЖ II | 17 |

a Estimate the probability of getting green on the spinner.
b Do you think the spinner is biased?
  Explain your answer.
..................................................................
a The spinner was green on 17 out of 50 occasions.
  Estimated probability of getting green $= \frac{17}{50}$
b You would expect each frequency to be about the same for a fair spinner.

  The spinner could be biased as there are many more green than yellow.

  However, James needs to spin the spinner many more times before he can make the decision.

The spinner is **biased** if the colours are NOT all equally likely.

The spinner is **fair** if the colours are all equally likely.

- The estimated probability becomes more and more reliable the greater the number of trials.

Each spin of the spinner is called a **trial**.

**1** A tetrahedron dice is rolled 50 times. The scores are shown.

```
4  3  2  2  1  4  2  3  1  4
3  2  1  4  4  3  2  1  1  2
4  2  2  3  1  1  2  4  4  3
3  3  2  1  4  3  4  2  2  1
2  1  4  2  4  3  4  2  1  1
```

**a** Copy and complete the frequency chart to show the 50 scores.

| Score | Tally | Frequency |
|-------|-------|-----------|
| 1     |       |           |
| 2     |       |           |
| 3     |       |           |
| 4     |       |           |

**b** State the modal score.

**c** Estimate the probability of rolling a

  **i** 1      **ii** 2      **iii** 3      **iv** 4

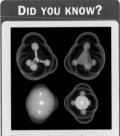

**DID YOU KNOW?**

The tetrahedron is a shape that is commonly seen in molecular structures, for example methane.

**2** A spinner is made from a regular octagon.
The spinner is spun 40 times and the colour is recorded.

```
Orange  Red     Orange  Green   Orange  Orange
Orange  Green   Red     Green   Orange  Orange
Orange  Green   Orange  Orange  Orange  Orange
Orange  Green   Orange  Orange  Red     Green
Green   Green   Orange  Green   Green   Green
Orange  Orange  Orange  Red     Green   Green
Green   Orange  Green   Red
```

**a** Copy and complete the frequency chart to show the 40 colours.

| Colour | Tally | Frequency |
|--------|-------|-----------|
| Orange |       |           |
| Green  |       |           |
| Red    |       |           |

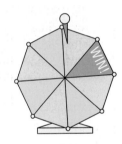

**b** State the modal colour.

**c** Estimate the probability of spinning

  **i** orange      **ii** green      **iii** red.

**3** A coin is spun 100 times. The outcomes are shown in the frequency table.

**a** Calculate the estimated probability of spinning a Head.

**b** Calculate the estimate probability of spinning a Tail.

**c** Do you think the coin is biased? Explain your answer.

|      | Frequency |
|------|-----------|
| Head | 45        |
| Tail | 55        |

This spread will show you how to:

- List all outcomes for two successive events in a systematic way

**Keywords**
Event
Outcome
Successive
Systematic

**Successive**
means following
on, for example,
6, 7, 8.

- You can list the possible **outcomes** for two successive events.

**Example**

A restaurant decides to offer a two-course meal for £5.99.

The meal must be one starter and one main course.

List the different choices that are possible.

Onion Soup – Beef Steak
Onion Soup – Grilled Salmon
Onion Soup – Veggie Pasta
Caesar Salad – Beef Steak
Caesar Salad – Grilled Salmon
Caesar Salad – Veggie Pasta

This list is
**systematic**.
It is in order.

**Example**

A spinner has colours red, yellow, blue and green.
A coin has two faces, Heads or Tails.

Matthew spins the spinner and the coin.

**a** List all the possible outcomes.
**b** What is the probability that he gets green and a Head?

**a**

| Colour on spinner | Red | Red | Yellow | Yellow | Blue | Blue | Green | Green |
|---|---|---|---|---|---|---|---|---|
| Head/Tail on coin | Head | Tail | Head | Tail | Head | Tail | Head | Tail |

**b** Green and Head occurs once.
There are 8 possible outcomes.

$P(\text{Green and a Head}) = \frac{1}{8}$

**1** At a sports club, there are three activities, but only two sessions. You have to choose one different activity for each session. Copy and complete the table to show the possible choices.

| Session 1 | Session 2 |
|-----------|-----------|
| Tennis | Badminton |
| Tennis | |
| | |
| | |
| | |
| | |

Choose 2 from
**Tennis**
**Badminton**
**Squash**

**2** Four people, Arthur, Ben, Chris and Darryl, enter a competition.
  **a** List the four possible winners of the competition.
   It is decided to give another award, for 'Most improved player'.
  **b** Copy and complete the table to show the 12 possible prize winners.

| Winner | Most improved player |
|--------|----------------------|
| A | B |
| A | |

**3** A spinner is labelled 1, 2, 3. Another spinner is labelled A, B, C. Both spinners are spun.
  **a** List the nine possible outcomes.
  **b** Calculate the probability of getting a 3 and a C.

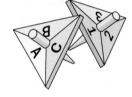

**4** A dice is numbered from 1 to 6. A coin has Head or Tail. The dice is rolled and the coin is spun.
  **a** List the 12 possible outcomes.
  **b** Calculate the probability of getting a 3 and a Head.
  **c** Calculate the probability of getting an even number and a Tail.

**5** Three tracksuit tops are in a drawer. Another drawer has three tracksuit bottoms. One top and one bottom are randomly taken out of the drawers.

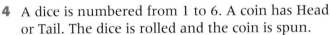

Red (R)　　Green (G)　　Blue (B)

Yellow (Y)　　Pink (P)　　Orange (O)

  **a** List the nine possible outcomes.
  **b** Calculate the probability of getting blue and yellow.
  **c** Calculate the probability of not getting blue and yellow.
  **d** Calculate the probability of getting blue and orange.
  **e** Calculate the probability of not getting blue and orange.

## Summary

### Check out

You should now be able to:

- Understand and use the vocabulary of probability scale
- Calculate probabilities of events, including equally likely outcomes, giving answers in their simplest form
- Calculate the expected frequency of an event
- Understand and use relative frequency
- List all outcomes for single events and for two successive events in a systematic way

### Worked exam question

Joshua rolls an ordinary dice once.
It has faces marked 1, 2, 3, 4, 5 and 6.

**a** Write down the probability that he gets

  **i**   a 6,                 **ii**   an odd number,

  **iii**   a number less than 3,     **iv**   an 8.           (4)

Ken rolls a different dice 60 times.
This dice also has six faces.
The table gives information about Ken's scores.

| Score on dice | Frequency |
| --- | --- |
| 1 | 9 |
| 2 | 11 |
| 3 | 20 |
| 4 | 2 |
| 5 | 8 |
| 6 | 10 |

**b** Explain what you think is different about Ken's dice.   (1)

(Edexcel Limited 2006)

**a** Write down the probability that he gets

  **i**   $\frac{1}{6}$

  **ii**   $\frac{3}{6} = \frac{1}{2}$

  **iii**   $\frac{2}{6} = \frac{1}{3}$

  **iv**   0

**b** Ken's dice is biased.

> Write each probability as a fraction.

> The frequencies vary from 2 to 20.

> Write the initial fraction as well as the simplified fraction.

## Exam questions

**1** There are 3 red pens, 4 blue pens and 5 black pens in a box.
Sameena takes a pen, at random, from the box.

Write down the probability that she takes a black pen. (2)

(Edexcel Limited 2008)

**2** Mary rolls a 6-sided dice and spins a 4-sided spinner.

The dice is labelled 1, 2, 3, 4, 5, 6
The spinner is labelled 1, 2, 3, 4

Mary adds the score on the dice and the score on the spinner to get the total score.

Write down all the ways Mary can get a score of 8 or more. (4)

**3** Mark throws a fair coin.
He gets a Head.

Mark's sister then throws the same coin.
**a** What is the probability that she will get a Head? (1)

Mark throws the coin 30 times.
**b** Explain why he may not get exactly 15 Heads and 15 Tails. (1)

(Edexcel Limited 2004)

# Introduction

The United Kingdom is not a very regular shape. However, cartographers have managed to work out its area as 244 820 km².

## What's the point?

Cartographers use lines of latitude and longitude to divide countries into much smaller regular shapes, such as trapeziums. They can then calculate the area of each of these smaller pieces, and add them together to calculate the area of the country.

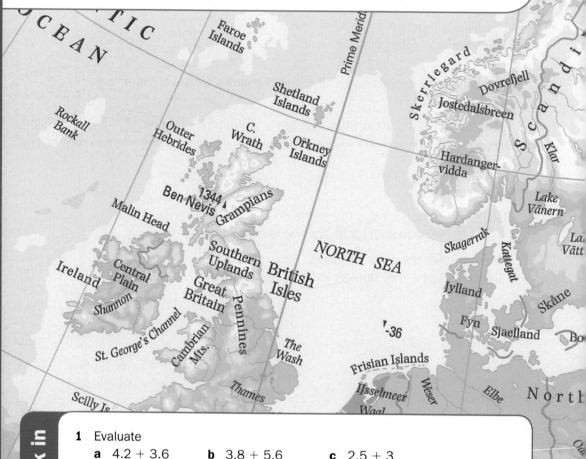

**1** Evaluate

   **a** 4.2 + 3.6     **b** 3.8 + 5.6     **c** 2.5 + 3

**2** Work out

   **a** 40 × 10      **b** 14 × 1000     **c** 3.1 × 10

   **d** 13.4 × 100    **e** 6.3 × 1000    **f** 400 ÷ 10

   **g** 6000 ÷ 100   **h** 430 ÷ 100    **i** 640 ÷ 1000

   **j** 3.1 ÷ 10

**3** Measure this line

   ——————————

   **a** in millimetres

   **b** in centimetres.

| What I need to know | What I will learn | What this leads to |
|---|---|---|
| Key stage 3 → | ■ Make sensible estimates of measurements<br>■ Convert measurements<br>■ Know rough metric equivalents of imperial units<br>■ Find perimeters and areas of simple shapes<br>■ Find the surface area of cuboids | → G2 + 7 |

A farmer has 240 m of fencing. He wants to enclose a field with the maximum area.

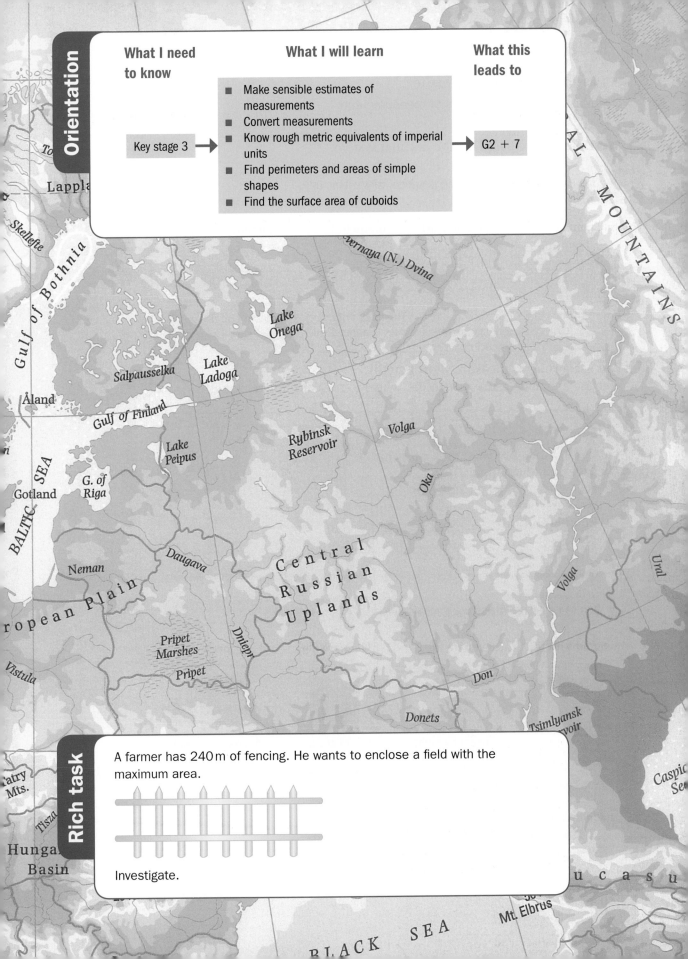

Investigate.

This spread will show you how to:

- Make sensible estimates of measurements

**Metric** units are based on the decimal system.

- You can **measure** length and distance using metric units.

**millimetre (mm)**

1 mm

0    1
cm

1 mm is $\frac{1}{10}$ of 1 cm
10 mm = 1 cm

**centimetre (cm)**

1 cm

The thickness of your little finger is about 1 cm.

**metre (m)**

2 m

The height of a door is about 2 m.

**kilometre (km)**

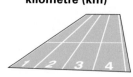

1    2    3    4

$2\frac{1}{2}$ times round the running track is about 1 km.

p.204

You use a ruler to measure short lengths.
You use a tape measure or trundle wheel to measure longer lengths.

**Example**

Give a sensible metric unit to measure

**a** the distance travelled on a car journey
**b** the mass of an apple
**c** the amount of water in a bath.

..........................................................................................

**a** kilometres (km)
**b** grams (g)
**c** litres

- You can measure **mass** using metric units.

Mass is linked to weight.

**milligrams (mg)**

1 mg is $\frac{1}{1000}$ of a gram
1000 mg = 1 g

**gram (g)**

A peanut weighs about 1 g.

**kilogram (kg)**

A bag of sugar weighs 1 kg.

**tonne (t)**

A small car weighs about 1 tonne.

- You can measure **capacity** or volume using metric units.

Capacity is the amount of liquid a container holds.

**millilitre (ml)**

A teaspoon holds about 5 ml.

**centilitre (cl)**

A can of drink holds 33 cl.

**litre (l)**

A carton of fruit juice holds 1 litre.

**Unit 2**

**1** Four metric units for measuring distance are

> metre   kilometre   centimetre   millimetre

**a** Write them in order of size starting with the smallest.
**b** Write the correct abbreviations next to your answers.

**2** Three metric units for measuring capacity are

> centilitre   litre   millilitre

**a** Write them in order of size, starting with the smallest.
**b** Write the appropriate abbreviation next to your answer.

**DID YOU KNOW?**

The world's tallest wooden house is around 43 m in height and extends to 13 floors. It was built by Nikolai Sutyagin in Arkhangelsk in Russia.

**A02 Functional Maths**

**3** Which metric unit of length would you use to measure
  **a** the length of a swimming pool
  **b** the thickness of a coin
  **c** the distance from London to Paris
  **d** the height of a house?

**4** Which of these measurements could be 2.5 cm?
  **a** height of a room       **b** height of a table
  **c** diameter of a coin     **d** length of a book

For questions 5–7 choose the most suitable answer.

**5** The length of a car is about
  **a** 30 cm      **b** 300 mm      **c** 3 m      **d** 0.5 m

**6** The length of a playing card is about
  **a** 9 mm      **b** 0.9 m      **c** 90 cm      **d** 9 cm

**7** The width of a playing card is about
  **a** 60 mm      **b** 60 cm      **c** 0.6 m      **d** 6 m

**8** Which metric unit of mass would you use to weigh
  **a** a person             **b** a bus
  **c** a banana             **d** a piece of paper?

For questions 9–11, choose the most suitable answer.

**9** The weight restriction for baggage on an aircraft could be
  **a** 15 g      **b** 15 t      **c** 15 mg      **d** 15 kg

**10** A tub of margarine could weigh
  **a** 500 kg      **b** 500 g      **c** 500 mg      **d** 500 t

**11** The weight of flour used to make pastry could be
  **a** 200 mg      **b** 200 g      **c** 200 kg      **d** 200 t

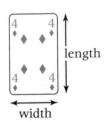

length

width

This spread will show you how to:

- Convert measurements from one unit to another

**Keywords**
Capacity
Convert
Length
Mass
Metric

- **Metric** units are based on the decimal system.

You can **convert** between units in the metric system, by multiplying or dividing by 10, 100, 1000, ...

p.224

### Length

10 mm = 1 cm        100 cm = 1 m        1000 m = 1 km

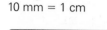

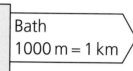

Bath
1000 m = 1 km

mm = millimetre
cm = centimetre
m = metre
km = kilometre

### Mass

1000 mg = 1 g
1000 g = 1 kg
1000 kg = 1 t

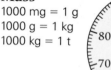

### Capacity

1000 ml = 1 litre
100 cl = 1 litre

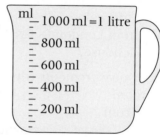

ml
— 1000 ml = 1 litre
— 800 ml
— 600 ml
— 400 ml
— 200 ml

mg = milligrams
g = gram
kg = kilogram
t = tonne

ml = millilitre
cl = centilitre
l = litre

---

**Example**

The height of a ceiling is 2.4 m.
Change 2.4 m to

**a** centimetres        **b** millimetres.

$\times 100$
metres ⟶ centimetres
$\div 100$

..................................................

**a**    1 m = 100 cm
2.4 m = 2.4 × 100 cm = 240 cm

$\times 10$
centimetres ⟶ millimetres
$\div 10$

**b**    1 cm = 10 mm
240 cm = 240 × 10 mm = 2400 mm

---

**Example**

A bottle of wine holds 75 cl.
Change 75 cl to

**a** litres        **b** millilitres.

$\times 100$
litres ⟶ centilitres
$\div 100$

..................................................

**a**    1 litre = 100 cl
75 cl = 75 ÷ 100 litre = 0.75 litre

$\times 1000$
litres ⟶ millilitres
$\div 1000$

**b**    1 litre = 1000 ml
0.75 litre = 0.75 × 1000 = 750 ml

**1** Convert these measurements to millimetres.
  **a** 5 cm        **b** 8 cm        **c** 15 cm        **d** 6 cm 7 mm        **e** 19 cm 3 mm
  **f** 4.5 cm      **g** 4.3 cm      **h** 10.6 cm      **i** 80 cm            **j** 1 m

**2** Convert these measurements to centimetres.
  **a** 60 mm       **b** 85 mm       **c** 240 mm       **d** 63 mm            **e** 4 mm
  **f** 4 m         **g** 10 m        **h** 3.5 m        **i** 1.6 m            **j** 1.63 m

**3** Convert these measurements to metres.
  **a** 400 cm      **b** 450 cm      **c** 475 cm       **d** 470 cm           **e** 50 cm
  **f** 1 km        **g** 4 km        **h** 0.5 km       **i** 3.5 km           **j** 18 km

**4** Convert these weights to kilograms.
  **a** 8000 g      **b** 7000 g      **c** 7500 g       **d** 500 g            **e** 200 g
  **f** 1 t         **g** 1.5 t       **h** 3.5 t        **i** 10 t             **j** 100 t

**5** Convert these weights to grams.
  **a** 1 kg        **b** 4 kg        **c** 0.5 kg       **d** 4.5 kg           **e** 3 kg 500 g
  **f** 2 kg 400 g  **g** 2.4 kg      **h** 1000 mg      **i** 500 mg           **j** 2500 mg

**6** Convert these capacities to litres.
  **a** 1000 ml     **b** 3000 ml     **c** 500 ml       **d** 4500 ml          **e** 4750 ml
  **f** 100 cl      **g** 200 cl      **h** 50 cl        **i** 250 cl           **j** 70 cl

**7** Write these lengths in order of size, smallest first.
  2.11 m        212 cm        2011 mm        209 cm

**8** Write these heights in order of size, smallest first.
  173 cm        1.7 m        1.75 m        176 cm        171 cm

**A02 Functional Maths**

**9** A lorry can carry a maximum load of five tonnes.
  Crates are made up, each weighing 625 kg.
  How many crates can the lorry take?

**10** A glass holds 200 ml. How many glasses can
  Dennis pour from a 1-litre bottle of lemonade?

**11** One ream (500 sheets) of A4 paper weighs 0.5 kg.
  Calculate the weight of one sheet of paper in grams.

**12** Sarah buys a 0.5 kg bag of rice. Each portion of rice is 150 g.
  How many complete portions can she get from the bag?

Unit 2

This spread will show you how to:

● Know rough metric equivalents to imperial units

**Keywords**
Capacity
Equivalents
Imperial units
Length
Mass
Metric units

Most people in the world use **metric units**.
Some people still use **imperial units**.
It is useful to know the metric **equivalents** of imperial units.

I'm 6 foot and I weigh 170 lb.

I'm 1.7 m tall and I weigh 60 kg.

≃ means approximately equal to.

lb is pounds.

oz is ounces.

A litre is more than a pint.

● **Length** metric imperial
2.5 cm ≃ 1 inch
30 cm ≃ 1 foot (12 inches)
1 m ≃ 1 yard (3 feet)
8 km ≃ 5 miles

● **Mass** 1 kg ≃ 2 lb (2.2 lb is better)
30 g ≃ 1 oz

● **Capacity** metric imperial
600 ml ≃ 1 pint
1 litre ≃ 1.75 pints
$4\frac{1}{2}$ litres ≃ 1 gallon

1 litre = 1 .75 pints

**Example**

In 2005 all Ireland's road signs were changed from imperial to metric units.
Change 50 miles to kilometres.

Dublin 50 miles

×10 ( 5 miles = 8 km ) ×10
50 miles = 80 km

Dublin 80 kilometres

**Example**

Linda puts 8 gallons of petrol in her car.
Approximately how many litres is that?

1 gallon ≃ $4\frac{1}{2}$ litres
8 gallons ≃ $4\frac{1}{2}$ × 8 litres
≃ 36 litres

**1** Convert these distances to miles.

| **a** | Madrid<br>8 km | **b** | Valencia<br>240 km | **c** | Benidorm<br>96 km | **d** | Barcelona<br>120 km |

| **e** | Granada<br>32 km | **f** | Alicante<br>104 km | **g** | Alicante<br>104 km | **h** | Bilbao<br>68 km |

**2** Convert these distances to kilometres.

| **a** | Leeds<br>20 miles | **b** | Sheffield<br>40 miles | **c** | York<br>100 miles | **d** | Manchester<br>70 miles |

| **e** | Liverpool<br>250 miles | **f** | London<br>45 miles | **g** | Nottingham<br>35 miles | **h** | Birmingham<br>55 miles |

**3** Convert these speeds to miles per hour.

**a** 64 km/h　　**b** 24 km/h　　**c** 16 km/h　　**d** 48 km/h　　**e** 80 km/h

km/h = kilometres per hour

**4** Convert these speeds to kilometres per hour.

**a** 30 mph　　**b** 50 mph　　**c** 70 mph　　**d** 40 mph　　**e** 20 mph

**5** Use 1 kg ≃ 2.2 lb, to convert these weights to pounds.
**a** 2 kg　　**b** 10 kg　　**c** 8 kg　　**d** 60 kg　　**e** 50 kg

**6** Use 1 kg ≃ 2 lb, to convert these weights to kilograms.
**a** 4 lb　　**b** 60 lb　　**c** 100 lb　　**d** 25 lb　　**e** 11 lb

**7** Use 1 litre ≃ 1.75 pints, to convert these capacities to pints.

**a** 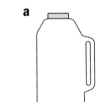 4 litres　　**b** 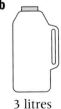 3 litres　　**c**  2 litres　　**d**  1 litre　　**e**  0.5 litres

**8** Use 1 gallon ≃ $4\frac{1}{2}$ litres, to convert these capacities to litres.
**a** 2 gallons　　**b** 8 gallons　　**c** 0.5 gallons
**d** 2.5 gallons　　**e** 40 gallons　　**f** 500 gallons

Unit 2

This spread will show you how to:
- Interpret scales on a range of measuring instruments, including those for time and mass
- Recognise the possible inaccuracy of measurements

**Keywords**
Accurate
Scale
Temperature
Time

Measuring instruments use **scales** to show measurements.

The scales are divided into small divisions.

You need to work out what one division stands for.

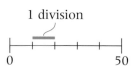
1 division

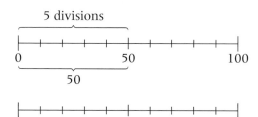

There are 5 divisions from 0 to 50.

$50 \div 5 = 10$

So each division stands for 10.

**Example**

Write the readings shown on the scales.

**a**

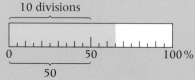
10 divisions
50

**b**

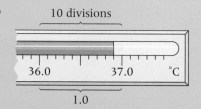
10 divisions
1.0

**a** There are 10 divisions from 0 to 50.
$50 \div 10 = 5$

Each division stands for 5%.
Reading shows
$50 + 5 + 5 + 5 = 65\%$.

**b** There are 10 divisions from 36.0 to 37.0.
$1.0 \div 10 = 0.1$

Each division stands for 0.1.
Reading shows
$36.0 + 0.9 = 36.9\,°C$.

The reading on this clock is only **accurate** to the nearest minute. The reading is not exact.

The reading shows 2 minutes past 12.

However, the line could be anywhere between 1.5 and 2.5 minutes past. The reading may be inaccurate by up to 30 seconds either way.

Two minutes past

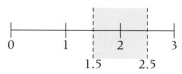

**1** For each scale, write what each division represents and the readings shown.

**a**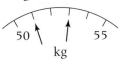
kg

**b**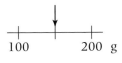
100    200 g

**c**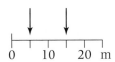
0   10   20 m

**d** cl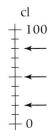

**e**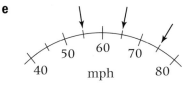

**2** For each scale, write what each division represents and the readings shown.

**a** 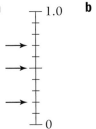   **b**   **c** 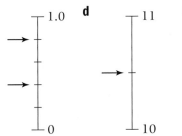 **d**  **e**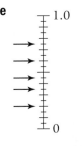

**3** This scale shows how to convert from stones to kilograms.

Use the scale to convert these weights in stones to kilograms.

    **a** 8 stones      **b** 3 stones      **c** 2.5 stones
    **d** 5.5 stones     **e** 8.5 stones    **f** 0.5 stones

**4** **a** Give the reading on the thermometer.

36.0°     37.0°     38.0°
°C

    **b** Calculate how much the temperature is above 36.9 °C.

**5** These measurements are given to the nearest centimetre.
Give the lowest and highest measurements they could represent.

    **a** 5 cm       **b** 8 cm       **c** 1 cm
    **d** 10 cm     **e** 20 cm     **f** 0 cm

This type of question is indicative of grade C.

Unit 2

141

This spread will show you how to:
- Find the perimeter of a shape by counting squares and measuring

**Keywords**
Length
Perimeter
Rectangle
Unit
Width

- The **perimeter** is the distance all round a shape.
- You measure perimeter in units of **length**, for example centimetre (cm), metre (m).

**Example**

Find the perimeter of each shape. State the **units** of your answers.

> p.402

**a**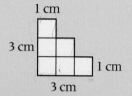

**b**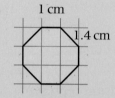

**a** Perimeter = 1 + 1 + 1 + 1 + 1 + 1 + 3 + 3
         = 12 cm

**b** Perimeter = 1 + 1.4 + 1 + 1.4 + 1 + 1.4 + 1 + 1.4
         = 9.6 cm

You can find the perimeter of a **rectangle** by counting lengths on a centimetre grid.

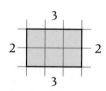

Perimeter = 3 + 2 + 3 + 2
      = 10 cm

You can find the perimeter without a centimetre grid.

- For any rectangle

  Perimeter = length + width + length + width
        = 2 × length + 2 × width
  Perimeter = $l + w + l + w$
        = $2l + 2w$

  width ($w$)

  length ($l$)

**Example**

The length of a rectangle is 5.8 cm.
The perimeter of the rectangle is 19.4 cm.
Calculate the width of the rectangle.

width

←length→

width + 5.8 + width + 5.8 = 19.4
    2 × width + 11.6 = 19.4
        2 × width = 19.4 − 11.6 = 7.8
          width = $\frac{7.8}{2}$ = 3.9
So    width = 3.9 cm

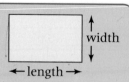

Check:
    5.8
    5.8
    3.9
  +3.9
  $\overline{19.4}$

**1** Find the perimeter of each shape. Each square represents 1 cm.

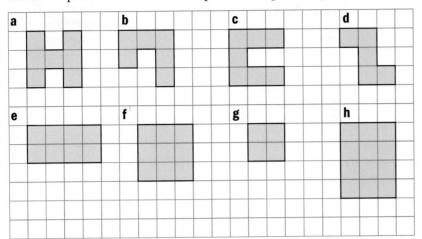

**2** Calculate the perimeters of these shapes. State the units of your answers.

**a** 3 cm  7 cm   **b** 5 m  10 m   **c** 15 mm  5 mm   **d** square 8 cm

**e** 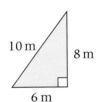 10 m  8 m  6 m   **f**  6 cm  6 cm  6 cm   **g** 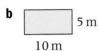 5 cm  8 cm  6 cm  3 cm   **h** 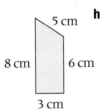 6 cm  regular hexagon

A regular hexagon has 6 equal sides.

**3** A rectangular field is 80 m long and 35 m wide.
Calculate the perimeter of the field. State the units of your answer.

**4 a** The perimeter of each rectangle is 24 cm. Calculate the unknown lengths.

**i** ? cm  8 cm   **ii** ? cm  5 cm   **iii** ? cm  10 cm   **iv** square ? cm  ? cm

**b** The perimeter of each rectangle is 36 cm. Calculate the unknown lengths.

**i**  ? cm  14 cm   **ii** ? cm  15 cm   **iii** 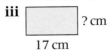 ? cm  17 cm   **iv** square  ? cm  ? cm

This spread will show you how to:
● Find the area of shapes by counting squares
● Find the area of a rectangle using the formula

**Keywords**
Area
Rectangle
Square
  centimetre
  (cm$^2$)
Square metre
  (m$^2$)

● **Area** is the amount of surface a shape covers.

You can find the area of a shape by counting the number of squares on a centimetre grid.
Each square is equal to an area of 1 cm$^2$.
The area of the circle is about 12 cm$^2$.

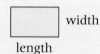 1 cm
1 cm

1 **square centimetre** or 1 cm$^2$.

You can find the area of a **rectangle** by counting squares.

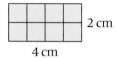
2 cm
4 cm

Area = 4 × 2
     = 8 cm$^2$

There are 2 rows of 4 squares.

This formula works for all rectangles.

● You can find the area of any rectangle by using the formula:

Area of rectangle = length × width

width
length

**Example**

Calculate the area of this rectangle.
State the units of your answer.

8 cm
12 cm

...........................................................

Area = 12 × 8 = 96 cm$^2$

**Example**

I buy 12 square paving slabs. Each slab measures 1 metre by 1 metre.
I want to make a rectangle using all 12 slabs.

**a** What sizes of rectangles can I make?
**b** Calculate the area of each rectangle.

...........................................................

**a**

3 m
4 m

**b** Area = 3 × 4 = 12 m$^2$

2 m
6 m

Area = 2 × 6 = 12 m$^2$

1 m
12 m

Area = 1 × 12 = 12 m$^2$

1 **square metre** = 1 m$^2$
1 **square millimetre** = 1 mm$^2$

Factors of 12 are 1, 2, 3, 4, 6, 12

## Exercise G1.6

**Grade F**



**1** Which is larger, one square centimetre or one square metre?

**2** Find the area of each shape. Each square represents 1 $cm^2$.

a
b
c
d
e
f
g
h

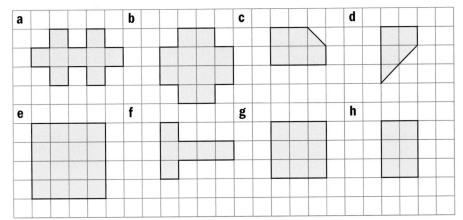

**3** Calculate the areas of these rectangles. Remember to give the units of your answers.

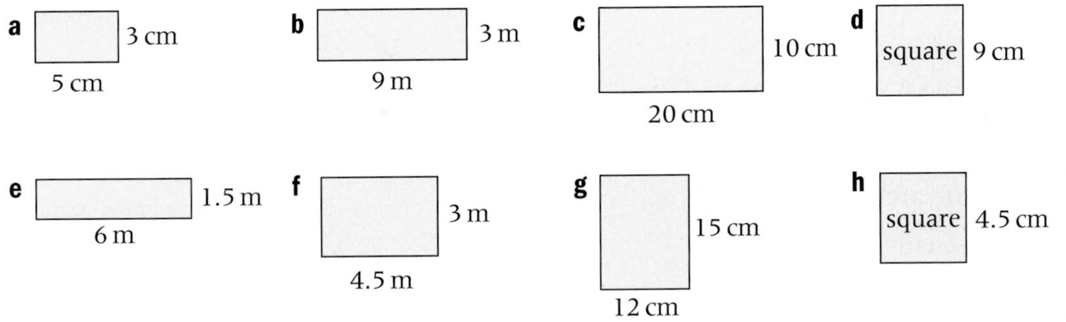

a
3 cm
5 cm
b
3 m
9 m
c
10 cm
20 cm
d
square
9 cm
e
1.5 m
6 m
f
3 m
4.5 m
g
15 cm
12 cm
h
square
4.5 cm

AO3 Problem

**4** Calculate the missing lengths. Give the units of your answers.

a
Area 48 cm²
6 cm
? cm
b
Area 60 m²
5 m
? m
c
Area 84 m²
? m
7 m
d
Area 36 cm²
? cm
a square
e
Area 10 cm²
4 cm
? cm
f
Area 28 m²
? m
8 m
g
Area 60 cm²
? cm
8 cm
h
Area 6.25 m²
? m
a square

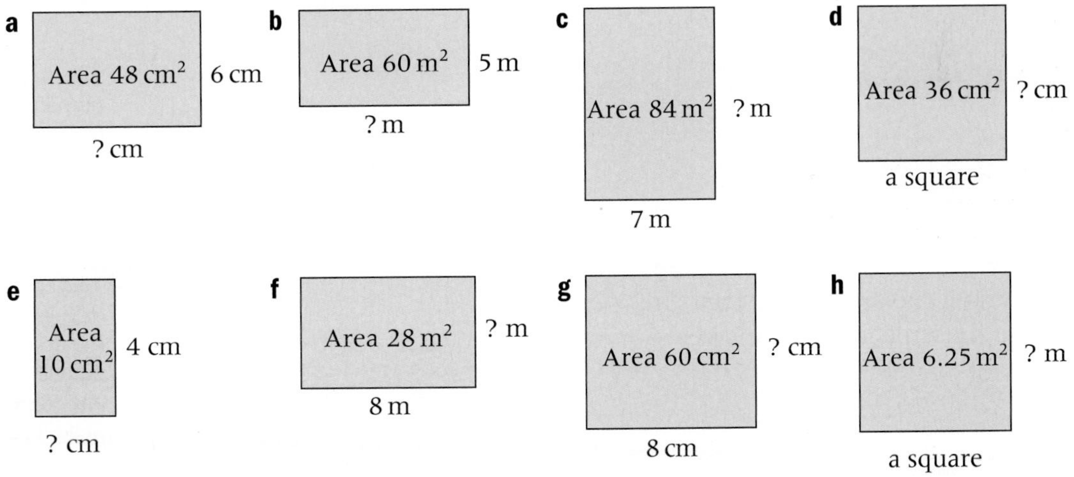

**Area of a rectangle and a triangle**

This spread will show you how to:

- Calculate the area of rectangles and triangles and shapes made from rectangles and triangles

**Keywords**
Area
Diagonal
Perimeter
Rectangle
Right-angled
 triangle
Square
 centimetre

- The **area** is the amount of surface a shape covers.

You can find the area of a **rectangle** using the formula

- Area of rectangle = length $\times$ width

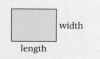

This formula also works for a square.

You can find the area of a **right-angled triangle** in several ways

Area = 6 squares and 4 half squares

   = 6 + 2

   = 8 cm$^2$

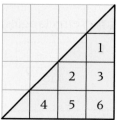

The **diagonal** line splits the square into two halves.

Area = $\frac{1}{2}$ of the area square

   = $\frac{1}{2}$ of 16 cm$^2$

   = 8 cm$^2$

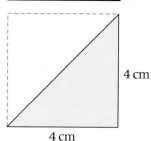

**Area** of the triangle is half the area of the square.

- Area of a right-angled triangle = $\frac{1}{2} \times$ base $\times$ height

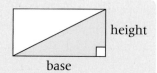

The height is perpendicular (at right angles) to the base.

**Example**

Calculate the area of the triangle.
State the units of your answer.

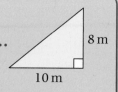

Area = $\frac{1}{2} \times 10 \times 8$

   = 40 m$^2$

The units are square metres or m$^2$.

This topic is extended to the area of a parallelogram and trapezium on page 428.

**1** Find the area of each of these triangles. Each square represents one square centimetre.

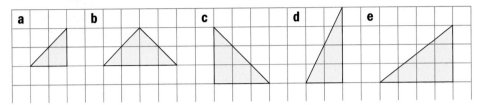

**2** Calculate the area of each of these right-angled triangles. State the units of your answers.

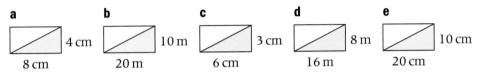

**3** Calculate the area of each of these triangles. State the units of your answers.

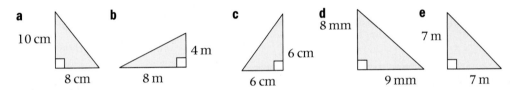

A03 Problem

**4 a** Calculate the perimeter of this triangle.
   **b** Calculate the area of the triangle.

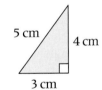

5 cm     4 cm

3 cm

**c** Two of these triangles are placed together to form five different shapes.

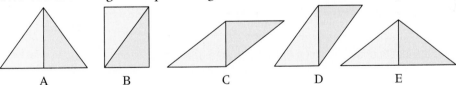

A          B          C          D          E

Copy and complete this table.

| Shape | Perimeter (cm) | Area (cm²) |
|-------|----------------|------------|
| A | | |
| B | | |
| C | | |
| D | | |
| E | | |

Unit 2

147

This spread will show you how to:
- Find the surface area of cuboids
- Find the length of a side of a cuboid, given the surface area

**Keywords**
Cuboid
Faces
Net
Surface area

A **cuboid** has six rectangular **faces**.

A cereal box is a cuboid.

You can unfold the cereal box to see its net.

When you unfold the cuboid, the six rectangles form the **net**.
The area of the net gives you the **surface area** of the cuboid.

- The surface area of a cuboid is the total area of its faces.

  p.404

There are two green rectangles, two red rectangles and two pink rectangles.

**Example**

Calculate the surface area of this cuboid.
State the units of your answer.

........................................................

Area of one red rectangle    $= 2 \times 4 = 8 \text{ cm}^2$
Area of one pink rectangle   $= 4 \times 8 = 32 \text{ cm}^2$
Area of one green rectangle  $= 2 \times 8 = \underline{16 \text{ cm}^2}$
                                            $56 \text{ cm}^2$

Total surface area           $= 56 \times 2$
                             $= 112 \text{ cm}^2$

Units of area are $\text{cm}^2$.

- You can find the length of a side, given the surface area of a cube.

**Example**

The surface area of a cube is $150 \text{ cm}^2$.
Calculate the length of one side of the cube.

........................................................

A cube has six square faces.

The area of one square $= 150 \div 6$
                       $= 25 \text{ cm}^2$

Length of one side $= \sqrt{25}$
                   $= 5 \text{ cm}$

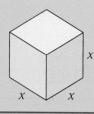

Area 25 cm²

**1** These nets make cuboids. Each square represents a 1 cm square.

a 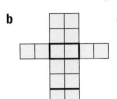  b 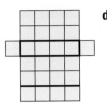  c 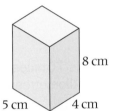  d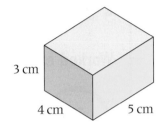

Calculate the surface area of each cuboid.
State the units of your answers.

**2** A 3 cm by 4 cm by 5 cm cuboid is shown. Calculate
  **a** the area of the red rectangle
  **b** the area of the orange rectangle
  **c** the area of the green rectangle
  **d** the surface area of the cuboid.

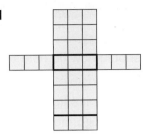

3 cm

4 cm        5 cm

**3** Calculate the surface area of each of these cuboids.
State the units of your answers.

a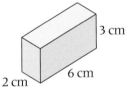
3 cm
2 cm   6 cm

b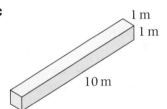
8 cm
5 cm   4 cm

c
1 m
1 m
10 m

d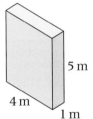
5 m
4 m
1 m

e
1 cm
4 cm   4 cm

f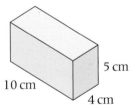
5 cm
10 cm   4 cm

**4** Calculate the surface area of each of these cubes.
State the units of your answers.
  **a** length 5 cm      **b** length 8 m      **c** length 2.5 cm
  **d** length 15 mm     **e** length 0.5 m

length

**5** Calculate the length of one side of a cube if the surface
area of the cube is
  **a** 600 cm$^2$      **b** 54 cm$^2$      **c** 294 cm$^2$
  **d** 9600 cm$^2$     **e** 37.5 cm$^2$

$x$

Unit 2

149

### Check out

You should now be able to:

- Make sensible estimates of measurements
- Convert measurements from one unit to another
- Know rough metric equivalents of imperial units
- Calculate the perimeter and area of shapes made from rectangles and triangles
- Calculate the surface area of cuboids

### Worked exam question

70 mph
Great Britain

120 k/h
Spain

The motorway speed limit in Great Britain is 70 miles per hour.
The motorway speed limit in Spain is 120 kilometres per hour.

Which of these speed limits is the lowest speed?
You must show working to explain your answer.          (3)

(Edexcel Limited 2007)

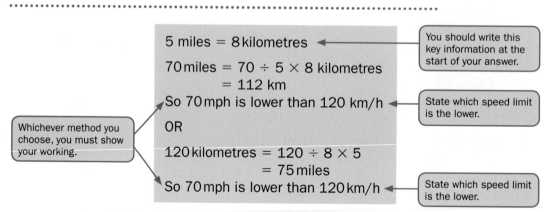

5 miles = 8 kilometres ← You should write this key information at the start of your answer.

70 miles = 70 ÷ 5 × 8 kilometres
= 112 km

So 70 mph is lower than 120 km/h ← State which speed limit is the lower.

OR

120 kilometres = 120 ÷ 8 × 5
= 75 miles

So 70 mph is lower than 120 km/h ← State which speed limit is the lower.

Whichever method you choose, you must show your working.

# Exam questions

A02

**1**

The picture shows a man standing next to a giraffe.
The giraffe and the man are drawn to the same scale.
Estimate the height, in metres, of the giraffe. (4)

**2** Here is a rectangle.

Diagram NOT
accurately drawn

10 cm

20 cm

**a** Work out the perimeter of the rectangle. (2)
**b** Work out the area of the rectangle. (2)

(Edexcel Limited 2008)

**3** Complete this table.
Write a sensible unit for each measurement.
Three have been done for you.

|  | Metric | Imperial |
|---|---|---|
| The length of a pencil | .............. | inches |
| The distance between England and France | kilometres | ............ |
| The amount of potatoes in a scale | .............. | pounds |

(3)

The focus on protecting the environment from further damage is now stronger than ever. Recycling and reusing waste materials have become an important part of everyday life both for manufacturers and consumers.

This time-series chart shows the total waste per person produced by households in the UK and the proportion of this waste that was recycled between 1983/4 and 2007/8.

What can you say in general about the amount of waste produced and recycled by households in the UK during this time? Justify your response by referring to the data.

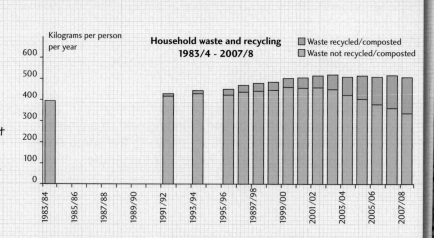

Kilograms per person per year

Household waste and recycling 1983/4 - 2007/8

☐ Waste recycled/composted
☐ Waste not recycled/composted

Copy and complete this table giving the values shown in the time-series chart.

| Year | 1983/84 | 1991/92 | 1993/94 | 1995/96 | 1996/97 | 1997/98 | 1998/99 | 1999/00 | 2000/01 | 2001/02 | 2002/03 | 2003/04 | 2004/05 | 2005/06 | 2006/07 | 2007/08 |
|---|---|---|---|---|---|---|---|---|---|---|---|---|---|---|---|---|
| Waste not recycled/composted | 394 | 417 | | 423 | 438 | 441 | 443 | 457 | 455 | 456 | 449 | 425 | | 376 | 359 | |
| Waste recycled/composted | 3 | 11 | 15 | 27 | 32 | 36 | | | 52 | 60 | 71 | 87 | 113 | 135 | 157 | 173 |
| Total waste | 397 | 427 | 445 | | 469 | 477 | 483 | 505 | 507 | | 521 | 512 | 517 | 511 | | 507 |

The data shows that less than 0.8% of UK household waste was recycled in the year 1983/4. Work out what percentage of UK household waste (to the nearest 0.01%) was recycled each year until 2007/8. Add this information to your table.

Can you think of any reason for the trend shown by this data?

By what percentage has the amount of

a) household waste

b) waste recycled by households

changed during this time in the UK?

What realistic predictions do you think the government could have made about household waste for the year 2008/09?

Manufacturers are responsible for designing packaging that is as environmentally friendly as possible while also protecting the product.

A drinks company sells its brand of Cola in 500ml plastic (PET) bottles. The company has reduced the weight of these bottles by a third since the 1970s. The bottles weighed 39g in the 1970s. What is the weight of a new bottle?
The company plans to start using bottles that weigh 24g. What further reduction in weight (%) would this be?

Glass milk bottles are 50% lighter than they were 50 years ago.

As well as reducing the consumption of raw materials, lighter packaging also saves money in other ways such as transport costs.

A supermarket sells tomatoes in packs of six. The packaging consists of a plastic tray with a lid as shown. How much lighter (as a %) would each package be if it were made with no lid?

Do you think that not having lids would risk the quality of the tomatoes?

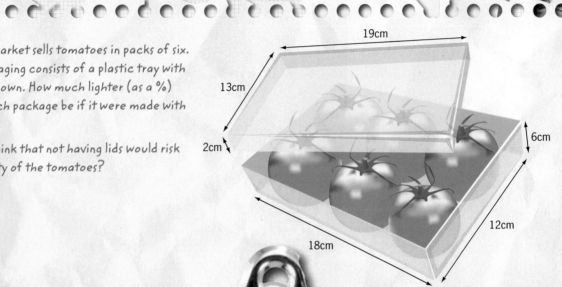

The product/pack ratio compares the weight of the packaging with the weight of the product it contains. Companies use this ratio to assess the suitability of the packaging used for each of their products. They often express it as a percentage to show how much of the overall weight is contributed by the packaging.

Look at some of the packaging you have at home. Could it be adapted to use less material without increasing the risk of damage to the product? If so, how?

How does the packaging used for perishable goods (e.g. food) differ from that used for non-perishable goods (e.g. electrical items)?

Research some well-known manufacturing companies on the Internet to find out about their packaging guidelines. Do they have different rules for different products (e.g. perishable/non-perishable goods)?

# Introduction

Engineers and scientists use algebraic expressions to model and explain the behaviour of real events and activities. Without algebra there would be no aircraft, mobile phones or plasma TVs.

## What's the point?

Algebra is an extension of arithmetic, but using letters instead of numbers. By using algebra, we can invent and use rules to explain real-life phenomena.

**Check in**

1 Work out
   **a** $3^2$  **b** $2^2$  **c** $4^2$

2 There are 5 CDs in a packet.
   How many CDs are there in 3 packets?

3 Work out
   **a** $4 - -3$  **b** $2 + -3$
   **c** $-3 + 5$  **d** $-4 - -1$

4 Work out
   **a** $-3 \times 2$  **b** $4 \times -2$
   **c** $6 \div -3$  **d** $-8 \div -2$

Key stage 3 →

- Use letters to represent numbers
- Simplify expressions by collecting like terms
- Substitute positive and negative numbers into an expression

→ A2 + 5

**Rich task**

Think of a number between 1 and 10.
- Double it.
- Add 4.
- Halve your answer.
- Take away the number you first thought of.
The answer is always 2.

Investigate.

**Letter symbols**

This spread will show you how to:

- Use letters to represent numbers in algebraic expressions

---

- You can use letters to represent numbers.

There are 6 eggs in a box.

In 2 boxes there are $6 \times 2 = 12$ eggs.
In 3 boxes there are $6 \times 3 = 18$ eggs.
In $n$ boxes there are $6 \times n = 6n$ eggs.

In algebra
$6n = 6 \times n$.
You do not write
the $\times$ sign.

**Example**

There are 12 sweets in one packet.

**a** How many sweets are there in 4 packets?
**b** How many sweets are there in $x$ packets?

**a** $12 \times 4 = 48$ sweets
**b** $12 \times x = 12x$ sweets

---

- An **expression** is a collection of letters and numbers with no $=$ sign.

**Example**

One apple costs 20 pence.

**a** Work out the cost of 3 apples.
**b** Write an expression for the cost of $y$ apples.

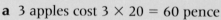

**a** 3 apples cost $3 \times 20 = 60$ pence
**b** $y$ apples cost $y \times 20 = 20y$ pence

$y \times 20 = 20 \times y$
Write numbers
before letters.

You can write expressions to represent real situations.

**Example**

There are $m$ pens in one box.

**a** How many pens are there in 3 boxes?
**b** Write an expression for the number of
pens in 3 boxes plus 5 extra pens.
**c** 6 pens are taken out of a box.
Write an expression for the number of
pens left in the box.

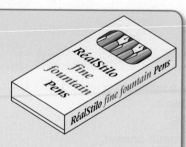

**a** $3 \times m = 3m$ pens
**b** $3m + 5$
**c** $m - 6$

$3m$ in 3 boxes,
plus 5 more.

**A02 Functional Maths**

**1** Stamps cost 30 pence each.
  **a** How much do 8 stamps cost?
  **b** How much do *n* stamps cost?

**2** Chews cost 20 pence each.
  **a** How much do 10 chews cost?
  **b** How much do *x* chews cost?

**3** Pencils cost 8 pence each.
  **a** How much do 8 pencils cost?
  **b** How much do *m* pencils cost?

**4** There are 12 biscuits in a packet.
How many biscuits are there in
  **a** 5 packets
  **b** 3 packets
  **c** *x* packets
  **d** *n* packets?

**5** Work out the cost of
  **a** 2 kg of potatoes
  **b** 3 kg of carrots
  **c** 10 kg of potatoes
  **d** 4 kg of carrots.
Write an expression for the cost of
  **e** *n* kg of potatoes
  **f** *x* kg of carrots
  **g** *y* kg of potatoes
  **h** *p* kg of carrots.

**6** Daniel has *x* DVDs.
  **a** Lisa has twice as many DVDs as Daniel.
    Write an expression in terms of *x* for the number of DVDs
    Lisa has.
  **b** Charlie has 4 more DVDs than Daniel.
    Write an expression in terms of *x* for the number of DVDs
    Charlie has.
  **c** Sareeta has 3 fewer DVDs than Lisa.
    Write an expression in terms of *x* for the number of DVDs
    Sareeta has.

**A03 Problem**

**7** Match each expression in box **A** with an expression in box **B**.

| A | B |
|---|---|
| $n + n$     $6n$ | $5n$     $7m$ |
| $3 \times n$     $4m$ | $m \times 4$     $3m$ |
| *n* oranges at 5p each | 6 stamps at *n* pence each |
| *m* toys at £3 each     $7 \times m$ | 3 chews at *n* pence each   $2n$ |

# Simplifying expressions

This spread will show you how to:

- Use the four rules of arithmetic
- Simplify expressions by collecting like terms

**Keywords**
Simplify
Squared
Term

- You can add and subtract in algebra, just like you do with numbers.

$m + m + m + m = 4$ lots of $m = 4 \times m = 4m$

**Addition**

$4m$       $+ 2m$      $= 6m$

$m + m + m + m$   $+ m + m$   $= m + m + m + m + m + m$

$2 + 2 + 2 + 2$
$= 4$ lots of 2
$= 4 \times 2 = 8$

**Subtraction**

$4m$          $- m$        $= 3m$

$m + m + m + m$   $- m$    $= m + m + m$

- You can **simplify** multiplications and divisions in **algebra**.

**Multiplication**

$3 \times a = 3a$
$x \times y = xy$
$y \times y = y^2$

You say '$y$ **squared**'
$3 \times 3 = 3^2 \ (=9)$

**Division**

$x \div 2 = \dfrac{x}{2}$    $4a \div 7 = \dfrac{4a}{7}$

This topic is extended to expanding and factorising on page 418.

---

**Example**

Simplify these expressions.

**a** $n + n + n$      **b** $c + c + c + c + c$      **c** $7x + 4x$
**d** $9y - y$        **e** $4p + 8p - 3p$

..................................................................................................

**a** $n + n + n = 3n$    **b** $c + c + c + c + c = 5c$    **c** $7x + 4x = 11x$
**d** $9y - y = 9y - 1y$   **e** $4p + 8p - 3p = 12p - 3p$
        $= 8y$                    $= 9p$

---

- A **term** is an individual part of an expression.

$4x - 2x$ is an expression.
$4x$ and $2x$ are terms.

To make calculations easier you can write terms in a different order.
Keep each term with its sign.

**Example**

Simplify these expressions.

**a** $3q - 5q + 2q$                 **b** $t - 4t + 8t$

..................................................................................................

**a** $3q - 5q + 2q = 3q + 2q - 5q$    **b** $t - 4t + 8t = t + 8t - 4t$
                    $= 5q - 5q$                    $= 9t - 4t$
                    $= 0$                        $= 5t$

**1** Write each statement as a single amount. Use a letter to represent each item.

For example, 6 apples + 2 apples can be written as $6a + 2a = 8a$.

**a** 8 apples + 7 apples      **b** 6 boys + 5 boys
**c** 3 CDs + 5 CDs      **d** 8 chairs and 13 chairs
**e** 9 toys and 23 toys      **f** 18 books + 8 books
**g** 13 chocolates − 8 chocolates    **h** 6 cakes − 6 cakes
**i** 15 sweets − 7 sweets      **j** 13 bananas − 6 bananas

**2** Simplify these expressions.

**a** $m + m + m$      **b** $n + n + n + n + n + n + n$
**c** $y + y + y + y + y + y$      **d** $z + z + z - z + z$

**3** Collect the terms and simplify each expression.

**a** $6a + 7a$    **b** $5n + 12n$    **c** $6t + 9t$    **d** $3x + 16x$
**e** $9r - 5r$    **f** $6f - 2f$    **g** $12g - 5g$    **h** $15r - 7r$
**i** $16n + 4n + 3n$ **j** $6c + 8c + 3c$

**4** Write each of these as a single term.

**a** $4 \times m$    **b** $p \times 3$    **c** $r \times s$    **d** $12 \times q$
**e** $5 \times g$    **f** $c \times 4$    **g** $d \times 8$    **h** $j \times k$
**i** $n \times n$    **j** $e \times 15$    **k** $t \times t$    **l** $6 \times m \times n$

**5** Simplify each expression.

**a** $8n + 3n + 4n$      **b** $3m + 2m + 7m$
**c** $8p + 6p + 3p$      **d** $5q + 7q + 6q$
**e** $12x - 7x - 4x$      **f** $8w - w - 3w$
**g** $4a + 6a - 3a$      **h** $12b - 3b - 4b$
**i** $3j - 4j + 2j$      **j** $k - 5k + 6k$

**6** Simplify these divisions.

**a** $d \div 4 = \dfrac{d}{4}$    **b** $x \div 3$    **c** $y \div 7$    **d** $t \div 9$
**e** $2a \div 3$    **f** $3n \div 4$    **g** $5p \div 7$    **h** $2v \div 4$

> The first one has been done for you.

**7** Use these four terms and three signs to make the different totals.

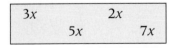

| $3x$ | | $2x$ | | | $+$ | | $-$ |
|---|---|---|---|---|---|---|---|
| | $5x$ | | $7x$ | | | $+$ | |

**a** $13x$      **b** $3x$      **c** $7x$      **d** $11x$

# Collecting terms

This spread will show you how to:

- Simplify expressions by collecting like terms
- Rearrange algebraic expressions involving different letters

---

- An expression can include terms with different letters.

**Example**

Bags of sweets come in two sizes.

**Small**

*n* **sweets**

There are *n* sweets in a small bag

**Large**

*p* **sweets**

There are *p* sweets in a large bag

**a** Rupal buys 1 large bag and 1 small bag.
How many sweets does he buy altogether?

**b** Maisie buys 2 small bags and 3 large bags.
How many sweets does she buy altogether?

........................................................................

**a** 1 small bag + 1 large bag
  $n$ sweets + $p$ sweets
  $n + p$ sweets

**b** 2 small bags + 3 large bags
  $2 \times n$ sweets + $3 \times p$ sweets
  $2n + 3p$ sweets

---

- Terms with the same letter are called like terms.
  You can simplify expressions by collecting like terms.

**Example**

Simplify

**a** $4m + 2p + 3m$          **b** $2x + 5y + 3x + y$

..................................................................

**a** $4m + 2p + 3m = 4m + 3m + 2p$
  $= 7m + 2p$

**b** $2x + 5y + 3x + y = 2x + 3x + y + 5y$
  $= 5x + 6y$

Rearrange the terms to collect like terms together.

$y = 1y$

**Example**

Simplify these expressions.

**a** $2e + 5f + 6e - 2f$   **b** $6u - v - 3u + 4v$   **c** $3m + 2n - m - 4n$

..................................................................

**a** $2e + 5f + 6e - 2f$
  $= 2e + 6e + 5f - 2f$
  $= 8e + 3f$

**b** $6u - v - 3u + 4v$
  $= 6u - 3u + 4v - v$
  $= 3u + 3v$

**c** $3m + 2n - m - 4n$
  $= 3m - m + 2n - 4n$
  $= 2m + {-2n}$
  $= 2m - 2n$

Keep each term with its sign.

**A02 Functional Maths**

**Unit 2**

**1** Bags of peanuts come in two sizes. There are $x$ peanuts in a small bag. There are $y$ peanuts in a large bag.

LARGE
$y$ Peanu...
SMALL
$x$ Peanuts

   **a** Sebastian buys 1 small bag and 1 large bag.
     How many peanuts does he buy?
   **b** Adam buys 3 large bags.
     How many peanuts does he buy?
   **c** Gabi buys 2 small bags and 1 large bag.
     Write an expression for the number of peanuts she buys.
   **d** Sushma buys 4 small bags.
     Write an expression for the number of peanuts she buys.
   **e** Kofi buys 3 small and 2 large bags.
     Write an expression for the number of peanuts he buys.

**2** Simplify each expression by collecting like terms together.
   **a** $a + b + a + b$       **b** $c + d + c + c + c$
   **c** $3e + 2f + 4e + 3f$      **d** $5g + 7h + 2g + h$
   **e** $3i + j + 4i + 5j$       **f** $3u + 5v + 2v + u$

**3** Simplify these expressions.
   **a** $4a + 2b - 3a + b$      **b** $6x + 4y - 2x + 2y$
   **c** $5m + 3n + 2m - n$      **d** $8s + 3t + s - 2t$
   **e** $3p + 2q - p + 3q$       **f** $2c + 3d + 3c - 2d$

**4** Simplify these by collecting like terms.
   **a** $4a - 6b - 3a + 8b$      **b** $3c - 4d - 2c + 5d$
   **c** $7u - 4v - 2u + 5v$      **d** $6x - 5y - 5x + 11y$
   **e** $12m - 5n - 3m + 10n$    **f** $9p - 4q - 3p + 6q$

**5** Simplify these expressions.
   **a** $5e - 3f - 2e + 2f$      **b** $4g - 6h - 3g + 4h$
   **c** $j - 3k + 4j + 2k$       **d** $2r - 4s - r + s$
   **e** $7t + 3u - 4t - 5u$      **f** $9v - 5w + 3v - 2w$

**A03 Problem**

**6** Make sets of three matching expressions, using one expression from each box in each set.

| A | B | C |
|---|---|---|
| $3x + 5y - x + 2y$ | $2x + 5y$ | $7y - 3x + 5x - 2y$ |
| $2x - 4y + 3x + 2y$ | $3y + 7x + 4y - 5x$ | $4x + 4y - 3x$ |
| $2x + 4y - x$ | $5x - 2y$ | $7y + 2x$ |
| $2y + 3x - x + 3y$ | $3x + 6y - 2x - 2y$ | $2x - 4y + 2y + 3x$ |

161

This spread will show you how to:

- Substitute numbers into an expression and work out its value
- Substitute numbers into a formula

You can replace letters with number values.
This is called **substituting**.

 p.282

**Example**

If $c = 4$, work out

**a** $5c$     **b** $2c + 1$     **c** $3c - 2$

...........................................................................................................

**a** $5c = 5 \times c$     Write the multiplication sign.
     $= 5 \times 4$     Write 4 instead of $c$.
     $= 20$     Follow the order of operations.

**b** $2c + 1 = 2 \times c + 1$          **c** $3c - 2 = 3 \times c - 2$
     $= 2 \times 4 + 1$               $= 3 \times 4 - 2$
     $= 8 + 1 = 9$                    $= 12 - 2 = 10$

- You can substitute values into expressions with more than one letter.

**Example**

Work out the value of each expression when $x = 2$ and $y = 1$.

**a** $x + 3$     **b** $y + 4$     **c** $x + y$
**d** $2x - y$     **e** $3y - 2x$     **f** $x^2$

...........................................................................................................

**a** $x + 3 = 2 + 3$     **b** $y + 4 = 1 + 4$     **c** $x + y = 2 + 1$
     $= 5$                    $= 5$                      $= 3$

**d** $2x - y = 2 \times x - y$ **e** $3y - 2x = 3 \times y - 2 \times x$ **f** $x^2 = x \times x$
     $= 2 \times 2 - 1$          $= 3 \times 1 - 2 \times 2$          $= 2 \times 2 = 4$
     $= 4 - 1 = 3$              $= 3 - 4 = -1$

**Remember:**
$x^2$ means '$x$ squared.'

- A **formula** shows a relationship between quantities.
  This formula works out pay: Pay = hours worked $\times$ hourly rate
  Using algebra, $P = h \times r = hr$
  Jims works 5 hours. His hourly rate is £5.60. Substitute $h = 5$
  and $r =$ £5.60, into the formula.
    $P = hr = 5 \times$ £5.60 $=$ £28     Jims pay is £28.

**1** If $a = 3$, work out the value of these expressions.

**a** $2a$      **b** $a + 1$      **c** $4a$      **d** $a - 2$

**e** $2a + 3$      **f** $3a - 4$      **g** $4a + 2$      **h** $4a - 5$

**2** If $c = 4$ and $d = 2$, calculate the value of these expressions.

**a** $3c$      **b** $2d$      **c** $d + c$      **d** $cd$

**e** $2c + 4d$      **f** $3c - 2d$      **g** $3d - c + 2$      **h** $4c + d - 5$

**3** Find the value of each expression when $m = 2$ and $n = 5$.

**a** $m + n$      **b** $n - m$      **c** $2m + n$      **d** $m - n$

**e** $m^2$      **f** $n - 4m$      **g** $3m + n - 5$      **h** $2m - 3n + 1$

**4** Work out the value of each expression when $x = 3$, $y = 5$ and $z = 2$.

**a** $4x + 3$      **b** $2z + y$      **c** $3y - z$      **d** $x + y + z$

**e** $2x - y + 3z$      **f** $3z - 2x + y$      **g** $4x^2$

**5** Work out the value of these when $a = 3$, $b = 5$, $c = 4$ and $d = 6$.

**a** $a^2$      **b** $2a^2$      **c** $b^2$      **d** $2b^2$

**e** $c^2$      **f** $2c^2$      **g** $d^2$      **h** $2d^2$

**A02** Functional Maths

**6** A taxi company calculates its fares using a formula

$$F = 2 + n$$

where $F$ is the fare in pounds and $n$ is the number of miles.

**a** What is the fare for a journey of 2 miles?

**b** What is the fare for a journey of 6 miles?

**7** A rent-a-car company charges for its cars using the formula

$$C = 30 + 20n$$

where $C$ is the cost in £s and $n$ is the number of days hired.

**a** What is the charge for 3 days' hire?

**b** What is the charge for 14 days' hire?

**c** If the charge is £210, for how many days was the car hired?

**A03** Problem

**8** Work out the value of each capital letter, then read the coded word.

| $m = 3$ | $n = 8$ | $p = 5$ | $q = -2$ |
|---|---|---|---|

| | | |
|---|---|---|
| H = $4n + 2q$ | L = $6m + 3p$ | O = $m^2 + 7$    A = $2q + 10$ |
| T = $pq$ | C = $2n - 3p$ | E = $np + 2m$ |

| 1 | 28 | 16 | 1 | 16 | 33 | 6 | −10 | 46 |
|---|---|---|---|---|---|---|---|---|

**More substituting**

This spread will show you how to:

- Substitute numbers into an expression and work out its value
- Substitute negative numbers into a formula

- You can substitute **negative** values into expressions.

- You use the rules for calculating with negative numbers.

---

**Example**

When $x = 2$ and $y = -3$, work out the value of

**a** $x - 3$ **b** $y + 5$ **c** $x - y$

.................................................................................

**a** $x - 3 = 2 - 3$
$\phantom{x - 3} = -1$

**b** $y + 5 = -3 + 5$
$\phantom{y + 5} = +2$

**c** $x - y = 2 - -3$
$\phantom{x - y} = 2 + 3$
$\phantom{x - y} = 5$

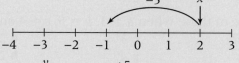

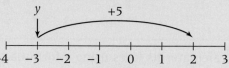

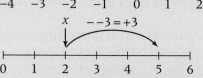

'Subtract $-3$'
is the same as
'add $+3$'.

---

**Example**

Find the value of these expressions when $p = -2$ and $q = 4$.

**a** $3p - q$ **b** $p^2$

.................................................................................

**a** $3p - q = 3 \times -2 - 4$
$\phantom{3p - q} = -6 - 4$
$\phantom{3p - q} = -10$

**b** $p^2 = p \times p$
$\phantom{p^2} = -2 \times -2$
$\phantom{p^2} = 4$

Negative $\times$ negative
= positive

---

- You can substitute values into expressions involving division.

---

**Example**

Work out the value of each expression when $a = 3$ and $b = -2$.

**a** $\dfrac{4a}{6}$ **b** $\dfrac{a - b}{5}$

.................................................................................

**a** $\dfrac{4a}{6} = \dfrac{4 \times a}{6}$
$\phantom{\dfrac{4a}{6}} = \dfrac{4 \times 3}{6} = \dfrac{12}{6} = 2$

**b** $\dfrac{a - b}{5} = \dfrac{3 - -2}{5}$
$\phantom{\dfrac{a - b}{5}} = \dfrac{3 + 2}{5} = \dfrac{5}{5} = 1$

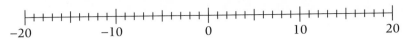

**1** Use this number line to work out the answers.

$$-20 \qquad -10 \qquad 0 \qquad 10 \qquad 20$$

**a** $-7 + 3$     **b** $4 - 8$     **c** $-4 + 11$     **d** $-3 - 7$
**e** $-6 + 4$     **f** $6 - 18$     **g** $4 - 6 - 7$     **h** $-3 - 8 + 5$

**2** If $x = -5$, work out the value of these expressions.
    **a** $3x$     **b** $x + 2$     **c** $2x - 1$     **d** $1 - x$
    **e** $x^2$     **f** $3 - 2x$     **g** $2x^2$     **h** $4x + 15$

**3** Work out the value of these expressions when $c = 3$ and $d = -2$.
    **a** $3c + 1$     **b** $3d$     **c** $d^2$     **d** $2d + 5$
    **e** $c^2$     **f** $2d + 4c$     **g** $2c - d$     **h** $d - c$

**4** If $x = -3$, $y = 2$ and $z = 4$, work out the value of these expressions.
    **a** $x + y$     **b** $y^2 - 5$     **c** $x^2 + 2$     **d** $2y + z$
    **e** $3y + 2x$     **f** $z^2 - 2y$     **g** $3z + 2x$     **h** $3x + 2y - z$

**5** Work out the value of each of these expressions when
$e = 4$, $f = 2$, $g = 5$ and $h = -3$.

    **a** $\dfrac{3e}{g}$     **b** $\dfrac{8g}{10}$     **c** $\dfrac{6f}{3}$     **d** $\dfrac{2g + 3}{7}$

    **e** $\dfrac{6g}{f}$     **f** $\dfrac{3h + 4g}{8}$     **g** $\dfrac{5e}{fg}$     **h** $\dfrac{(2g + 6)}{(e - f)}$

**6** Calculate the value of each expression when $r = 2$, $s = 4$ and $t = -3$.

    **a** $\dfrac{s}{2}$     **b** $\dfrac{6r}{3}$     **c** $\dfrac{t}{3}$     **d** $\dfrac{s + r}{3}$

    **e** $\dfrac{t - 5}{2}$     **f** $\dfrac{s \times r}{3}$     **g** $\dfrac{3r}{t}$     **h** $\dfrac{st}{r}$

---

**A02 Functional Maths**

**7** You can use this **formula** to convert temperatures in °C to °F

$$F = \frac{9C}{5} + 32$$

where $F$ represents the temperature in °F and $C$ represents the
temperature in °C.
    **a** Substitute the temperature 15 °C into the formula to convert
       it to °F.
    **b** Convert $-5$ °C to °F.

**DID YOU KNOW?**

The coldest temperature
on Earth was recorded
in 1983 at Vostock
Station in Antarctica.
The Russian research
station recorded
$-89.2$ °C (that's a chilly
$-128.6$ °F).

Unit 2

# Summary

## Check out
You should now be able to:

- Use letters to represent numbers in algebraic expressions
- Simplify algebraic expressions by collecting like terms
- Substitute positive and negative numbers into an expression
- Write expressions to solve problems

## Worked exam question
Andrew, Brenda and Callum each collect football stickers.
Andrew has $x$ stickers.
Brenda has three times as many stickers as Andrew.

**a** Write down an expression for the number of stickers that
Brenda has. (1)

Callum has 9 stickers less than Andrew.

**b** Write down an expression for the number of stickers that
Callum has. (1)

(Edexcel Limited 2005)

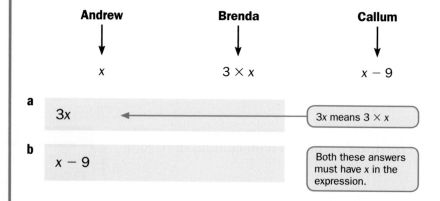

|  Andrew | Brenda | Callum |
|---|---|---|
| $x$ | $3 \times x$ | $x - 9$ |

**a** $3x$ &larr; 3x means $3 \times x$

**b** $x - 9$     Both these answers must have x in the expression.

## Exam questions

**1** Ben is $n$ years old.
Colin is three years younger than Ben.
**a** Write down an expression, in terms of $n$, for Colin's age. (1)

Daniel is twice as old as Ben.
**b** Write down an expression, in terms of $n$, for Daniel's age. (1)
(Edexcel Limited 2008)

**2** Simplify
**a** $c + c + c$ (1)
**b** $e + f + e + f + e$ (1)
**c** $2a + 3a$ (1)
**d** $2xy + 3xy - xy$ (1)
**e** $3a + 5b - a + 2b + 8$ (2)
(Edexcel Limited 2006)

**3** $F = 1.8C + 32$
**a** Work out the value of $F$ when $C = -8$ (2)
**b** Work out the value of $C$ when $F = 68$ (2)
(Edexcel Limited 2009)

**4** A pencil costs 30p.
A pen costs 50p.
Write down an expression for the total cost, in pence, of $x$ pencils and $y$ pens. (2)

**A03**

**5** The perimeter of a rectangle is $(4x + 12)$ cm.
Give two possible alternatives for the length and width of the rectangle.
Your answers should include $x$. (4)

# Introduction

The very first fractions can be traced back to the ancient Egyptians.

They wrote all their fractions as unit fractions (such as $\frac{1}{2} + \frac{1}{3}$ to mean the fraction $\frac{5}{6}$).

Since then, fractions have evolved through different cultures over the centuries.

It was not until the 17th century that fractions as we know them today existed in Europe.

## What's the point?

Understanding how fractions work enables us to make a lot of connections in mathematics, for instance in solving real life problems involving ratio and proportion.

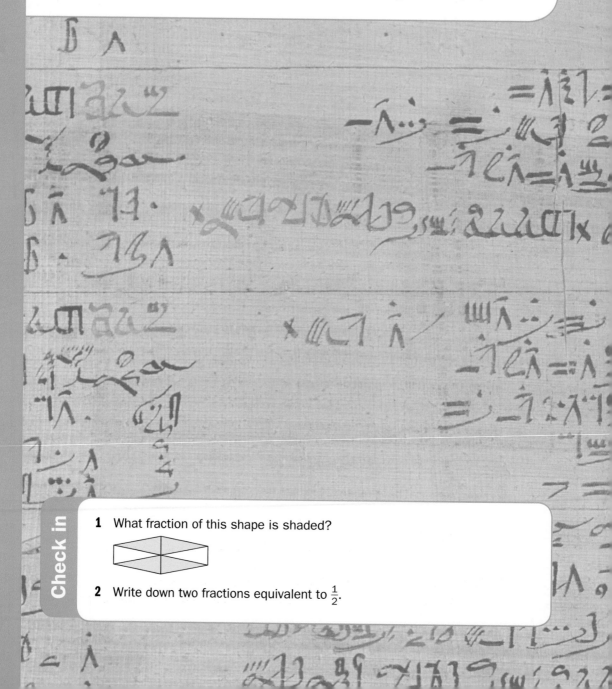

**Check in**

1 What fraction of this shape is shaded?

2 Write down two fractions equivalent to $\frac{1}{2}$.

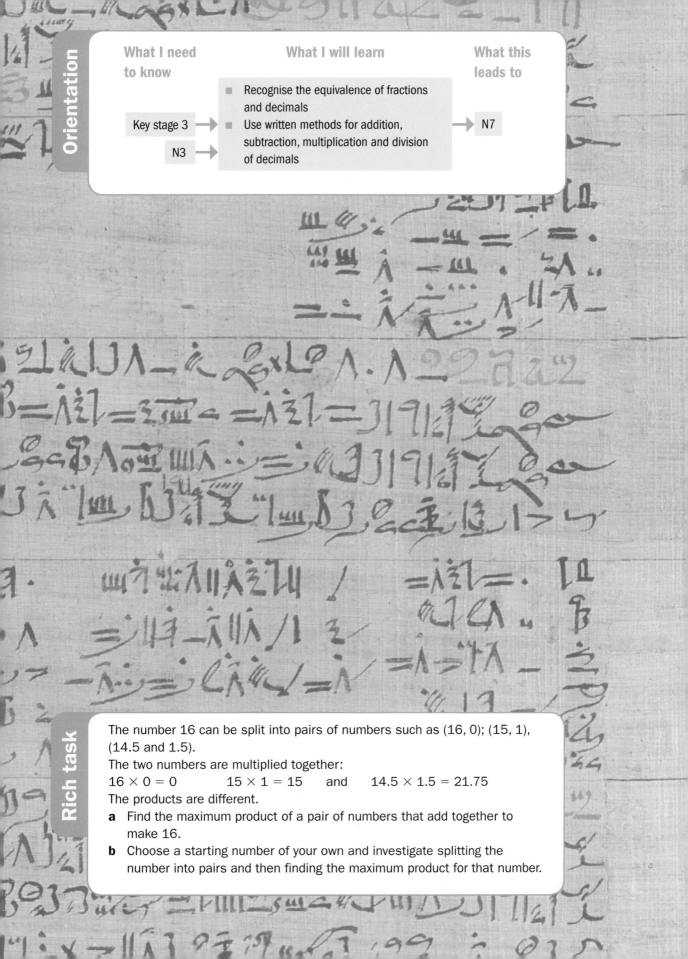

| What I need to know | What I will learn | What this leads to |
|---|---|---|
| Key stage 3 → <br> N3 → | ■ Recognise the equivalence of fractions and decimals <br> ■ Use written methods for addition, subtraction, multiplication and division of decimals | → N7 |

**Rich task**

The number 16 can be split into pairs of numbers such as (16, 0); (15, 1), (14.5 and 1.5).

The two numbers are multiplied together:

$16 \times 0 = 0$      $15 \times 1 = 15$    and    $14.5 \times 1.5 = 21.75$

The products are different.

**a** Find the maximum product of a pair of numbers that add together to make 16.

**b** Choose a starting number of your own and investigate splitting the number into pairs and then finding the maximum product for that number.

This spread will show you how to:
- Convert terminating decimals into fractions
- Convert fractions into decimals
- Order decimals on a number line

**Keywords**
Decimal
Equivalent
Fraction
Terminating
decimal

A **decimal** is another way of writing a **fraction**.

You should learn some common fractions and their decimal **equivalents**.

A decimal is often called a **decimal fraction**.

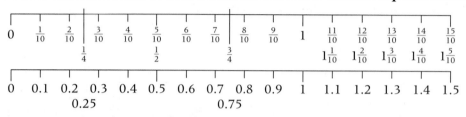

- You can write a **terminating decimal** as a fraction by using place value.

| | Decimal | | | | Fraction |
|---|---|---|---|---|---|
| **Units** **1** | **•** | **tenths** $\frac{1}{10}$ | **hundredths** $\frac{1}{100}$ | **thousandths** $\frac{1}{1000}$ | |
| 0 | • | 3 | | | $\frac{3}{10}$ |
| 0 | • | 4 | 8 | | $\frac{48}{100}$ |
| 3 | • | 1 | 5 | 8 | $3\frac{158}{1000}$ |

$$0.48 = \frac{48}{100}$$

$$\frac{48}{100} \overset{\div 4}{\underset{\div 4}{=}} \frac{12}{25}$$

- You can convert a fraction into a decimal

### Using equivalent fractions

$$\frac{3}{20} \overset{\times 5}{\underset{\times 5}{=}} \frac{15}{100}$$

Convert the fraction to an equivalent fraction with a denominator of 10, 100, 1000 etc.

$$\frac{3}{20} = \frac{15}{100} = 0.15$$

Change the equivalent fraction to a decimal.

### Using division

$$\frac{3}{20} = 3 \div 20 = 0.15$$

Divide the numerator by the denominator.

p.108

Every number can be represented as a position on a number line.

**Example**

What number is the arrow pointing to?

The arrow is pointing between 6 and 7.
There are 10 spaces between 6 and 7. So 10 spaces represent 1 unit.
Each space represents $1 \div 10 = \frac{1}{10} = 0.1$ unit.
The arrow is pointing to the number 6.3.

1 Write these decimals as fractions.
   **a** 0.3          **b** 0.9          **c** 0.23          **d** 0.39
   **e** 0.88         **f** 0.274        **g** 0.814         **h** 0.037

2 Write these decimals as fractions in their simplest form.
   **a** 0.4          **b** 0.8          **c** 0.75          **d** 0.36
   **e** 0.85         **f** 0.08         **g** 0.005         **h** 2.65

3 Change these fractions to decimals without using a calculator.
   **a** $\frac{7}{10}$     **b** $\frac{1}{2}$     **c** $\frac{47}{50}$     **d** $\frac{13}{25}$     **e** $\frac{22}{25}$
   **f** $\frac{11}{10}$    **g** $\frac{31}{25}$    **h** $\frac{145}{500}$   **i** $\frac{2}{8}$      **j** $\frac{32}{40}$

4 Change these fractions into decimals using an appropriate method.
   Give your answers to two decimal places where necessary.
   **a** $\frac{19}{50}$    **b** $\frac{1}{3}$     **c** $\frac{7}{20}$     **d** $\frac{3}{50}$
   **e** $\frac{11}{16}$    **f** $\frac{5}{2}$     **g** $\frac{51}{60}$    **h** $\frac{8}{13}$

5 Write the number each of the arrows is pointing to.
   **a**

   **b**

   **c**

6 **a** Copy this decimal number line.

   **b** Mark on these fractions.
   **i** $\frac{8}{10}$          **ii** $\frac{28}{20}$          **iii** $\frac{7}{8}$

7 Put these lists of numbers in order, starting with the smallest.
   **a** 2.13        2.09        2.2        2.12        2.07
   **b** 0.345       0.35        0.325      0.3         0.309
   **c** 1.32        1.4         1.35       1.387       1.058
   **d** 5.306       5.288       5.308      5.29        5.3

**DID YOU KNOW?**

The decimal number system is also called the 'Hindu - Arabic' system. Although the exact origins are unclear, most historians agree that a decimal place value system came from India originally.

Unit 2

171

This spread will show you how to:

- Round numbers to any given power of 10
- Round to the nearest integer and to one significant figure
- Estimate answers to problems involving decimals

**Keywords**
Decimal places (dp)
Estimate
Rounding
Significant figure

You can **round** a number to the nearest 10, 100, 1000, and so on.

You can also round a number to the nearest whole number or to a given number of **decimal places**.

---

**Example**

Round 16.473
**a** to the nearest whole number
**c** to 2 decimal places
**b** to 1 decimal place
**d** to the nearest 10.

........................................................................

**a** 16.473 ≈ 16. Look at the tenths digit.
**b** 16.473 ≈ 16.5. Look at the hundredths digit.
**c** 16.473 ≈ 16.47. Look at the thousandths digit.
**d** 16.473 ≈ 20. Look at the units digit.

Look at the next digit. If it is 5 or more then the number is rounded up, otherwise it is rounded down.

---

- The first digit that is not zero in a number is called the **first significant figure**. It has the highest value in the number.

This topic is extended to more significant figures on page 408.

You can round a number to one significant figure.

---

**Example**

Round the numbers to one significant figure.
**a** 7560          **b** 52.3          **c** 1.5

........................................................................

| | Thousands | Hundreds | Tens | Units | • | tenths |
|---|---|---|---|---|---|---|
| **a** | 7 | 5 | 6 | 0 | • | |
| **b** | | | 5 | 2 | • | 3 |
| **c** | | | | 1 | • | 5 |

**a** First significant figure is 7, so round up to 8000.
**b** First significant figure is 5, so round down to 50.
**c** First significant figure is 1, so round up to 2.

---

You can **estimate** the answer to a calculation by first rounding the numbers in the calculation.

p.338

---

**Example**

Estimate the answer to this calculation.          $\dfrac{4.23 \times 5.89}{9.7}$

........................................................................

You can round each of these numbers to the nearest whole number.
$$\frac{4.23 \times 5.89}{9.7} \approx \frac{4 \times 6}{10} = \frac{24}{10} = 2.4$$

You have to decide how much to round the numbers to make a good estimate for the calculation.

---

**1** Write the value of the red digit in each of these numbers.
  **a** 1324    **b** 21894    **c** 234897    **d** 54327

**2** Round each of these numbers to the nearest
  **i** 10           **ii** 100           **iii** 1000.
  **a** 2568         **b** 4297           **c** 7853         **d** 1432
  **e** 12473        **f** 18258

**A02 Functional Maths**

**3** Here is a table showing the populations of five cities.

| Town | Population |
|------|-----------|
| London | 7 172 091 |
| Paris | 2 142 800 |
| New York | 8 085 742 |
| Mumbai | 16 368 084 |
| Beijing | 7 441 000 |

Round the population of each city to the nearest
10 000 and then place the cities in order of size
from smallest to largest.

**4** Round each of these numbers to the nearest
  **i** 10           **ii** 100.
  **a** 458.2        **b** 1329.5         **c** 342.52       **d** 354.82

**5** Round each of these numbers to the nearest whole number.
  **a** 3.7          **b** 8.7            **c** 18.63        **d** 69.49
  **e** 109.9        **f** 6.899

**6** Round each of these numbers to 1 decimal place.
  **a** 0.27         **b** 2.89           **c** 3.82         **d** 12.48

**7** Round each of these numbers to
  **i** 2 decimal places    **ii** one significant figure.
  **a** 0.327        **b** 2.869          **c** 3.802        **d** 14.458

**8** **a** Irwin estimates the value of to
  $$\frac{47.3 \times 18.9}{8.72}$$ to be 100.
  Write three numbers Irwin could use to get his estimate.
  **b** Sarah estimates the value of
  $$\frac{21.4 \times 4.87}{49.8}$$ to be 2.
  Write three numbers Sarah could use to get her estimate.

For more
questions on
rounding, see
page 408.

This spread will show you how to:

- Use written methods for addition and subtraction of whole numbers and decimals
- Add and subtract mentally numbers with up to two decimal places

There is a standard written method for **addition** of **decimals**.

**Example**

Liam measures the lengths of three vehicles.
  Car 2.4m   Lorry 5m   Motorbike 1.68m
What is the total length of the three vehicles?

**Estimate** the answer first.
$2.4 + 5 + 1.68 \approx 2 + 5 + 2$
$\qquad\qquad = 9m$
Set out the calculation in columns, lining up the decimal points.

| Units | • | tenths | hundredths |
|-------|---|--------|------------|
| 2 | • | 4 | |
| 5 | • | | |
| + 1₁ | • | 6 | 8 |
| = 9 | • | 0 | 8 |

Start by adding hundredths to hundredths, then tenths to tenths, units to units and so on.

So the combined length = 9.08m.

There is a standard written method for **subtraction** of decimals.

**Example**

Calculate 27.8 litres − 14.45 litres.

Estimate the answer first.
$27.8 - 14.45 \approx 28 - 14$
$\qquad\qquad\quad = 14$ litres
Set out the calculation in columns, lining up the decimal points.
You could write the numbers in a place value table.

$$\begin{array}{r} 27.\overset{71}{8}0 \\ -14.45 \\ \hline 13.35 \end{array}$$

Add a zero here so that both numbers have the same number of decimal places.

Start with the smallest place value (in this case hundredths), and subtract hundredths from hundredths, tenths from tenths, and so on.
27.8 litres − 14.45 litres = 13.35 litres

You could also use 'shopkeepers subtraction'.

**1** Use an appropriate method for each of these calculations.

   **a** 83 + 57             **b** 93 + 32           **c** 275 + 958

   **d** 843 + 872         **e** 838 + 697         **f** 834 + 787

> Get into the habit of estimating your answer first.

**2** Use an appropriate method for each of these calculations.

   **a** 62 − 47             **b** 83 − 68           **c** 487 − 356

   **d** 852 − 728         **e** 548 − 387         **f** 589 − 387

**3** Use an appropriate method for each of these calculations.

   **a** 25 + 38 + 68      **b** 123 + 76 − 58

   **c** 173 − 27 + 56      **d** 327 + 176 − 255

**4** Use a mental or written method to work out these calculations.

   **a** 33.4 + 15.2       **b** 34.6 + 13.7      **c** 19.8 + 8.8      **d** 18.7 + 26.5

**5** Use a mental or written method to work out these calculations.

   **a** 8.7 − 2.5         **b** 15.8 − 8.4      **c** 26.3 − 7.9      **d** 53.6 − 27.8

---

**A02 Functional Maths**

**3** Jodie buys

   3 pens at 14p each
   2 writing pads at £1.89 each
   1 calculator at £2.79

She pays with a £10 note.
Work out how much change Jodie should get from £10.

---

**7** Use a written method to work out these additions.

   **a** 3.52 + 4.6        **b** 13.62 + 2.9      **c** 8.5 + 14.81      **d** 75.8 + 28.39

**8** Use a written method to work out these subtractions.

   **a** 17.3 − 4.22       **b** 16.6 − 3.47      **c** 37.7 − 18.86      **d** 57.28 − 38.4

**9** Use a written method for each of these calculations.

   **a** 16.4 + 9.87       **b** 49.2 + 7.72      **c** 9.42 − 5.9

   **d** 26.9 + 9.82      **e** 36.57 − 8.59      **f** 36.28 − 17.4

---

**A02 Functional Maths**

**10** Use a mental or written method to solve each of these problems.

   **a** Sean sells olives at the weekend. On Saturday he sells 8.9 kg; on Sunday he sells 3.38 kg. What weight of olives has Sean sold altogether during the weekend?

   **b** Naomi is building a wooden cold frame for growing vegetables. She needs three lengths of wood to finish the frame. The lengths are 1.82 m, 1.3 m and 1.79 m. What is the total length of wood she will need to buy?

This spread will show you how to:

- Use written methods for multiplication and division of whole numbers and decimals

- Use approximation to estimate the answers to problems

**Keywords**
Divisor
Estimate
Grid method
Standard
  method
Whole number

You can multiply decimals by replacing them with an equivalent **whole number** calculation that is easier to work out.

**Example**

Bruce buys 28 lengths of wood. Each length is 4.8m long.
What is the total length of wood he buys?

**Estimate** the answer first.
$28 \times 4.8 \approx 30 \times 5$
$\qquad = 150 \text{ m}$
Rewrite as a whole number calculation $\quad 28 \times 4.8 = 28 \times 48$
Work out $28 \times 48$ using the standard method.

$$
\begin{array}{r}
48 \\
\times 28 \\
\end{array}
$$

$20 \times 48 \quad\quad 960$
$\phantom{2}8 \times 48 \quad +384$
$28 \times 48 = 1344$

Bruce buys
$28 \times 4.8 = 28 \times 48 \div 10$
$\qquad\qquad = 1344 \div 10$
$\qquad\qquad = 134.4\text{m of wood}$

You could also use
the grid method:

| ×  | 40  | 8   |
|----|-----|-----|
| 20 | 800 | 160 |
| 8  | 320 | 64  |

$28 \times 48 =$
$800 + 320 +$
$160 + 64 = 1344$

Adjust your answer
for the decimals.

You can divide any number including decimals by a whole number using the 'chunking method'.

**Example**

Andrew packs tins into boxes. Each box will hold 12 tins.
Andrew has 159 tins. How many boxes will he fill?

Estimate the answer first.
$159 \div 12 \approx 150 \div 10$
$\qquad\quad = 15 \text{ boxes}$

$$
\begin{array}{r}
12\overline{)159} \\
-120 \\
\hline
39 \\
-36 \\
\hline
3
\end{array}
$$

$12 \times \mathbf{10}$

$12 \times \mathbf{3}$
$159 \div 12 = \mathbf{13}$ remainder 3

Andrew will fill 13 boxes with 3 tins left over.

1 Calculate these using an appropriate written method.
  Remember to do a mental approximation first.
  **a** $13 \times 16$      **b** $18 \times 13$      **c** $13 \times 13$
  **d** $16 \times 19$      **e** $17 \times 19$

2 Use an appropriate method of calculation to work out:
  **a** $23 \times 8$      **b** $9 \times 64$      **c** $8 \times 147$
  **d** $17 \times 21$      **e** $16 \times 28$      **f** $24 \times 23$
  **g** $12 \times 114$      **h** $25 \times 135$      **i** $28 \times 154$

3 Use an appropriate method of calculation to work out each of these.
  Where appropriate leave your answer in remainder form.
  **a** $56 \div 6$      **b** $84 \div 8$      **c** $95 \div 5$
  **d** $116 \div 7$      **e** $123 \div 9$      **f** $144 \div 8$
  **g** $155 \div 12$      **h** $185 \div 14$      **i** $284 \div 12$

**A02 Functional Maths**

**4 a** Beatrice plants 8 seeds in a pot. She has 114 seeds.
   How many pots will she fill with seeds? How many seeds will
   there be left?
  **b** Melinda packs 7 boxes into every crate. She has 103 boxes.
   How many crates will she be able to fill?

5 Use an appropriate method of calculation to work out:
  **a** $13 \times 2.1$      **b** $3.7 \times 13$      **c** $5.4 \times 13$
  **d** $23 \times 3.3$      **e** $28 \times 3.2$      **f** $6.3 \times 29$

6 Use an appropriate method of calculation to work out:
  **a** $25.9 \div 7$      **b** $34.8 \div 6$      **c** $66.4 \div 8$
  **d** $73.8 \div 6$      **e** $117.9 \div 9$      **f** $122.4 \div 8$

7 Use an appropriate method of calculation to work out:
  **a** $12 \times 1.64$      **b** $13 \times 1.42$      **c** $13 \times 1.35$
  **d** $15 \times 1.32$      **e** $18 \times 1.43$      **f** $28 \times 1.52$

**A02 Functional Maths**

**8 a** Wally buys 13 bags of potatoes. Each bag costs £1.23.
   How much does this cost in total?
  **b** Ashley buys six CDs. Each CD costs £8.79. How much is this
   in total?
  **c** Christina buys 12 ready meals. Each meal costs £1.79.
   What is the cost of the 12 ready meals?

9 Use an appropriate method of calculation to work out:
  **a** $54.16 \div 4$      **b** $85.32 \div 6$      **c** $130.72 \div 8$
  **d** $62.23 \div 7$      **e** $188.7 \div 6$      **f** $219.51 \div 9$

## Summary

### Check out

You should now be able to:

- Recognise the equivalence of fractions and decimals
- Order decimals and fractions on a number line
- Round numbers to any given power of 10, the nearest whole number and one significant figure
- Use rounding to estimate answers to calculations
- Use written methods for addition, subtraction, multiplication and division of whole numbers and decimals

### Worked exam question

Work out an estimate for the value of $5.1 \times 98$ (2)

(Edexcel Limited 2007)

Write your approximations for 5.1 and 98

$$5.1 \longrightarrow 5$$
$$98 \longrightarrow 100$$
$$5 \times 100 = 500$$

### Worked exam question

Work out £1.70 × 5

£ ..................... (1)

(Edexcel Limited 2008)

The answer must be in pounds (£).

$$\begin{array}{r} 1.70 \\ 5 \times \\ \hline 8.50 \end{array}$$ £8.50

OR

| × | 100 | 70 | 0 |
|---|-----|-----|---|
| 5 | 500 | 350 | 0 |

£8.50

```
 500
 350
  0 +
-----
 850
```

Do NOT write £8.5 This would give no marks

## Exam questions

**1**

| Cinema tickets | |
|---|---|
| Adult ticket | £8.65 |
| Child Ticket | £4.90 |
| Senior ticket | £5.85 |

Tony buys one child ticket and one senior ticket.
**a** Work out the total cost. (1)

Stephanie buys adult tickets only.
The total cost is £60.55
**b** How many adult tickets does she buy? (2)

Kamala buys one adult ticket and two child tickets.
She pays with a £20 note.
**c** How much change should she get? (3)

(Edexcel Limited 2009)

**2** **a** Write down the fraction of this shape that is shaded.
Give your fraction in its simplest form.

(2)

**b** Shade $\frac{2}{7}$ on a copy of this shape. (1)

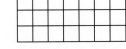

**c** Write $\frac{3}{10}$ as a decimal. (1)
**d** Write 0.39 as a fraction. (1)

(Edexcel Limited 2009)

# Introduction

When you hire a car, the price often increases in equal amounts for each extra day of hiring. This is an example of a linear function, and the graph will be a straight line.

## What's the point?

Linear functions occur commonly in man-made situations, such as in currency conversion and in working out tariffs and charges. If you understand how to create and use linear graphs, you can often solve real-life problems much quicker than calculating from scratch.

1 Work out the value of the letter.
   **a** $2 + p = 5$      **b** $3 + q = 11$
   **c** $5 - r = 3$      **d** $2 - s = -3$

2 Work out the value of each expression when $x = 2$.
   **a** $x + 6$          **b** $3x - 1$
   **c** $2x + 4$         **d** $\frac{x}{4} + 3$

3 Substitute $x = 0$ into these expressions.
   **a** $2x + 5$         **b** $3x - 4$
   **c** $10x + 1$        **d** $4x + 11$

4 Substitute $x = -1$ into these expressions.
   **a** $2x + 1$         **b** $3x - 2$
   **c** $4x + 5$         **d** $2x - 5$

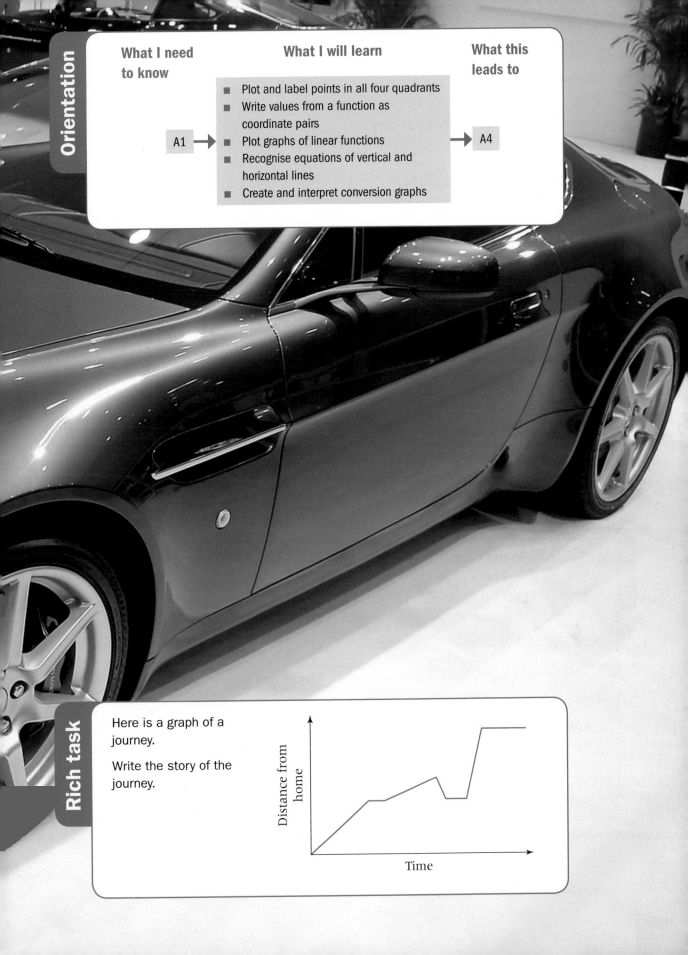

**What I need to know**

**What I will learn**

**What this leads to**

A1 →

- Plot and label points in all four quadrants
- Write values from a function as coordinate pairs
- Plot graphs of linear functions
- Recognise equations of vertical and horizontal lines
- Create and interpret conversion graphs

→ A4

**Rich task**

Here is a graph of a journey.

Write the story of the journey.

Distance from home

Time

# Coordinates

This spread will show you how to:

- Plot coordinates
- Locate points with given coordinates

**Keywords**
Coordinates
Negative
Origin
Positive
Quadrant
x-axis
y-axis

- **Coordinates** are a pair of numbers (x, y) that fix a point on a grid.

You can plot coordinates on a grid.

- A grid has two perpendicular axes: the *x*-axis and the *y*-axis.

You write the coordinates as a pair
    (*x*-coordinate, *y*-coordinate)
The *x*-value comes first.

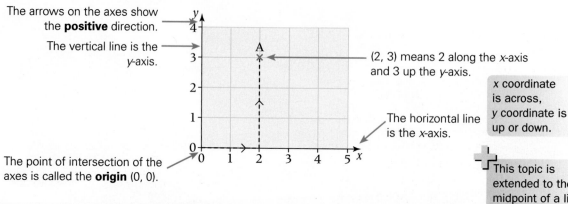

The arrows on the axes show the **positive** direction.

The vertical line is the *y*-axis.

(2, 3) means 2 along the *x*-axis and 3 up the *y*-axis.

The horizontal line is the *x*-axis.

The point of intersection of the axes is called the **origin** (0, 0).

*x* coordinate is across, *y* coordinate is up or down.

This topic is extended to the midpoint of a line on page 434.

**Example**

**a** Plot and join the points
A(1, 3), B(3, 3) and C(3, 1).
Name the shape you have drawn.

**b** Add and join the point D(0, 0).
Name the new shape.

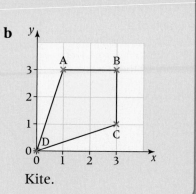

Kite.

**1** Give the coordinates of the points A to Z.
The first one is done for you.
A(2, 8)
B(__ , __)

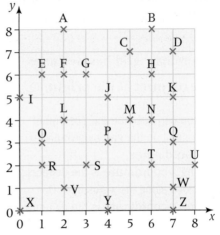

**2 a** Copy this coordinate grid onto square
  grid paper.
  **b** Plot and label these points.
  A(2, 3)   B(8, 3)   C(8, 9)   D(2, 9)
  **c** Join the points in order.
  **d** Write the name of the shape ABCD.

**3 a** Copy the coordinate grid in question
  **2** onto square grid paper.
  **b** Plot, label and join each of these sets
  of points, then write the name of the
  shape you have made.
  **i** A(7, 6), B(7, 9), C(3, 9), D(3, 6)
  **ii** E(5, 1), F(3, 4), G(1, 1)
  **iii** H(8, 3), I(10, 5), J(7, 5), K(5, 3)
  **iv** L(8, 6), M(9, 8), N(8, 9), P(7, 8)

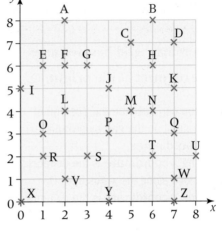

**4** Write the coordinates of all the corner points
of this shape.
Start at the origin, then point A, ...

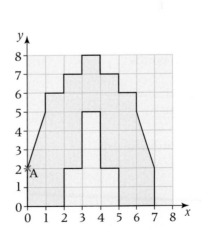

**Coordinates in all four quadrants**

This spread will show you how to:
- Plot points in all four quadrants

**Keywords**
Axes
Coordinates
Origin
Quadrant
*x*-coordinate
*y*-coordinate

A coordinate grid has two **axes**.

The axes meet at the **origin**, O.

- You can describe the position of a point on the grid by giving its **coordinates**.
  The **x-coordinate** is the distance you move along the x-axis from O.
  The **y-coordinate** is the distance you move parallel to the y-axis from O.

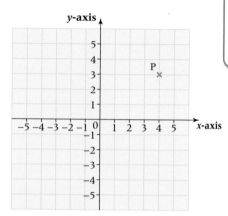

The coordinates of *P* are (4, 3). *x* comes before *y* in the alphabet.

You can extend the *x*- and *y*-axes into negative numbers.
The axes divide the grid into four sections, called **quadrants**.

The coordinates of Q are (−3, 2). From 0 you move −3 along the *x*-axis and then +2 parallel to the *y*-axis.

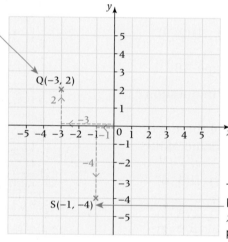

The coordinates of S are (−1, −4). From 0 you move −1 along the *x*-axis and then −4 (downwards) parallel to the *y*-axis.

- You can plot and label points in all four quadrants.

**Example**

Plot the points
A(1, 4),
B(−2, 3),
C(4, −2)
D(−2, −3)
on a coordinate grid.

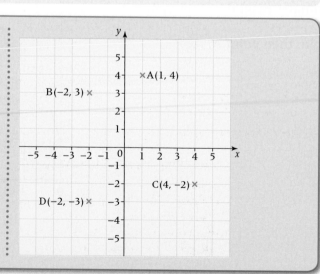

**1** Write the coordinates of the points O, P, Q, R, S and T.

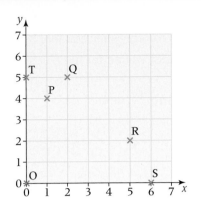

**2** Write the coordinates of the points in each diagram.

**a**

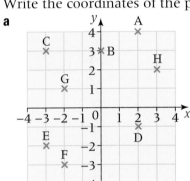

**b**

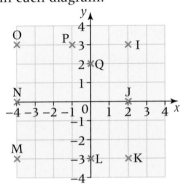

**3 a** Plot these sets of points on a copy of this grid.

   **i** (3, 2)   (−1, 2)   (−1, −1)

   **ii** (1, 2)   (−1, 0)   (3, 0)

**b** Join each set of points in order.

**c** What is the name of each shape?

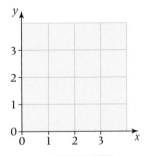

**4 a** Copy a coordinate grid from question **2** onto square grid paper.

   **b** Plot and label these points on your grid.

   A (3, 3)          B (−2, 3)          C (−4, −1)

   **c** A, B and C are three corners of a parallelogram.
   Write the coordinate of the fourth corner, D.

**5 a** Copy a coordinate grid from question **2** onto square grid paper.

   **b** On your grid, draw a triangle with each corner in a different quadrant. Label the corners A, B and C.

   **c** Write the coordinates of A, B and C.

   **d** Repeat for
   **i** a square          **ii** a kite, with each corner in a different quadrant.

Do **not** copy the points.

**A03  Problem**

**Unit 2**

185

**Function machines 1**

This spread will show you how to:
- Use function machines to represent equations
- Write the input and output values for functions as pairs in a table

Here is a **function machine**

input      output

| 0 | | 0 |
| 1 | ×2 | 2 |
| 2 | | 4 |
| 3 | | 6 |

When you know the **input**, you can calculate the **output**.

*y* is the output.

In this machine    input $\longrightarrow$ output
               $x$          $2x$

You can write this as an **equation**   $y = 2x$.

When you know the value of $x$ you can calculate $y$.   When $x = 1$, $y = 2 \times 1 = 2$.
When $x = 2$, $y = 2 \times 2 = 4$.

You will learn about **solving** equations on page 326.

**Example**

For each function machine, write the output for the inputs given.

**a**   $x \longrightarrow \boxed{\times 3} \longrightarrow y$

inputs 0, 2, 5, 10

**b**   $x \longrightarrow \boxed{\div 2} \longrightarrow y$

inputs 2, 4, 10, 18

**a**

| Input | Output |
|-------|--------|
| 0 | 0 |
| 2 | 6 |
| 5 | 15 |
| 10 | 30 |

**b**

| Input | Output |
|-------|--------|
| 2 | 1 |
| 4 | 2 |
| 10 | 5 |
| 18 | 9 |

- You can draw a function machine to represent an equation.

**Example**

Draw function machines to represent the equations.
**a** $y = x + 2$          **b** $y = \frac{x}{4}$

**a**   $x \longrightarrow \boxed{+2} \longrightarrow y$

**b**   $x \longrightarrow \boxed{\div 4} \longrightarrow y$

$\frac{x}{4}$ means $x \div 4$.

Functions can have more than one step.

**Example**

**a** Draw a function machine for the equation $y = 3x - 2$.
**b** Work out the outputs for these inputs: 0, 2, 4.

**a**   $x \longrightarrow \boxed{\times 3} \longrightarrow \boxed{-2} \longrightarrow y$

**b** $0 \rightarrow 0 \times 3 - 2 = 0 - 2 = -2$
$2 \rightarrow 2 \times 3 - 2 = 6 - 2 = 4$
$4 \rightarrow 4 \times 3 - 2 = 12 - 2 = 10$

$3x = 3 \times x$

First multiply $x$ by 3 then subtract 2.

**1** Copy and complete the tables for these function machines.

**a**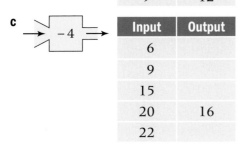

| Input | Output |
|-------|--------|
| 0 | 3 |
| 1 | 4 |
| 4 | |
| 7 | |
| 9 | 12 |

**b** ×3

| Input | Output |
|-------|--------|
| 0 | |
| 3 | 9 |
| 6 | |
| 7 | |
| 9 | 27 |

**c** − 4

| Input | Output |
|-------|--------|
| 6 | |
| 9 | |
| 15 | |
| 20 | 16 |
| 22 | |

**d** ÷ 3

| Input | Output |
|-------|--------|
| 6 | |
| 12 | |
| 15 | |
| | 8 |
| 30 | |

**2** Draw function machines for these equations.

**a** $y = x + 5$    **b** $y = x − 3$    **c** $y = 3x$    **d** $y = x + 1$

**e** $y = \frac{x}{3}$    **f** $y = x − 2$    **g** $y = 6x$    **h** $y = \frac{x}{2}$

**3** Draw a function machine for each equation.
Use your machines to calculate the outputs when

**i** $x = 1$        **ii** $x = 2$        **iii** $x = 3$

**a** $y = 2x$    **b** $y = x + 4$    **c** $y = x − 1$    **d** $y = \frac{x}{4}$

**4** Copy and complete the tables for these two-step function machines.

**a** 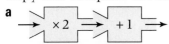 ×2 → +1

| Input | Output |
|-------|--------|
| 0 | 1 |
| 1 | 3 |
| 2 | |
| 3 | |
| 4 | |
| 10 | 21 |

**b** ×3 → − 1

| Input | Output |
|-------|--------|
| 2 | |
| 4 | 11 |
| 5 | |
| 6 | |
| 7 | 20 |
| 10 | |

**5** Draw function machines for these equations.
Use your machines to calculate the outputs when

**i** $x = −2$        **ii** $x = 2$        **iii** $x = 4$

**a** $y = 2x − 1$    **b** $y = 3x + 2$    **c** $y = \frac{x}{2} − 1$    **d** $y = 4x − 5$

**Drawing tables of values**

This spread will show you how to:
- Write the input and output values for functions as pairs in a table
- Identify explicit and implicit functions

**Keywords**
Equation
Function
Implicit equation
Table of values

This function machine represents the equation $y = x - 3$.

Input                    Output
$x \longrightarrow$ $\boxed{-3}$ $\longrightarrow y$

You can work out the value of $y$ for different values of $x$.

Input                    Output
$x = 3$                  $y = 0$
$x = 5$                  $y = 2$
$x = 7 \longrightarrow$ $\boxed{-3}$ $\longrightarrow y = 4$
$x = 12$                 $y = 9$
$x = 15$                 $y = 12$

You can write the pairs of $x$ and $y$ values in a table of values.

| $x$ | 3 | 5 | 7 | 12 | 15 |
|---|---|---|---|---|---|
| $y$ | 0 | 2 | 4 | 9 | 12 |

Input this $x$-value and you get this $y$-value.

**Example**

Complete the table of values for this function machine.

$x \longrightarrow$ $\boxed{+4}$ $\longrightarrow y$

| $x$ | 0 | 2 | 3 | 6 | 9 |
|---|---|---|---|---|---|
| $y$ | | | | | |

Input each $x$ value in turn.

$x = 0 \longrightarrow$ $\boxed{+4}$ $\longrightarrow y = 4$

$x = 2 \longrightarrow$ $\boxed{+4}$ $\longrightarrow y = 6$

| $x$ | 0 | 2 | 3 | 6 | 9 |
|---|---|---|---|---|---|
| $y$ | 4 | 6 | 7 | 10 | 13 |

**Example**

Complete the table of values for the equation $x + y = 5$.

| $x$ | 0 | 2 | 4 | 5 |
|---|---|---|---|---|
| $y$ | | | | |

$x + y = 5$ is an **implicit** equation. $x$ and $y$ appear on the same side of the equals sign.

When $x = 0$ the equation is $0 + y = 5$, so $y = 5$
When $x = 2$                $2 + y = 5$, so $y = 3$
When $x = 4$                $4 + y = 5$, so $y = 1$
When $x = 5$                $5 + y + 5$, so $y = 0$

| $x$ | 0 | 2 | 4 | 5 |
|---|---|---|---|---|
| $y$ | 5 | 3 | 1 | 0 |

**1** Copy and complete the table of values for each function machine.

**a** Input → $x$ → $+5$ → $y$ → Output

| $x$ | 0 | 2 | 3 | 6 | 9 |
|---|---|---|---|---|---|
| $y$ | | | | | |

**b** Input → $x$ → $\times 3$ → $y$ → Output

| $x$ | 0 | 2 | 3 | 6 | 9 |
|---|---|---|---|---|---|
| $y$ | | | | | |

**c** Input → $x$ → $-6$ → $y$ → Output

| $x$ | 6 | 7 | 8 | 9 | 10 |
|---|---|---|---|---|---|
| $y$ | | | | | |

**d** Input → $x$ → $\div 4$ → $y$ → Output

| $x$ | 4 | 8 | 12 | 16 | 20 |
|---|---|---|---|---|---|
| $y$ | | | | | |

**2** Copy and complete the table of values for each function machine.

**a** Input → $x$ → $+3$ → $y$ → Output

| $x$ | −5 | −2 | 3 | 6 | 9 |
|---|---|---|---|---|---|
| $y$ | | | | | |

**b** Input → $x$ → $\times 6$ → $y$ → Output

| $x$ | −2 | 0 | 3 | 5 | 7 |
|---|---|---|---|---|---|
| $y$ | | | | | |

**c** Input → $x$ → $-4$ → $y$ → Output

| $x$ | −2 | 0 | 3 | 5 | 7 |
|---|---|---|---|---|---|
| $y$ | | | | | |

**d** Input → $x$ → $\div 3$ → $y$ → Output

| $x$ | −6 | −3 | 3 | 6 | 9 |
|---|---|---|---|---|---|
| $y$ | | | | | |

A03 Problem

**3** Match each equation to a table of values.

**a** $y = 3x$

**i**

| $x$ | −2 | 0 | 2 | 4 | 6 |
|---|---|---|---|---|---|
| $y$ | −2 | 4 | 10 | 16 | 22 |

**b** $y = x + 4$

**ii**

| $x$ | −1 | 2 | 3 | 5 | 7 |
|---|---|---|---|---|---|
| $y$ | −1 | 11 | 15 | 23 | 31 |

**c** $y = 3x + 4$

**iii**

| $x$ | −2 | 0 | 2 | 4 | 6 |
|---|---|---|---|---|---|
| $y$ | −6 | 0 | 6 | 12 | 18 |

**d** $y = 4x + 3$

**iv**

| $x$ | −4 | −2 | 1 | 2 | 4 |
|---|---|---|---|---|---|
| $y$ | 0 | 2 | 5 | 6 | 8 |

Unit 2

**Plotting graphs from tables of values**

This spread will show you how to:

- Plot graphs of functions in which $y$ is or is not the subject
- Read values from a graph

**Keywords**
Coordinate pairs
Satisfy

Here is a table of values for the equation

$$y = 3x$$

| $x$ | $-2$ | $-1$ | 0 | 1 | 2 | 3 |
|---|---|---|---|---|---|---|
| $y$ | $-6$ | $-3$ | 0 | 3 | 6 | 9 |

In the table, each $y$-value links to an $x$-value.

$(-2, -6)$ $(-1, -3)$ $(0, 0)$ $(1, 3)$ $(2, 6)$ $(3, 9)$

- You can write the linked $x$- and $y$-values as coordinate pairs.

- You can plot the coordinate pairs on a grid.

Plot each point.

Join the points with a straight line.

All the points on the line **satisfy** the equation $y = 3x$. This means that for every point on the line,

$y$-value = $x$-value $\times$ 3

- You can read values from a graph.

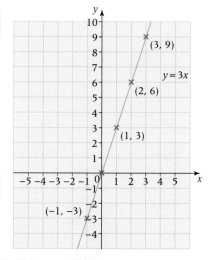

---

Here is the graph of $y = 2x + 3$.
Use the graph to find

**a** the value of $x$ when $y = 7$
**b** the value of $y$ when $x = 3\frac{1}{2}$.

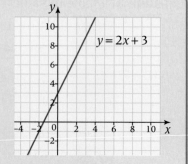

This topic is extended to the intersection of two lines on page 420.

.........................................................

**a** Find $y = 7$ on the $y$-axis.
   Draw a horizontal line to the graph line.
   Draw a vertical line to the $x$-axis.
   Read off the value of $x$.
   $x = 2$

**b** Find $x = 3\frac{1}{2}$ on the $x$-axis.
   Draw a vertical line to the graph line.
   Draw a horizontal line to the $y$-axis.
   Read off the value of $y$.
   $y = 10$

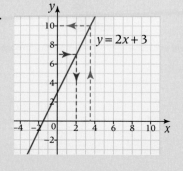

**1** Here is the graph of $y = 2x - 1$.
Find the value of $x$ when

**a** $y = 7$

**b** $y = 0$

**c** $y = -9$

**d** $y = -6$

Find the value of $y$ when

**e** $x = 4$

**f** $x = -4$

**g** $x = 2\frac{1}{2}$

**h** $x = -1\frac{1}{2}$

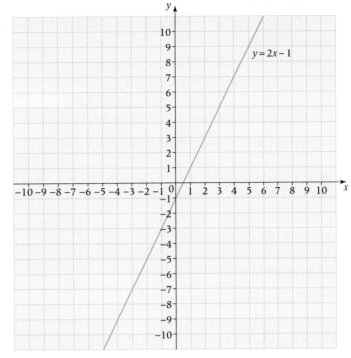

$y = 2x - 1$

**2 a** Copy and complete this table of values for the equation $y = 3x + 1$.

| x | −3 | −2 | 0 | 1 | 2 |
|---|---|---|---|---|---|
| y | | | | 4 | |

**b** Copy and complete this list of coordinate pairs from your table.
(−3, __) (−2, __) (0, __) (1, 4) (2, __)

**c** Copy the grid in question **1** onto square grid paper.

**d** Plot the points from part **b** on your grid.
Join them with a straight line.

**e** From your graph, find the value of $x$ when $y = -2$.

Do not copy the graph line.

**3 a** Copy and complete this table of values for the equation $y = \frac{x}{2}$.

| x | −4 | −2 | 0 | 2 | 6 |
|---|---|---|---|---|---|
| y | −2 | | | | |

**b** Write a list of coordinate pairs from your table.

**c** Copy the grid in question **1** onto square grid paper.

**d** Plot the points from part **b** on your grid.
Join them with a straight line.

**e** From your graph, find the value of $y$ when $x = 9$.

Do not copy the graph line.

**4** Repeat question **3** for the equation $x + y = 7$.

This spread will show you how to:

● Recognise the form of equations of vertical and horizontal lines

**Keywords**
Horizontal
Parallel
Vertical

Horizontal and vertical lines are easy to identify on a graph.
You can also identify them by their equation.

● The equation of a **vertical** line is $x$ = a number.

● The equation of a **horizontal** line is $y$ = a number.

A and B are **vertical** lines.
They are **parallel** to the $y$-axis.

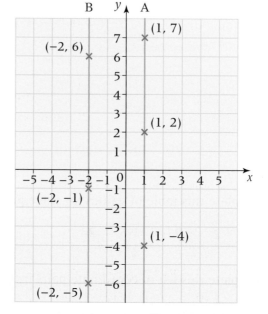

For line A the points labelled are
$(1, -4)$ $(1, 2)$ $(1, 7)$.
Every point on this line has
$x$-coordinate 1.

The equation of line A is $x = 1$.

For line B the points labelled are
$(-2, -5)$ $(-2, -1)$ $(-2, 6)$.
Every point on this line has
$x$-coordinate $-2$.

The equation of line B is $x = -2$.

C and D are **horizontal** lines.
They are parallel to the $x$-axis.

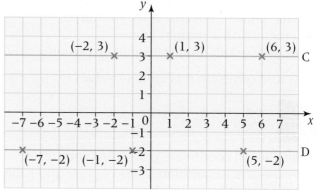

For line C the points labelled are
$(-2, 3)$ $(1, 3)$ $(6, 3)$.
Every point on this line has
$y$-coordinate 3.

The equation of line C is $y = 3$.

For line D the points labelled are
$(-7, -2)$ $(-1, -2)$ $(5, -2)$.
Every point on this line has
$y$-coordinate $-2$.

The equation of line D is $y = -2$.

**1** Name the lines on the grid.

Copy and complete

The equation of the $x$-axis is $y = $ _____

The equation of the $y$-axis is _____

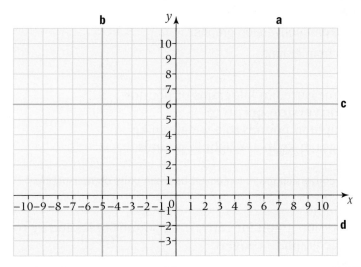

**2** Copy the axes from question **1** onto square grid paper.
For each part, plot the points and join them to make a straight line.
Name each line.

Do not copy the graph lines in blue.

  **a** Line 1: $(-4, -6)$ $(-4, -3)$ $(-4, 1)$ $(-4, 7)$
  **b** Line 2: $(-7, 1)$ $(-2, 1)$ $(4, 1)$ $(6, 1)$
  **c** Line 3: $(-3, -3)$ $(-1, -3)$ $(4, -3)$ $(8, -3)$

**3** Name these lines without plotting the points.
  **a** Line 1: $(-5, 5)$ $(-2, 5)$ $(5, 5)$ $(9, 5)$
  **b** Line 2: $(-8, -3)$ $(-8, 3)$ $(-8, 6)$ $(-8, 10)$

**4** Copy the axes from question **1** onto square grid paper.
  **a** Draw these lines on your grid.
   $x = -2$   $y = -4$   $x = 7$   $y = 1$
  **b** What shape do your lines enclose?

**5** Copy the axes from question **1** onto square grid paper.
  **a** Draw four lines to enclose a square.
  **b** Write the equations of your four lines.
  **c** Write the coordinates of the vertices of your square.

**6** Match the points in set B with lines they lie on in set A.

Some points may lie on more than one line.

**Set A**

| | | | |
|---|---|---|---|
| $x = 3$ | $x = -5$ | $x = 6$ | $x = -2$ |
| $y = 4$ | $y = -2$ | $y = 5$ | $y = -3$ |

**Set B**

| | | | | |
|---|---|---|---|---|
| $(-2, 6)$ | $(3, 3)$ | $(-5, -5)$ | $(6, 5)$ | $(2, 4)$ |
| $(6, -3)$ | $(-2, -3)$ | $(-5, 4)$ | $(-5, 7)$ | $(3, 6)$ |
| $(6, 1)$ | $(8, -3)$ | $(3, 4)$ | $(1, -3)$ | $(5, -2)$ |
| $(6, 3)$ | $(-3, 4)$ | $(3, -3)$ | $(-2, -2)$ | $(-5, 5)$ |

This spread will show you how to:
- Use and interpret conversion graphs
- Read values from graphs

**Keywords**
Conversion
    graph
Convert
Scale
Unit

Weights can be measured in kilograms or pounds.
You can use a **conversion graph** to
- **convert** a weight in pounds to a weight in kg
- convert a weight in kg to a weight in pounds.

- You can use a conversion graph to convert between units of measurement.

kg is the metric
**unit**, pound is the
imperial unit.

**Example**

Here is a conversion graph for converting pounds to kg and kg to pounds. Use the graph to convert
**a** 12 pounds to kilograms      **b** 7 kilograms to pounds.

p.284

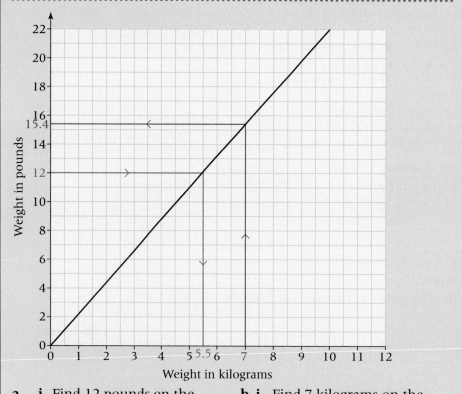

The vertical scale
goes up in 2s.

**a  i** Find 12 pounds on the pounds (vertical) axis.
  **ii** Draw a line across to the graph.
  **iii** Draw a line down from the graph to the kilograms (horizontal) axis.
  **iv** Read the value off the axis.
       12 pounds = 5.5 kilograms

**b  i** Find 7 kilograms on the kilograms (horizontal) axis.
  **ii** Draw a line up to the graph.
  **iii** Draw a line across from the graph to the pounds (vertical) axis.
  **iv** Read the value off the axis. Use the scale to estimate the value.
       7 kilograms = 15.4 pounds

The horizontal
scale goes up
in 1s.

**A02 Functional Maths**

**1** Use the conversion graph on page 194 to convert
    **a** 22 pounds to kilograms     **b** 11 pounds to kilograms
    **c** 3 kilograms to pounds     **d** 9 kilograms to pounds
    **e** 8.5 pounds to kilograms     **f** 3.5 pounds to kilograms
    **g** 7.5 kilograms to pounds     **h** 2.5 kilograms to pounds.

**2** Here is a conversion graph for
    • euros to pounds
    • pounds to euros.

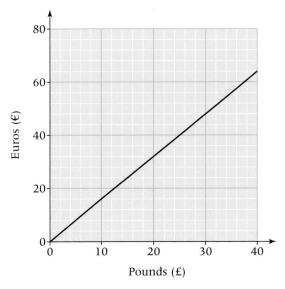

    **a** Use the graph to convert
       **i** €32 to pounds
      **ii** €48 to pounds
     **iii** £40 to euros
     **iv** £25 to euros
      **v** €50 to pounds
     **vi** €35 to pounds
    **b** Which is worth more: £1 or €1?
       Explain how you know.

**3** Here is a conversion graph for
    • miles to kilometres
    • kilometres to miles.
    **a** Use the graph to convert
       **i** 4 km to miles
      **ii** 5 miles to km
     **iii** 1 mile to km
     **iv** 1 km to miles.
    **b** Which is longer, 1 mile or 1 km?
       Explain how you know.

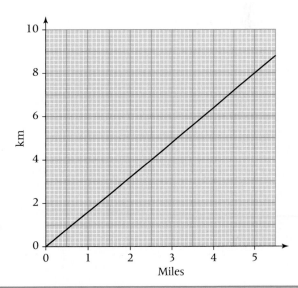

Unit 2

This spread will show you how to:
- Use and interpret conversion graphs
- Read values from graphs

**Keywords**
Degrees
  Celsius (°C)
Degrees
  Fahrenheit (°F)

You can use this conversion graph to convert
- temperatures in °C to °F
- temperatures in °F to °C.

A weather forecast often gives temperatures in degrees Fahrenheit (°F) and degrees Celsius (°C).

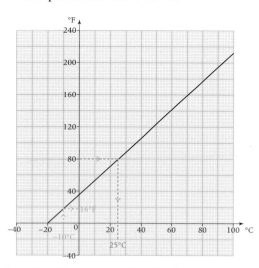

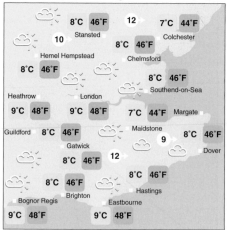

**Example**

Use the conversion graph to convert
**a** 80 °F to °C
**b** −10 °C to °F.

**a** To convert 80 °F to °C
  **i** Find 80 °F on the °F (vertical) axis. (This scale goes up in 40s.)
  **ii** Draw a line across to the graph.
  **iii** Draw a line down from the graph to the °C (horizontal) axis.
  **iv** Read the value off the axis.
    80 °F = 25 °C

**b** To convert −10 °C to °F
  **i** Find −10 °C on the °C (horizontal) axis.
  **ii** Draw a line up to the graph.
  **iii** Draw a line across from the graph to the °F (vertical) axis.
  **iv** Read the value off the axis.
    −10 °C = 16 °F

**Example**

Use the conversion graph to help you write these temperatures in order, from coldest to hottest.
    10 °F     60 °F     10 °C     80 °C     160 °F

To compare temperatures, they need to be measured in the same units.

From the graph, 10 °C = 50 °F
              80 °C = 176 °F

So in order the temperatures are

Use the original values in the answer.

Use the conversion graph for °F to °C on page 340 to answer questions **1** to **3**.

**1** Convert these temperatures.
  **a** 120 °F to °C     **b** 60 °F to °C     **c** 40 °C to °F     **d** 65 °C to °F
  **e** 75 °F to °C      **f** 8 °F to °C       **g** −5 °C to °F     **h** −20 °C to °F

**2** Which is hotter?
  **a** 20 °C or 20 °F    **b** 150 °F or 40 °C      **c** 18 °C or 60 °F
  **d** 90 °F or 30 °C    **e** −8 °C or 8 °F        **f** −30 °F or −30 °C

**3** **a** The melting point of ice is 32 °F. What is this in °C?
  **b** The boiling point of water is 100 °C. What is this in °F?
  **c** Average body temperature for humans is 37 °C.
    What is this in °F?

**A02 Functional Maths**

**4** Here is a conversion graph for inches to centimetres.
  **a** Use the conversion graph to convert
    **i** 6 inches to cm          **ii** 10 cm to inches
    **iii** 4 cm to inches        **iv** 10 inches to cm.
  **b** Use the graph to help you write these sets of lengths in order.
    **i** 2 inches   12 cm   13 inches   9 cm        4 inches
    **ii** 23 cm     1 inch   16 cm       5 inches    3 cm
  **c** For a handling data project, a group of students measured the lengths of their feet. Some measured in inches instead of centimetres.
    **i** Convert all the measurements in inches to centimetres.
    **ii** Write the students' feet in order of size.

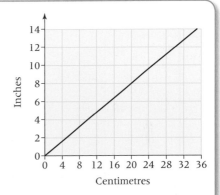

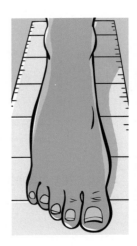

| Name | Length of foot |
|---|---|
| Nadia | 19 cm |
| Mel | 10 inches |
| Jonathan | 13 inches |
| Omar | 23 cm |
| Shelley | 10.5 inches |
| Dustin | 12 inches |
| Jake | 29 cm |

# Summary

## Check out

You should now be able to:

- Use axes and coordinates to describe the position of a point in all four quadrants
- Plot straight line graphs of functions in which y is or is not the subject
- Read values from a graph
- Use and interpret conversion graphs

## Worked exam question

The conversion graph can be used to change pounds (£) and Euros (€).

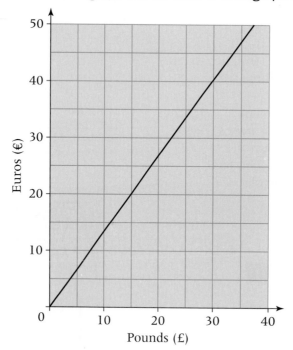

a Use the graph to change 30 pounds to Euros. (1)

b Use the graph to change 16 Euros to pounds. (1)

(Edexcel Limited 2007)

a 40 Euros

b 12 pounds

Make sure you use the correct scale for each conversion.

# Exam questions

**1**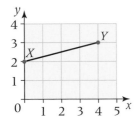

    **a** Write down the coordinates of the point
      **i** X
      **ii** Y                                        (2)
    **b** On a copy of the grid, mark with a cross (×) the midpoint of the line *XY*.   (1)

**2**  **a** Copy and complete the table of values for $y = 3x + 1$

| x | −3 | −2 | −1 | 0 | 1 | 2 |
|---|----|----|----|---|---|---|
| y | −8 |    | −2 |   |   |   |

    **b** On a copy of the grid, draw the graph of $y = 3x + 1$                 (2)

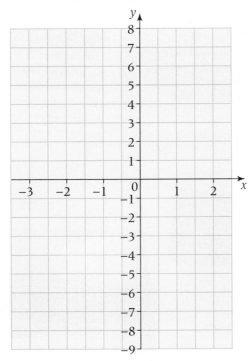

                                                                (2)

(Edexcel Limited 2008)

# Functional Maths 4: Holiday

Mathematics can help you to plan and budget for a holiday, as well as to understand currency, temperature and other units of measure at your destination.

## holiday *Paris*

**LOUISE'S** family are planning to go on holiday. Her parents will pay for the trip, but she must raise her own spending money.

**1** How much money could Louise save in the three months from March to May if she hired a DVD once a week instead of going to the cinema?

**2** A neighbour offers to pay Louise £10 per week if she takes her dog for a 30-minute walk every weekday before school. What hourly rate of pay does this represent? How much would Louise earn if she walked the dog every weekday throughout March, April and May?

**3** Louise's brother sold 18 of his CDs for £45. How much did he sell each CD for? He then sold another two CDs and 11 DVDs for £43.50. How much did he charge for each DVD?'

How could you raise money towards a holiday fund or to buy a new item? How long would it take you to reach your target amount?

Screen 13 Cinemaland
29/11/09
17:50
A GOOD NIGHT £4.50
YOU WERE SERVED BY DS AT TERMINAL 4. PAID BY: Cash

Hire charge £1.99 per film!

SIGN UP NOW!!

If you are going on holiday outside of the UK, then you will need to convert your money from £ Sterling to the local currency of your destination. Many European countries now use the Euro, €.

In 2005, the average £ Sterling : Euro exchange rate was 1 : 1.46.

In that year, how many
a) Euros would you receive in exchange for £150
b) £ Sterling would you receive in exchange for 120EUR?

Suppose that you are charged £70 (with no commission) to buy 91.7EUR.

What is the exchange rate? Give your answer as a ratio £ Sterling : Euro.

Some companies charge a commission fee to exchange currency. With an added charge of 1%, how many Euros would you now receive (at the same exchange rate) for £70?

What is the £ Sterling/ Euro exchange rate today? Research the commission rates that some companies are charging to exchange currency. What is the most/ least amount that the companies you have found would charge you to exchange £150 into Euros?

200

Deciding on your method of transport is an important part of planning a holiday.

*Some travel options between Oxford and Paris are shown.*

**1**

| Class | Outward | RETURN |
|---|---|---|
| STD | SATURDAY 06:36 ARRIVE 07:37 | MONDAY 17:14 ARRIVE 18:14 |

From
OXFORD
To
BIRMINGHAM INT.

Price
£21.00

**2–PART RETURN**

ECONOMY
Boarding Pass

PASSENGER
LOUISE
FROM
BIRMINGHAM INT (BHX)
TO
PARIS (CDG)

OUTWARD
SAT 0920, ARRIVE 1150
RETURN
MON 1555, ARRIVE 1625

| SEAT | ADDITIONAL INFO |
|---|---|
| 50K | COST: £115.16 |

**2**

Oxford
Buses
Route 777

Valid From:
**Oxford**

Valid To:
**London Heathrow**

Outward depart every hour and half hour.
Return every hour and half hour.

Adult Single £25

PA...
LOUISE
FROM
LONDON HEATHROW
TO
PARIS (CDG)

OUTWARD
SAT 0955, ARRIVE 1210
RETURN
MON 1610, ARRIVE 1625

| SEAT | ADDITIONAL INFO |
|---|---|
| 50K | COST: £136.37 |

**3**

| Class | Outward | RETURN |
|---|---|---|
| STD | SATURDAY 08:01 ARRIVE 09:29 | MONDAY 19:20 ARRIVE 20:49 |

From
OXFORD
To
LONDON ST. PANCRAS

Price
£14.00

**2–PART RETURN**

TICKET RESERVATION
**EUROSTAR**

01 ADULT

| DEPARTURE | FROM | TO | RETURN | CLASS |
|---|---|---|---|---|
| SAT 10:25 ARRIVE 13:47 | LONDON ST. PANCRAS | PARIS | MON 17:13 ARRIVE 18:34 | 2 |

| TRAIN 9141 ES | COACH 4 | SEAT 44 | PRICE |
|---|---|---|---|
| 01 SEAT Non Smkg | | CARRE | £104.00 |

ELGAR/MXTHPFWU 10080 U066    IV248500394 VO    4244A2
9538989954349 5
BW RT30AD 152485003940 BWXASE    181007 12h59    PNR/TYTFSO 1/1

**WHICH** travel option would you choose? Explain your response with reference to the travel times and costs. All times given are local. Paris is in the time zone GMT + 1 hour.

The foreign travel legs of the same journey options can be paid for in Euros for the following prices:

Return flight BHX to Paris CDG 151.49€; return Eurostar journey 130€, return flight London Heathrow to Paris CDG 162.82€.

How does each of the prices in Euros compare with the corresponding price in GBP?

*Explore travel options from your hometown to different destinations. Be careful, there are some times hidden costs such as additional taxes and fees.*

■ Different countries often use different units of measure for quantities such as temperature.

An Internet site states that the maximum and minimum temperatures in Rome on a particular day are 99°F and 63°F respectively.

A formula that can be used to convert between °C and °F is temp(°C) = 5(temp(°F) − 32)/9

What are the corresponding maximum and minimum temperatures in Rome?

The maximum and minimum temperatures in London on the same day were 25°C and 16°C. What are these temperatures in °F?

*What are the maximum and minimum temperatures in your home town today? Use the formula in the example to convert the temperatures you have found from °C to °F.*

STREET MAP
**Paris**

1:13,000 and 1:8,600

# Introduction

In computer games 3D characters and objects are made from thousands of triangles. The triangles are then given different colours to create the illusion of three dimensions. Computer programmers can write a piece of computer code to represent a triangle and then repeat this over and over again to represent much more complex shapes.

## What's the point?

Triangles are the most basic polygon. By using triangles in areas as diverse as computer graphics and architecture, we can create sophisticated shapes that we would otherwise not be able to create.

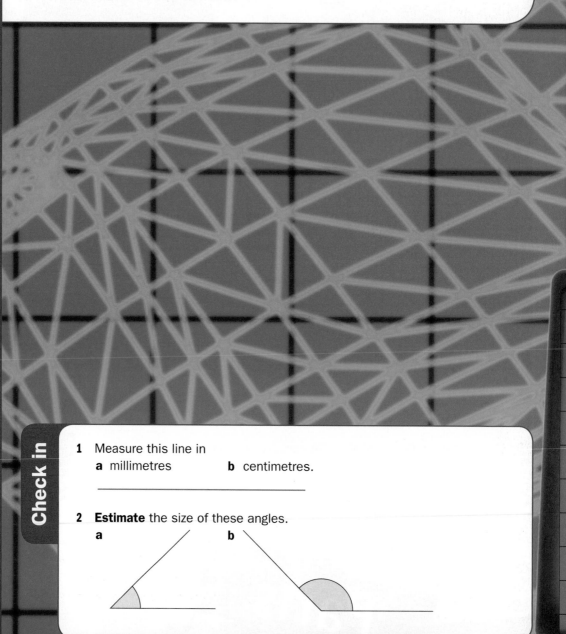

**Check in**

1   Measure this line in
    **a**  millimetres          **b**  centimetres.

2   **Estimate** the size of these angles.
    **a**                        **b**

What I need
to know

What I will learn

What this
leads to

Key stage 3 →

- Identify types of angles
- Recall and use properties of parallel and
  perpendicular lines
- Recall and use properties of angles
- Use angle properties of triangles
- Measure lines and angles

G1 →

→ G3

You will need a circular pinboard.

A triangle has been made on a circular geoboard. Measure its angles.
Investigate the angles in different triangles you can make on the pinboard.
Can you find some rules?

This spread will show you how to:

● Measure and draw lines to the nearest millimetre

p.134

A ruler **measures length** in **millimetres** (mm) or **centimetres** (cm).

```
┌────────────────────────────
│ 0    10   20   30   40
│ mm
```

This line measures 2.5 cm or 25 mm.

```
┌────────────────────────────
│ 0    1    2    3    4
│ cm
```

10 mm = 1 cm

```
┌────────────────────────────
│ 0    1    2    3    4
│ cm
```

$2.5\,cm = 2\frac{1}{2}\,cm$

This line measures 2.7 cm or 27 mm.

```
┌────────────────────────────
│ 0    10   20   30   40
│ mm
```

| H | T | U | • | $\frac{1}{10}$ | $\frac{1}{100}$ |
|---|---|---|---|---|---|
|   |   | 2 | • | 7 |   |

$2.7\,cm = 2\frac{7}{10}\,cm$

To measure a line, line up the ruler so that the zero mark is at the start of the line.

You can construct shapes using a ruler and a protractor.

**Example**

Using a ruler and a protractor, construct a square of length 5 cm.
Draw and measure the diagonal in   **a** centimetres
                                     **b** millimetres.

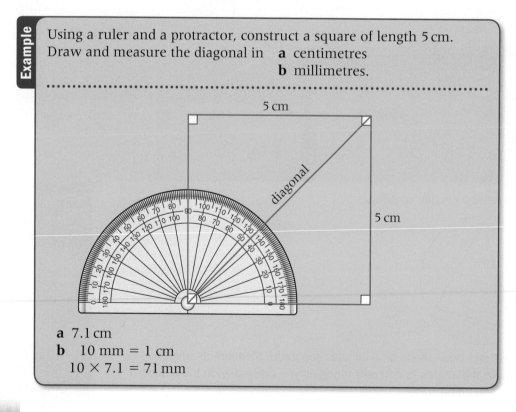

Use the ruler to draw the 5 cm lines.

Use the protractor to construct the 90° angles.

**a** 7.1 cm
**b**  10 mm = 1 cm
    10 × 7.1 = 71 mm

**1** Measure the lengths of these lines in
  **a** centimetres
  **b** millimetres.

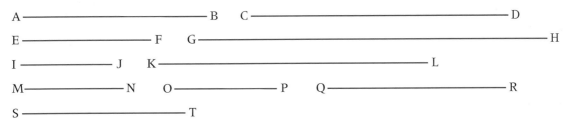

A——————————B  C——————————————D
E——————————F  G——————————————————H
I—————J  K——————————————L
M—————N  O—————P  Q——————————R
S—————————T

**2 a** Draw a line AB, so that AB = 9 cm.
  **b** Find the midpoint of AB and mark it with a cross.

**3 a** Draw a line CD, so that CD = 11.6 cm.
  **b** Find the midpoint of CD and mark it M.
  **c** Measure CM, stating the units of your answer.

**4** Measure and state the diameter of each circle in centimetres.

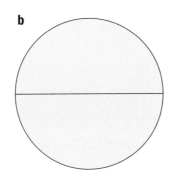

**a**                    **b**                    **c**

> The diameter
> is the distance
> across a circle
> through the
> centre.

**5** Measure and calculate the perimeter of this
rectangle in
  **a** centimetres
  **b** millimetres.

> The **perimeter** is
> the **distance** round
> the edge of a
> shape.

**6** Using a ruler and protractor, construct a
rectangle of length 7 cm and width 5 cm.
Draw and measure the diagonal in
  **a** centimetres
  **b** millimetres.

5 cm

7 cm

# Measuring angles

This spread will show you how to:

- Understand angle measure
- Measure and draw angles to the nearest degree
- Estimate the size of an angle in degrees

You can **measure** and draw an **angle** in **degrees** with a **protractor**.
A protractor measures angles up to 180°.
There are 180° in a half turn.

180°        180°

° means degrees.

- There are 180° on a straight line.

**Example**

Measure the size of angle $p$.

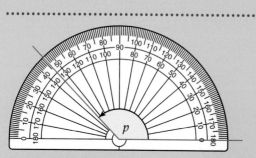

You have to decide which scale to use, either the inner scale or the outer scale.

1 **Estimate** the size of angle $p$. (Guess 120°, as greater than 90°.)
2 Place the protractor over the angle.
3 The angle point should be at the cross in the protractor.
4 One arm of the angle should be along the zero line.
5 Start counting from this zero line.

$$p = 134°$$

For this angle use the inner scale.

- You can measure a reflex angle by measuring the associated acute or obtuse angle.

A full turn is 360°.

**Example**

Measure the reflex angle AB̂C.

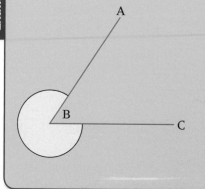

The acute angle AB̂C = 56°.
So the reflex angle AB̂C is
360° − 56° = 304°

Angles at a point add to 360°.

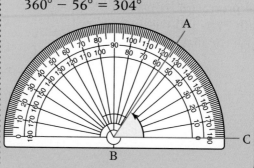

In questions **1–9**, for each angle state

**a** the type of angle – acute, right angle, obtuse or reflex
**b** your estimate in degrees
**c** the measurement in degrees.

Set out your answers like this:

| Question | Type of angle | Estimate | Measurement |
|----------|---------------|----------|-------------|
| 1 | acute | 40° | 30° |
| 2 | | | |

**1**

**2**

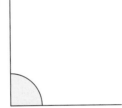

**3**

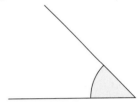

**4**

**5**

**6**

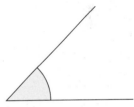

**7**

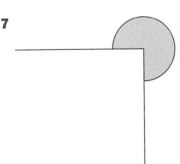

**8**

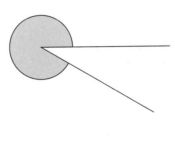

**9**

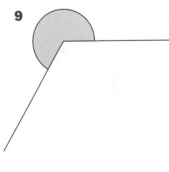

**10** Draw and label these angles using a protractor.
State whether each angle is acute, obtuse,
reflex or a right angle.

| | | | |
|---|---|---|---|
| **a** 40° | **b** 140° | **c** 90° | **d** 36° |
| **e** 144° | **f** 56° | **g** 124° | **h** 38° |
| **i** 142° | **j** 85° | **k** 300° | **l** 200° |
| **m** 320° | **n** 245° | **o** 265° | |

This spread will show you how to:

- Identify acute, obtuse, reflex and right angles
- Recall and use properties of parallel and perpendicular lines

**Keywords**
Acute
Angle
Degrees (°)
Intersect
Obtuse
Parallel
Perpendicular
Reflex
Right angle

- An **angle** is a measure of turn. You measure the turn in **degrees**.

| Amount of turn | $\frac{1}{4}$ turn | $\frac{1}{2}$ turn | $\frac{3}{4}$ turn | full turn |
|---|---|---|---|---|

| Angle in degrees | 90° | 180° | 270° | 360° |
|---|---|---|---|---|

° means degrees.

- You can describe an angle by its size.

| an **acute** angle is less than 90° | a **right angle** is exactly 90° | an **obtuse** angle is between 90° and 180° | a **reflex** angle is more than 180° |
|---|---|---|---|

What type of angle is shown by the letter
**a** $x$      **b** $y$?

.......................................................................

**a** $x$ is acute.    **b** $y$ is reflex.

- **Parallel** lines are always the same distance apart.
  Parallel lines are shown by sets of arrows.

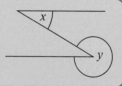

Parallel lines never **intersect** (cross) each other.

- **Perpendicular** lines meet at a right angle.

A line AB is drawn on a grid.
**a** Draw another line that is parallel to AB.
 Label the line CD and mark with arrows (>).
**b** Draw another line that is perpendicular to AB.
 Label the line EF and mark with a square (∟).

.........................................................................

CD is parallel to AB.
EF is perpendicular to AB.

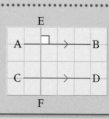

**1** How many right angles make up the angle shown in each diagram?

**a** 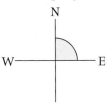   **b** 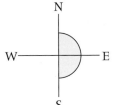   **c**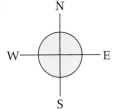

**d** 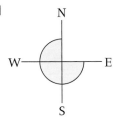   **e** 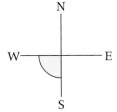   **f**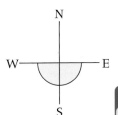

**2** Choose one of these words to describe each angle.

| acute | right angle | obtuse | reflex |
|---|---|---|---|

**a**    **b** 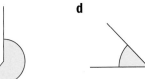   **c**    **d**

**e**   **f**   **g**    **h**

**i**    **j**   **k**    **l**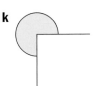

**DID YOU KNOW?**

Perpendicular and parallel lines are all around you!

**3** Choose one of these words to describe each angle.

| acute | right angle | obtuse | reflex |
|---|---|---|---|

**a** 90°  **b** 40°  **c** 140°  **d** 200°  **e** 270°  **f** 36°
**g** 137°  **h** 248°  **i** 302°  **j** 33°  **k** 96°  **l** 239°

**4  a** Draw two lines that are parallel. Label them with >.
  **b** Draw two lines that are perpendicular. Label them with ⌐.

This spread will show you how to:

- Recall and use properties of angles at a point, angles on a straight line, perpendicular lines and opposite angles at a vertex

**Keywords**
Angle
Degrees (°)
Point
Straight line
Vertically opposite

This information is useful for your Unit 1 assessment, as well as Unit 2.

- These are 360° in a full turn at a **point**.

- There are 180° on a **straight line**. This is a half turn at a point.

- There are 90° in a quarter turn at a point.

**Example**

Calculate the values of $p$, $q$ and $r$. Give a reason for each of your answers.

**a**

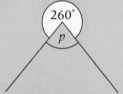

**b**

**c**

**a** $360° - 260° = 100°$
$p = 100°$
(angles at a point add to 360°)

**b** $76° + 65° = 141°$
$180° - 141° = 39°$
$q = 39°$
(angles on a straight line add to 180°)

**c** $35° + 90° = 125°$
$180° - 125° = 55°$
$r = 55°$
(angles on a straight line add to 180°)

When two lines intersect they make four angles.
The two acute angles are equal.
The two obtuse angles are equal.

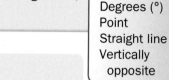

This topic is extended to alternate and corresponding angles on page 430.

- **Vertically opposite** angles are equal.

**Example**

Calculate the values of $x$ and $y$.
Give a reason for each of your answers.

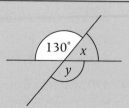

$x = 180° - 130° = 50°$ (angles on a straight line add to 180°)
$y = 130°$ (vertically opposite angles are equal)

**1** Give the values in degrees of the coloured angles.

　**a**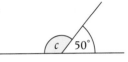

　**b**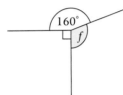

**2** This diagram is wrong.
　Explain why.

**3** Calculate the size of the angles marked by letters in each diagram.
　Give a reason for each answer. The diagrams are not accurately drawn.

**a** 　　**b** 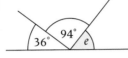　　**c**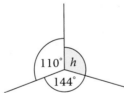

**d** 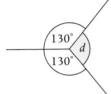　　**e** 　　**f**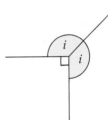

**g** 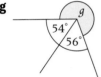　　**h** 　　**i**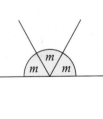

**j** 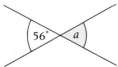　　**k** 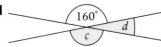　　**l** 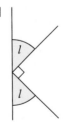　　**m**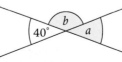

**4** Calculate the size of the angles marked by letters in each diagram.
　Give a reason for each of your answers.

These diagrams are not drawn to scale.

**a** 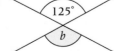　　**b** 　　**c**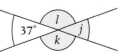

**d**　　**e**

211

This spread will show you how to:

- Use angle properties of equilateral, isosceles and right-angled triangles

**Keywords**
Angle
Degrees (°)
Equilateral
Isosceles
Right-angled
Scalene
Triangle

- There are 180° on a straight line.

You can draw any triangle ... tear off the corners ... and put them together to make a straight line.

- The angles in a **triangle** add to 180°.

Calculate the values of $x$, $y$ and $z$. Give a reason for each of your answers.

**a**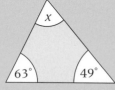

**b**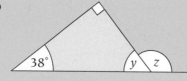

**a**  $63° + 49° = 112°$
  $180° - 112° = 68°$
    $x = 68°$

  (angles in a triangle add to 180°)

**b**  $38° + 90° = 128°$
  $180° - 128° = 52°$
    $y = 52°$   (angles in a triangle add to 180°)
  $180° - 52° = 128°$   (angles on a straight
    $z = 128°$   line add to 180°)

- You should know these names for special triangles

| **Right-angled** | **Equilateral** | **Isosceles** | **Scalene** |
|---|---|---|---|
|  |  |  |  |
| One 90° angle marked ∟ | 3 equal angles 3 equal sides | 2 equal angles 2 equal sides | No equal angles no equal sides |

For an equilateral triangle each angle is 60° as $180° ÷ 3 = 60°$

Lines with the same mark are equal length.

Calculate the values of $x$ and $y$.
Give reasons for your answers.

$180° - 129° = 51°$
    $x = 51°$   (angles on a straight line add to 180°)
  $51° + 51° = 102°$
  $180° - 102° = 78°$
    $y = 78°$   (angles in a triangle add to 180°)

As the triangle is isosceles, two of the angles are equal.

**A03 Problem**

**1 a** State the total of the three angles in this triangle.
  **b** Choose three of these angles that could be put
    together to make the angles in a triangle.

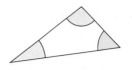

 20°

 40°

 50°

 60°

 70°

**2** Calculate the size of the unknown angles in each diagram.
The diagrams are not drawn to scale.

**a**
40°  a

80°  b  30°

**c**
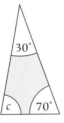
30°
c  70°

**d**

d
65°  55°

**e**
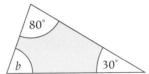
74°
e  36°

**f**
27°
f  28°

**g**

g
108°  36°

**h**
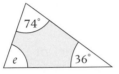
60°
60°  h

**i**
i
74°  74°

**j**
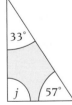
33°
j  57°

**k**

l
45°  k  68°

**l**
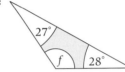
n
m  128°

**m**
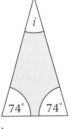
p
121°  o  60°

**n**

30°
65°  q  r

**o**
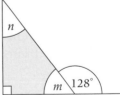
t
72°  s  111°

**3** List any triangles in question **2** that are
right-angled                                    isosceles.

# Properties of triangles

This spread will show you how to:

- Know the properties of right-angled, equilateral, isosceles and scalene triangles
- Know that the angles in a triangle add to 180°
- Understand similarity and congruence

**Keywords**
Congruent
Equilateral
Isosceles
Right-angled
Scalene
Similar
Triangle

- The angles in a triangle add to 180°.

$\angle A + \angle B + \angle C = 180°$

You need to know the properties of these triangles.

| Triangle | | Properties | Reflection symmetry | Rotational symmetry |
|---|---|---|---|---|
| Right-angled | | One 90° angle marked ⌐ | No lines of symmetry | Order 1 |
| Equilateral | | 3 equal angles 3 equal sides | 3 lines of symmetry | Order 3 |
| Isosceles | | 2 equal angles 2 equal sides | 1 line of symmetry | Order 1 |
| Scalene | | No equal angles No equal sides | No lines of symmetry | Order 1 |

You will learn about reflection and rotational symmetry on pages 254–257.

- **Similar** shapes are the same in shape but differ in size.

- **Congruent** shapes are the same size and shape.

**Example**

Here are two similar triangles.
**a** State the type of triangle.
**b** How many small congruent triangles will fit inside the large triangle?
**c** Draw the arrangement.

........................................................................

**a** Right-angled scalene triangle     **b** 4     **c**

**1** State the type of each triangle.

a    b 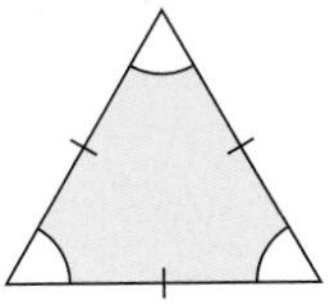   c 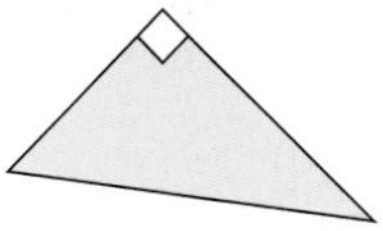   d

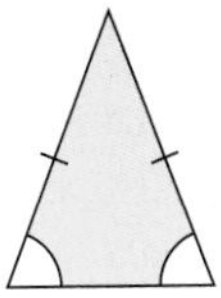

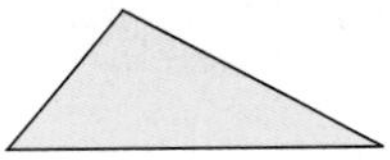

**2** State the type of each triangle, if the sides of the triangle are
  **a** 8 cm, 8 cm, 8 cm
  **b** 6 cm, 7 cm, 8 cm
  **c** 3 cm, 5 cm, 5 cm

**3** Calculate the third angle of the triangle and state the type of each of these triangles.
  **a** 30°, 60°
  **b** 70°, 40°
  **c** 60°, 60°
  **d** 35°, 65°
  **e** 45°, 45°

**Problem**

**4** How many equilateral triangles are in this pattern?

**5** Plot and join up each set of points on a separate copy of this grid.
  **a** (−2, −1), (−2, 2), (0, 2)
  **b** (−2, −3), (−1, 0), (0, −3)
  **c** (1, −2), (3, 2), (1, 3)
  **d** (1, −3), (3, −3), (3, −1)
  In each case, state the type of triangle.

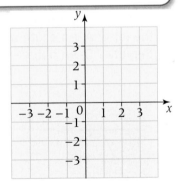

**Problem**

**AO3**

**6** Using three more congruent (identical) equilateral triangles, draw a larger similar equilateral triangle on isometric paper.

## Check out

You should now be able to:

- Identify acute, obtuse, reflex and right angles
- Understand and use properties of parallel and perpendicular lines
- Understand and use properties of angles at a point, on a straight line and of opposite angles at a vertex
- Identify and use the properties of right-angled, equilateral, isosceles and scalene triangles
- Know that the angles in a triangle add to 180°
- Identify congruent shapes
- Measure lines and angles

## Worked exam question

Here is a diagram drawn on a square grid.

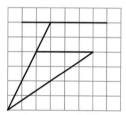

**a** Mark, with arrows (>>), a pair of parallel lines.     (1)
**b** Mark, with the letter A, an acute angle.     (1)
**c** Mark, with the letter O, an obtuse angle.     (1)

(Edexcel Limited 2007)

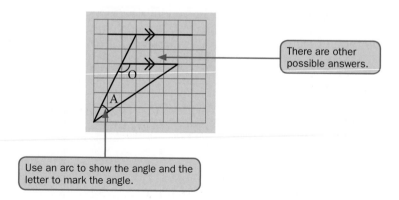

There are other possible answers.

Use an arc to show the angle and the letter to mark the angle.

# Exam questions

**1** Here are some triangles on a grid.

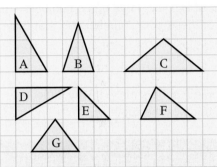

Two of these triangles are congruent.
**a** Write down the letters of these two triangles. (1)

One of these triangles is both right-angled and isosceles.
**b** Write down the letter of this triangle. (1)

(Edexcel Limited 2007)

**2 a**

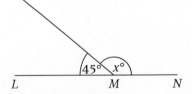

Diagram NOT
accurately drawn

*LMN* is a straight line.
**i** Work out the value of *x*.
**ii** Give a reason for your answer. (2)

**b**

Diagram NOT
accurately drawn

Work out the value of *y*. (2)

(Edexcel Limited 2008)

**A03**

**3** The points *A* and *B* have coordinates (6, 2) and (2, 4) respectively. Write the coordinates of a third point *C* so that *ABC* is an isosceles right-angled triangle.

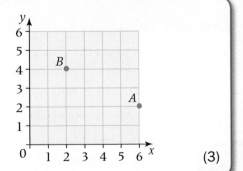

(3)

# Introduction

When you use the internet to pay for goods you need to know that your financial details are safe. To make these details secure they are turned into a secret code (encrypted). The message can be encrypted using the product of two very large prime numbers – the person receiving the message has to know both of these prime numbers so that they can decrypt the message.

## What's the point?

The problems involved in identifying very large prime numbers make it very difficult for someone intercepting an encrypted message to crack the code.

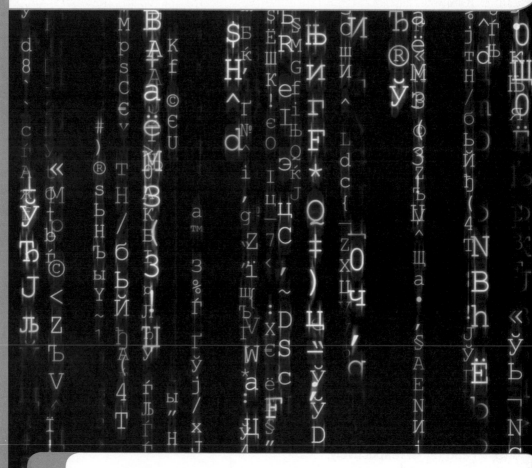

**Check in**

1 Calculate
   a $7 \times 7$
   b $2 \times 2 \times 2$
   c $10 \times 10 \times 10$
   d $32 \div 100$

2 Find the missing number in this expression.
   ___ × ___ = 25

3 Does 244 divide by 4?
   Explain how you know.

Orientation

## What I need to know

## What I will learn

## What this leads to

N1 →

- Recognise and use squares and cubes, and corresponding roots
- Multiply and divide by powers of 10
- Recognise prime numbers and use divisibility tests
- Understand and use the terms factor and multiple
- Find the highest common factor and least common multiple

→ +3

## Rich task

This diagram shows a 5 by 3 rectangular grid of squares.

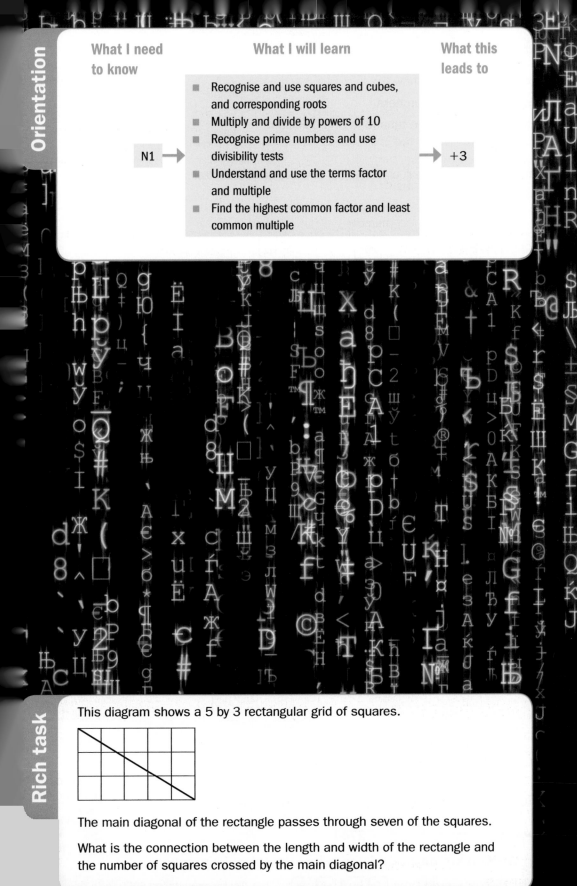

The main diagonal of the rectangle passes through seven of the squares.

What is the connection between the length and width of the rectangle and the number of squares crossed by the main diagonal?

This spread will show you how to:

- Use square and cube numbers
- Use the square and cube functions of a calculator

**Keywords**
Cube
Index
Power
Square

- A **square** number is the result of multiplying a **whole** number by itself.

| 1st square number | 2nd square number | 3rd square number | 4th square number |
|---|---|---|---|
| 1 | 4 | 9 | 16 |

$1 \times 1 = 1^2$      $2 \times 2 = 2^2$      $3 \times 3 = 3^2$      $4 \times 4 = 4^2$

Square numbers can be written using **index** notation.

$$5^2 = 5 \times 5 \qquad\qquad 12^2 = 12 \times 12$$
$$= 25 \qquad\qquad\qquad = 144$$

Use the $x^2$ function key on a calculator to find the square of a number.

To find $34^2$, type  [3] [4] [$x^2$] [=]     The display should read 1156.

You can say $5^2$ in lots of different ways

$5^2$ = '5 to the **power** of 2'
= '5 squared'
= 'the square of 5'

- A **cube** number is the result of multiplying a whole number by itself and then multiplying by that number again.

Cube numbers can be represented using 3-D drawings of cubes.

| 1st cube number | 2nd cube number | 3rd cube number | 4th cube number |
|---|---|---|---|
| 1 | 8 | 27 | 64 |

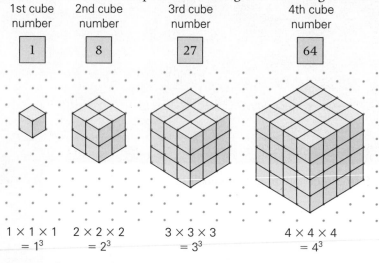

$1 \times 1 \times 1$      $2 \times 2 \times 2$      $3 \times 3 \times 3$      $4 \times 4 \times 4$
$= 1^3$             $= 2^3$             $= 3^3$             $= 4^3$

Cube numbers can be written using index notation.

$$4^3 = 4 \times 4 \times 4 \qquad\qquad 14^3 = 14 \times 14 \times 14$$
$$= 64 \qquad\qquad\qquad\qquad = 2744$$

Use the $x^3$ function key on a calculator to find the cube of a number.

To find $19^3$, you would type  [1] [9] [$x^3$] [=]     The display should read 6859.

You can say $4^3$ in lots of different ways:

$4^3$ = '4 to the power of 3'
= '4 cubed'
= 'the cube of 4'

**1** Find these numbers.
   **a** the 4th square number    **b** the 8th square number
   **c** the 20th square number   **d** the 5th cube number
   **e** the 7th cube number      **f** the 10th cube number

**2** Use your calculator to work out each of these squares and cubes.
   **a** $6^2$        **b** $11^2$       **c** $14^2$       **d** $23^2$
   **e** $31^2$       **f** $47^2$       **g** $4^3$        **h** $6^3$
   **i** $8^3$        **j** $13^3$       **k** $18^3$       **l** $21^3$

> **Remember:**
> You will not be allowed to use a calculator in your unit 2 assessment.

**A03 Problem**

**3** Some numbers can be represented as the sum of two square numbers.
For example $1^2 + 2^2 = 1 + 4 = 5$.
Try to find all the numbers less than 50 that can be represented as the sum of two square numbers.

**4** Use your calculator to work out each of these.
   **a** $3^2 + 2^2$       **b** $5^2 - 3^2$       **c** $6^2 - 2^3$
   **d** $4^3 + 4^2$       **e** $10^2 - 8^2$      **f** $13^2 + 4^3$
   **g** $14^2 - 5^3$      **h** $6^3 - 13^2$      **i** $12^2 + 13^2 + 14^2$
   **j** $6^3 + 7^3 + 8^3$

**5** Use the $x^2$ and $x^3$ function keys on your calculator to work out each of these. Give your answer to two decimal places as appropriate.
   **a** $2.5^2$      **b** $49^2$       **c** $3.2^3$      **d** $4.8^2$
   **e** $7.3^2$      **f** $4.9^3$      **g** $1.2^2$      **h** $0.5^2$
   **i** $9.9^2$      **j** $9.9^3$      **k** $(5 \text{ cm})^2$   **l** $(4 \text{ m})^3$

**A03 Problem**

**6 a** Work out these.
   $3^2 - 2^2 = \underline{\quad}$      $4^2 - 3^2 = \underline{\quad}$      $5^2 - 4^2 = \underline{\quad}$
   **b** Write anything you have noticed about your answers.
   **c** Copy and complete this table and investigate for the next seven pairs of consecutive integers.

| Square number | Square number | | Answer |
|---|---|---|---|
| $3^2$ | $2^2$ | $3^2 - 2^2 = 9 - \underline{\quad}$ | |
| $4^2$ | $3^2$ | $4^2 - 3^2 = 16 - \underline{\quad}$ | |
| $5^2$ | | | |
| $6^2$ | | | |

> Consecutive means 'next to', for example 4 and 5

This spread will show you how to:

- Estimate and use square roots and cube roots
- Use the square root and cube root functions of a calculator

**Keywords**
Cube root
Square root

- A **square root** is a number that when multiplied by itself is equal to a given number.

$7 \times 7 = 49$ so you can say that the square root of $49 = 7$.
- Square roots are written using $\sqrt{\phantom{x}}$ notation. $\sqrt{49} = 7$

You should try to learn the first 10 square numbers, then you will also know their square roots.

| | | |
|---|---|---|
| 1st square number | $= 1 \times 1 = 1$ | $\sqrt{1} = 1$ |
| 2nd square number | $= 2 \times 2 = 4$ | $\sqrt{4} = 2$ |
| 3rd square number | $= 3 \times 3 = 9$ | $\sqrt{9} = 3$ |

You can estimate the square root of a square number.

**Example**

289 is a square number. Work out $\sqrt{289}$ without using a calculator.

$15 \times 15 = 225$   This is too low, so $\sqrt{289}$ is greater than 15
$20 \times 20 = 400$   This is too high, so $\sqrt{289}$ is less than 20
$17 \times 17 = 289$   Correct
So $\sqrt{289} = 17$

You can use the grid method if you are stuck!

| × | 10 | 7 | |
|---|---|---|---|
| **10** | $10 \times 10 = 100$ | $10 \times 7 = 70$ | 100 |
| **7** | $7 \times 10 = 70$ | $7 \times 7 = 49$ | 70 |
| | | | 70 |
| | | | $+\,49$ |
| | | | 289 |

Use the $\sqrt{x}$ function key on a calculator to find the square root of a number.

To find $\sqrt{289}$, you would type  The display should read 17.

You will not be allowed to use a calculator in your Unit 2 assessment.

- A **cube root** is a number that when multiplied by itself and then multiplied by itself again is equal to a given number.

$2 \times 2 \times 2 = 8$ so the cube root of $8 = 2$ or $\sqrt[3]{8} = 2$

Use the $\sqrt[3]{x}$ function key on a calculator to find the cube root of a number.
To find $\sqrt[3]{1728}$, you would type  The display should read 12.

Square roots and cube roots are often not whole numbers so you usually round your answer to two decimal places.
$\sqrt{300} = 17.320\ 508\ 08...$
$= 17.32$ (2 dp)

**1** Find these numbers.
   **a** $\sqrt{25}$          **b** $\sqrt{9}$          **c** $\sqrt{16}$          **d** $\sqrt{1}$          **e** $\sqrt{4}$

**2** Calculate these using a calculator, giving your answer to 2 dp as appropriate.
   **a** $\sqrt{40}$          **b** $\sqrt{61}$          **c** $\sqrt{180}$          **d** $\sqrt{249}$          **e** $\sqrt{676}$

**3** Calculate these using the $\sqrt[3]{\ }$ key on your calculator. Give your answers to 2 dp where appropriate.
   **a** $\sqrt[3]{27}$          **b** $\sqrt[3]{512}$          **c** $\sqrt[3]{3375}$          **d** $\sqrt[3]{100}$          **e** $\sqrt[3]{24\,389}$

**A03** **Problem**

**4** Harry has mixed up his answers to these questions.
   **a** Without using a calculator, match each of these questions to the correct answer.

| Questions | | Estimates | |
| --- | --- | --- | --- |
| 1 | $\sqrt{169}$ | A | 9 |
| 2 | $\sqrt[3]{343}$ | B | 8 |
| 3 | $\sqrt{121}$ | C | 7 |
| 4 | $\sqrt{81}$ | D | 4 |
| 5 | $\sqrt{64}$ | E | 11 |
| 6 | $\sqrt[3]{1000}$ | F | 13 |
| 7 | $\sqrt{196}$ | G | 10 |
| 8 | $\sqrt[3]{64}$ | H | 14 |

   **b** Check your answers using your calculator.
      See how many of the questions and answers you matched correctly.

**A02** **Functional Maths**

**5 a** A square has an area of 144 m². What is the side length of the square?
   **b** John thinks of a number. He multiplies the number by itself. The answer is 529. What number did John think of?
   **c** Mr Mow designs a paddock. The paddock has to be in the shape of a square. The area of the paddock has to be 4000 m². What length should each of the sides of the paddock be? (Give your answer to the nearest metre.)
   **d** Nelly digs a hole in the shape of a cube. The volume of the earth she digs out to make the hole is 64 000 cm³. How deep is the hole?

**6** Do not use a calculator for these questions.
   **a** Between which two numbers does $\sqrt{95}$ lie?
   **b** Between which two numbers does $\sqrt{150}$ lie?
   **c** Between which two numbers does $\sqrt{300}$ lie?
   **d** Between which two numbers does $\sqrt[3]{80}$ lie?

# Powers of 10

This spread will show you how to:

- Understand and use index notation
- Multiply and divide by powers of 10

- **Index notation** is used to represent powers of any number.

  The **index** (or **power**) tells you how many times the number must be multiplied by itself.

  $$7^4 = 7 \times 7 \times 7 \times 7 = 2401$$
  $$6^3 = 6 \times 6 \times 6 \quad = 216$$

OUR POWERS COMBINED WE ARE 2401.

The small number is the index (or power).

Use your calculator to work out powers of a number.

To work out $13^5$, you might type ⎡1⎤ ⎡3⎤ ⎡$y^x$⎤ ⎡5⎤ ⎡=⎤

The display should read 371 293.

Your calculator may work differently.
If you are unsure, ask your teacher or check your manual.

- The decimal system is based upon **powers of 10**.

| | | | |
|---|---|---|---|
| 1 ten | = 10 | = 10 | = $10^1$ |
| 1 hundred | = 100 | = $10 \times 10$ | = $10^2$ |
| 1 thousand | = 1000 | = $10 \times 10 \times 10$ | = $10^3$ |
| 10 thousand | = 10 000 | = $10 \times 10 \times 10 \times 10$ | = $10^4$ |
| 100 thousand | = 100 000 | = $10 \times 10 \times 10 \times 10 \times 10$ | = $10^5$ |
| 1 million | = 1 000 000 | = $10 \times 10 \times 10 \times 10 \times 10 \times 10$ | = $10^6$ |

- It is easy to multiply and divide by **powers of 10**.

p.4

  $\times 10^1 \Rightarrow$ digits move 1 place left
  $\times 10^2 \Rightarrow$ digits move 2 places left

p.136

| | Thousands | Hundreds | Tens | Units | | tenths | hundredths |
|---|---|---|---|---|---|---|---|
| | | | | 3 | • | 2 | |
| $3.2 \times 10^1$ | | | 3 | 2 | • | | |
| $3.2 \times 10^2$ | | 3 | 2 | 0 | • | | |

The '0' holds the digits in place so that the '3' digit is in the Hundreds column and the '2' digit is in the Tens column.

  $\div 10^1 \Rightarrow$ digits move 1 place right
  $\div 10^2 \Rightarrow$ digits move 2 places right

| | Thousands | Hundreds | Tens | Units | | tenths | hundredths |
|---|---|---|---|---|---|---|---|
| | | | 4 | 5 | • | | |
| $4.5 \div 10^1$ | | | | 4 | • | 5 | |
| $4.5 \div 10^2$ | | | | 0 | • | 4 | 5 |

1 Find the value of
   **a** $5^2$      **b** $2^3$      **c** $3^3$      **d** $8^2$      **e** $12^2$

2 Find the value of
   **a** $3^4$      **b** $1^5$      **c** $2^7$      **d** $3^6$      **e** $10^6$

3 Use the $y^x$ function key on your calculator to work out these.
   **a** $12^3$      **b** $6^6$      **c** $21^3$      **d** $16^5$      **e** $13^3$

4 Use your calculator to work out these powers. In each case copy the question and fill in the missing numbers.
   **a** $3^? = 9$      **b** $5^? = 25$      **c** $4^? = 64$      **d** $2^? = 8$
   **e** $24^? = 576$

   Use a place value diagram.

5 Calculate each of these.
   **a** $1.2 \times 10$    **b** $655 \div 10$    **c** $3.4 \times 10^3$
   **d** $48 \div 100$    **e** $74 \times 100$    **f** $43.3 \div 10^2$

6 Here are some conversion rates for metric measurements.

| | | | | | | | |
|---|---|---|---|---|---|---|---|
| 1 km | = | 1000 m | 1 tonne | = | 1000 kg | 1 litre | = 1000 ml |
| 1 m | = | 100 cm | 1 kg | = | 1000 g | 1 m³ | = 1000 litres |
| 1 cm | = | 10 mm | | | | | |

Change these lengths to the units indicated in brackets.
You will need to multiply and divide by powers of 10.

You will need to revise how to change between units to answer these questions.

   **a** 30 mm    (centimetres)    **b** 7 cm    (millimetres)
   **c** 3 km    (metres)    **d** 2500 m    (kilometres)
   **e** 240 cm    (metres)    **f** 7.2 m    (centimetres)
   **g** 2.4 tonnes    (kg)    **h** 3750 kg    (tonnes)
   **i** 450 g    (kg)    **j** 2.04 kg    (grams)
   **k** 330 ml    (litres)    **l** 4.54 litres    (ml)
   **m** 15 m³    (litres)    **n** 2300 litres    (m³)

7 Copy these and fill in the missing numbers.
   **a** $34 \div 10 = \_\_\_$      **b** $2800 \div \_\_\_ = 28$
   **c** $6.1 \times \_\_ = 610$      **d** $5.7 \times 10^3 = \_\_\_$

This spread will show you how to:
- Understand the terms 'factor' and 'multiple'
- Find the common factors and common multiples of two numbers

Any number can be written as the product of two **factors**.

$20 = 2 \times 10$   so 2 and 10 are factors of 20.

- The factors of a number are those numbers that divide into it exactly, leaving no remainder.

You can often write a number as the **product** of two factors.

24 can be written as $4 \times 6$ or $3 \times 8$ or $2 \times 12$ or $1 \times 24$.

The factor pairs are $1 \times 24$, $2 \times 12$, $3 \times 8$ and $4 \times 6$.

You can write the factors in a list: 1, 2, 3, 4, 6, 8, 12, 24.

- A **common factor** is a factor that is common to two different numbers.

Product means multiply together.

p.230

**Example**

Write the common factors of 30 and 42.

The factors of 30 are   1  2  3  5  6  10  15  30

The factors of 42 are   1  2  3  6  7  14  21  42

The common factors of 30 and 42 are 1, 2, 3 and 6.

You can use factor pairs:
$1 \times 30$
$2 \times 15$
$3 \times 10$
$5 \times 6$

The first five **multiples** of 20 are 20, 40, 60, 80 and 100.

$1 \times 20 = 20$       $2 \times 20 = 40$       $3 \times 20 = 60$
$4 \times 20 = 80$       $5 \times 20 = 100$

- A **common multiple** is a multiple that is common to two different numbers.

**Example**

Write the first three common multiples of 8 and 12.

The multiples of 8 are   8  16  24  32  40  48  56  64  72  80  ...

The multiples of 12 are  12  24  36  48  60  72  84  ...

The first three common multiples of 8 and 12 are 24, 48 and 72.

**1** This factor diagram shows all the factor pairs of 12.

| 1 |
| 12 |

| 2 |
| 6 |

| 3 |
| 4 |

1 × 12 = 12    2 × 6 = 12    3 × 4 = 12

The factors of 12 are 1, 2, 3, 4, 6 and 12.

Copy and complete these factor diagrams.

**a** 18

| 1 |
|   |

| 2 |
|   |

| 3 |
|   |

**b** 20

| 1 |
|   |

| 2 |
|   |

|   |
|   |

**c** 30

| 1 |
|   |

|   |
|   |

|   |
|   |

| 5 |
|   |

**d** 14

|   |
|   |

|   |
|   |

**2** Draw factor diagrams for
   **a** 15      **b** 22      **c** 28      **d** 36      **e** 40

**3** Write all the factor pairs for each number.
   **a** 8      **b** 16      **c** 23      **d** 34      **e** 10
   **f** 26      **g** 42      **h** 48      **i** 39      **j** 44

**4** Write the first three multiples of each number.
   **a** 7      **b** 9      **c** 12      **d** 15      **e** 17
   **f** 25      **g** 30      **h** 32      **i** 45      **j** 50

**5** Find the common factors of
   **a** 10 and 20      **b** 12 and 15      **c** 20 and 25
   **d** 8 and 20      **e** 21 and 28      **f** 30 and 40
   **g** 12 and 28      **h** 9 and 36      **i** 24 and 30

**6** Find the first two common multiples of
   **a** 6 and 10      **b** 9 and 12      **c** 4 and 6
   **d** 10 and 15      **e** 14 and 21      **f** 20 and 30

**7 a** Write a multiple of 20 that is bigger than 200.
   **b** Write a multiple of 15 that is between 100 and 140.
   **c** Write a multiple of 6 that is bigger than 70 but less than 100.

Problem

A03

This spread will show you how to:
- Recognise prime numbers
- Use simple divisibility tests to check if a number is prime

**Keywords**
Factor
Prime number
Prime factor

Any whole number can be written as the product of two **factors**.

To list all the factors of 12, draw rectangles.

$1 \times 12 = 12$

$2 \times 6 = 12$

$3 \times 4 = 12$

The factors of 12 are {1, 2, 3, 4, 6 and 12}.

1, 2, 3, 4, 6 and 12 are factors of 12 because all these numbers divide exactly into 12 with no remainder.

- A **prime number** is a number with only two factors, these are 1 and the number itself.

29 is a prime number because it has only two factors, the numbers 1 and 29.

The first ten prime numbers are: 2, 3, 5, 7, 11, 13, 17, 19, 23, 29.

- A **prime factor** is a prime number that is also a factor of another number.

Factors of 20 = {1, 2, 4, 5, 10, 20}
Prime factors of 20 = {2, 5}

You can use simple divisibility tests to help you check if a number is a prime number.
Here are the divisibility tests for the first five prime numbers.

This topic is extended to prime factor decomposition on page 412.

| | |
|---|---|
| ÷2 | the number ends in 0, 2, 4, 6 or 8 |
| ÷3 | the sum of the digits is divisible by 3 |
| ÷5 | the number ends in 0 or 5 |
| ÷7 | there is no check for divisibility by 7 |
| ÷11 | the alternate digits add up to the same sum |

**Example**

Which of the numbers in this list are prime numbers: 42, 27, 43, 55?

42 ⟹ 2 is a factor (because it ends in a 2)
       42 is not a prime number.

27 ⟹ 2 is not a factor
       3 is a factor (because 2 + 7 = 9, a multiple of 3)
       27 is not a prime number.

43 ⟹ 2 is not a factor
       3 is not a factor
       5 is not a factor
       7 is not a factor (because $6 \times 7$ is 42)
       43 is a prime number.

55 ⟹ 2 is not a factor
       3 is not a factor
       5 is a factor (because it ends in a 5)
       55 is not a prime number.

**1** Write all the factors of these numbers.

| | | | |
|---|---|---|---|
| **a** 8 | **b** 12 | **c** 11 | **d** 14 |
| **e** 28 | **f** 30 | **g** 40 | **h** 50 |

**Problem**

**A03**

**2** Your task is to find all the prime numbers from 1 to 100.

**a** Copy this 1–100 number square.

**b** Follow these instructions.

- 1 is not a prime number so you can cross it out.
- 2 is the lowest prime number. Cross out all the multiples of 2 except for the number 2.
- 3 is the next number not crossed out. It is the next prime number. Cross out all the multiples of 3 except for the number 3.
- 5 is the next number not crossed out. It is the next prime number. Cross out all the multiples of 5 except for the number 5.

| 1 | 2 | 3 | 4 | 5 | 6 | 7 | 8 | 9 | 10 |
|---|---|---|---|---|---|---|---|---|---|
| 11 | 12 | 13 | 14 | 15 | 16 | 17 | 18 | 19 | 20 |
| 21 | 22 | 23 | 24 | 25 | 26 | 27 | 28 | 29 | 30 |
| 31 | 32 | 33 | 34 | 35 | 36 | 37 | 38 | 39 | 40 |
| 41 | 42 | 43 | 44 | 45 | 46 | 47 | 48 | 49 | 50 |
| 51 | 52 | 53 | 54 | 55 | 56 | 57 | 58 | 59 | 60 |
| 61 | 62 | 63 | 64 | 65 | 66 | 67 | 68 | 69 | 70 |
| 71 | 72 | 73 | 74 | 75 | 76 | 77 | 78 | 79 | 80 |
| 81 | 82 | 83 | 84 | 85 | 86 | 87 | 88 | 89 | 90 |
| 91 | 92 | 93 | 94 | 95 | 96 | 97 | 98 | 99 | 100 |

**c** Carry on until you have only prime numbers left.

**d** Make a list of all the prime numbers from 1 to 100.

**3** Use the divisibility tests to answer each of these questions. In each case explain your answer.

**a** Is 5 a factor of 135?    **b** Is 5 a factor of 210?

**c** Is 2 a factor of 321?    **d** Is 11 a factor of 231?

**e** Is 7 a factor of 91?

**4** Look at these numbers.

| 1 | 2 | 3 | 5 | 6 | 8 | 9 |
|---|---|---|---|---|---|---|
| 10 | 11 | 12 | 13 | 16 | 18 | 20 |

**a** Write all the numbers that are factors of 10.

**b** Write all the numbers that are square numbers.

**c** Write all the numbers that are prime factors of 44.

**d** Write all the numbers that are prime numbers.

**5** Use the mental method of halving and doubling to calculate each of these. Show the method you have used.

| | | | |
|---|---|---|---|
| **a** $4 \times 21$ | **b** $3 \times 16$ | **c** $23 \times 4$ | **d** $16 \times 15$ |

Hint for question 6: List all the factors. Find the ones that are prime.

**6** Write all the prime factors of each of these numbers.

| | | | |
|---|---|---|---|
| **a** 20 | **b** 27 | **c** 55 | **d** 35 |
| **e** 22 | **f** 70 | **g** 120 | **h** 110 |

This spread will show you how to:

- Understand and use the terms factor and multiple
- Understand and use simple divisibility tests
- Understand the terms highest common factor and least common multiple

**Keywords**

Common factor
Common multiple
Factor
HCF
LCM
Multiple

You can use a range of strategies to find all the **factors** of larger numbers.

**Example**

Find all the factors of 252.
..................................................................................................

You can list the factors by factor pairs.
Factors of 252 are

| | | |
|---|---|---|
| 1 × 252 | 4 × 53 | 9 × 28 |
| 2 × 126 | 6 × 42 | 12 × 21 |
| 3 × 84 | 7 × 36 | 14 × 18 |

Factors of 252 are
{1, 2, 3, 4, 6, 7, 9, 12, 14, 18, 21, 28, 36, 42, 53, 84, 126, 252}.

You can use doubling and halving to help find factors:

$$7 × 36 = 252$$
$$14 × 18 = 252$$

p.226

You can find the **highest common factor (HCF)** of two numbers by listing all the factors of both numbers.

This topic is extended to prime factors on page 412.

**Example**

Find the HCF of 24 and 60.
..................................................................................................

The factors of 24 are:  1  2  3  4  6  8  12  24
The factors of 60 are:  1  2  3  4  5  6  10  12  15  20  30  60

1, 2, 3, 4, 6 and 12 are **common factors** of 24 and 60.
12 is the **highest common factor** of 24 and 60.

- The **multiples** of a number are those numbers that divide by it exactly, leaving no remainder.

The multiples of 18 are 18, 36, 54, 72, ...
        1 × 18 = 18      3 × 18 = 54
        2 × 18 = 36      4 × 18 = 72

You can find the **least common multiple (LCM)** of two numbers by listing the first few multiples of each number.

You can think of multiples as being the numbers in the 'times tables'.

**Example**

Find the least common multiple of 24 and 60.
..................................................................................................

The first six multiples of 24 are:  24  48  72  96  120  144
The first six multiples of 60 are:  60  120  180  240  300  360

120, 240, 360 are **common multiples** of 24 and 60.
120 is the **least common multiple** of 24 and 60.

**1** Write all the factor pairs of each of these numbers.
**a** 18 **b** 14 **c** 30 **d** 48

**2** Look at these numbers.

| 2 | 3 | 4 | 5 | 6 | 8 | 10 |
|---|---|---|---|---|---|---|
| 12 | 15 | 16 | 17 | 18 | 19 | 20 |

**a** Write all the numbers that are factors of 40.
**b** Write all the numbers that are factors of 90.
**c** Write all the numbers that are multiples of 2.
**d** Write all the numbers that are prime numbers.

**3** Write the first three multiples of each of these numbers.
**a** 6 **b** 11 **c** 19 **d** 25
**e** 65 **f** 105 **g** 187 **h** 308

**4** Use divisibility tests to answer each of these questions.
In each case explain your answer.
**a** Is 5 a factor of 95? **b** Is 10 a factor of 710?
**c** Is 9 a factor of 321? **d** Is 11 a factor of 451?
**e** Is 6 a factor of 98?

**5** Find the highest common factor of
**a** 6 and 4 **b** 12 and 18 **c** 14 and 16
**d** 28 and 35 **e** 30 and 54 **f** 56 and 64

**6** Find the least common multiple of
**a** 6 and 4 **b** 6 and 8 **c** 12 and 18
**d** 15 and 25 **e** 21 and 28 **f** 26 and 39

**A03 Problem**

**4 a** Copy and complete this table.

| Numbers | Product | HCF | LCM |
|---|---|---|---|
| 6 and 4 | $6 \times 4 = 24$ | 2 | 12 |
| 8 and 10 | $8 \times 10 = $ —— | | |
| 12 and 18 | | | |
| 6 and 9 | | | |
| 15 and 20 | | | |
| 15 and 25 | | | |
| | | | |
| | | | |

**b** Write anything you notice about the numbers in your table.
**c** Write a quick way to find the LCM if you know the HCF.

# Summary

## Check out

You should now be able to:

- Use the terms square, square root, cube and cube root
- Understand and use index notation for squares, cubes and powers of 10
- Multiply and divide by powers of 10
- Identify factors, multiples and prime numbers from a list of numbers
- Find the highest common factor and the least common multiple of two numbers

## Worked exam question

Find the Least Common Multiple (LCM) of 24 and 36       (2)

(Edexcel Limited 2008)

> Use multiplication sums to find the multiples of 24

| 24 | 24 | 24 | 24 | 24 |
|----|----|----|----|----|
| 1 × | 2 × | 3 × | 4 × | 5 × |
| 24 | 48 | 72 | 96 | 120 |

Multiples of 24 are 24, 48, (72), 96, 120 ......

> Write the first few multiples of 24

| 36 | 36 |
|----|----|
| 1 × | 2 × |
| 36 | 72 |

Multiples of 36 are 36, (72) ......

> Write the multiples of 36

The Least Common Multiple is 72

## Exam questions

1 Here is a list of numbers.

| 5 | 6 | 7 | 8 | 9 | 10 |

From the list of numbers write down
**a** an even number (1)
**b** a square number (1)
**c** a multiple of 4 (1)
**d** a factor of 14 (1)

2 Here is a list of numbers.

| 4 | 5 | 6 | 7 | 8 | 9 | 10 | 11 | 12 |

From the list write down
**a** two odd numbers, (1)
**b** a prime number (1)
**c** the highest common factor (HCF) of 32 and 40 (2)

3 **a** Work out the value of $4^2 + 2^5$ (2)
**b** Write down the cube root of 64 (1)

(Edexcel Limited 2006)

4 Use a calculator to work out
$$\sqrt{2.56} + 8.4$$
(2)

(Edexcel Limited 2008)

5 Find the Highest Common Factor (HCF) of 60 and 84 (2)

**AO2 + 3**

**6** Two airport towers flash at regular intervals.
One flashes every 12 seconds and the other flashes every 9 seconds.
An aircraft pilot sees both towers flashing at the same time.
How many seconds will pass before they both flash together again? (3)

# Introduction

There are lots of different types of sequences in mathematics: from the most basic arithmetic sequences such as the set of even numbers, to the curious Fibonacci sequence used to describe plant growth, through to the elegant and complex world of iterative sequences used in chaos theory.

## What's the point?

Sequences allow you to find patterns in nature, so that you can understand it better.

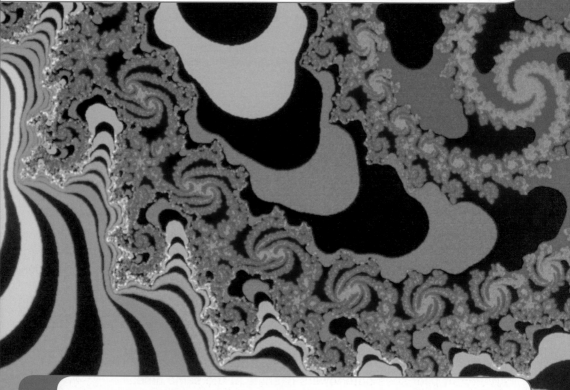

**Check in**

1 Find the missing numbers in these multiplication calculations.
  **a** $4 \times \square = 12$     **b** $3 \times \square = 27$
  **c** $8 \times \square = 32$     **d** $6 \times \square = 18$

2 Work out the square numbers from $1^2$ to $10^2$.

3 Copy and complete.
  **a** $2 + \square = 7$     **b** $16 - \square = 12$
  **c** $11 + \square = 18$     **d** $25 - \square = 19$

4 Copy and complete.
  **a** $3 \times \square = 6$     **b** $12 \div \square = 6$
  **c** $7 \times \square = 21$     **d** $18 \div \square = 6$

5 Substitute $n = 3$ into these expressions.
  **a** $n + 5$          **b** $2n$          **c** $3n + 3$          **d** $4n - 2$

**Rich task**

You have 15 circles. Here is a sequence of patterns that you can make.

Devise the first three terms of a different sequence using all 15 circles
Find the *n*th term of your sequence.

Can you find another sequence that uses all 15 circles?
Investigate finding the first three terms of sequences for different numbers of circles.

# Number sequences

This spread will show you how to:

- Understand and use the vocabulary associated with sequences
- Generate terms of a sequence using a term-to-term rule

**Keywords**
Ascending
Consecutive
Descending
Difference
Sequence
Term

- The numbers in a **sequence** follow a pattern.
  Each number in a sequence is called a **term**.

- You can see how a sequence grows by looking at the **differences** between **consecutive** terms.

Consecutive terms are next to each other.

The first five terms of a sequence are

1,   4,   7,   10,   13, ...

Difference:   +3   +3   +3   +3

You can follow the pattern to work out more terms.
13 + 3 = 16, 16 + 3 = 19, etc.

The numbers are getting higher. The sequence is **ascending**.

- A linear sequence goes up (or down) in equal sized steps.

**Example**

The first five terms of a sequence are
    14, 12, 10, 8, 6, ...
Work out the next two terms in the sequence.

The numbers are getting lower. The sequence is **descending**.

14,   12,   10,   8,   6, ...

Difference:   −2   −2   −2   −2

The next two terms are 6 − 2 = 4 and 4 − 2 = 2.

In a sequence that is not linear, the differences between terms may follow a pattern.

**Example**

The first five terms of a sequence are
    1, 2, 5, 10, 17, ...
Work out the next two terms.

1,   2,   5,   10,   17, ...

Difference:   +1   +3   +5   +7

The next term is 17 + 9 = 26.

The term after is 26 + 11 = 37.

The difference pattern is the odd numbers.
The next odd number is 9.
The next odd number is 11.

**1** Find the next two terms for each sequence.
  **a** 3, 5, 7, 9, ...        **b** 2, 5, 8, 11, ...
  **c** 1, 5, 9, 13, ...       **d** 4, 6, 8, 10, ...

**2** Work out the next two terms for each sequence.
  **a** 26, 21, 16, 11, ...    **b** 32, 28, 24, 20, ...
  **c** 22, 19, 16, 13, ...    **d** 86, 76, 66, 56, ...

**3** Find the next two terms for each sequence.
  **a** 6, 9, 12, 15, ...      **b** 15, 13, 11, 9, ...
  **c** 2, 9, 16, 23, ...      **d** 50, 42, 34, 26, ...

**4** Write the next two terms of the sequence 15, 17, 19, 21, ...
  Explain why 72 is **not** a term in this sequence.

**5** For each sequence,
  **i** Work out the differences between consecutive terms.
  **ii** Follow the pattern to work out the next two terms.
  **a** 2, 3, 5, 8, 12, ...    **b** 21, 20, 18, 15, ...
  **c** 4, 5, 8, 13, 20, ...   **d** 20, 15, 11, 8, ...

**6** Follow the patterns in these sequences to work out the next two terms.
  **a** 1,   2,   4,   ...     **b** 128,   64,   32,   ...
      ×2   ×2   ×2                  ÷2   ÷2   ÷2

  **c** 5, 10, 20, ...         **d** 81, 27, 9, ...

**7** The first three terms of a sequence are 3, 6, 12, ...
  Jim says 'Double a term to get the next one.'
  Sophie says 'The differences are +3 then +6. Add 9 to get the next term.'
  **a** Write the first four terms of
    **i** Jim's sequence     **ii** Sophie's sequence.
  **b** Write the first four terms of two different sequences that
    begin 1, 2, 4, ...

**8** Work out the next two terms in each sequence.
  **a** −5, −3, −1, 1, 3, ...  **b** 15, 12, 9, 6, 3, ...
  **c** −4, −3, −1, 2, 6       **d** 21, 19, 16, 12, 7, ...

**9** In each part, two sequences have been mixed up.
  Write out each sequence in the correct order.
  **a** 2, 4, 6, 6, 8, 10, 10, 12, 14, 18    **b** 1, 4, 5, 7, 9, 10, 13, 13, 17

**Generating sequences**

This spread will show you how to:

- Use term-to-term rules to work out missing terms in a sequence
- Generate terms of a sequence using a position-to-term rule
- Describe a sequence by giving its start number and term-to-term rule

**Keywords**

$n$th term
position-to-term
term-to-term

- A **term-to-term** rule tells you how to work out the next term in a sequence.

For the sequence    5,    8,    11,    14,    17, ...
$$+3 \quad +3 \quad +3 \quad +3$$

the term-to-term rule is 'add 3'.

- The term-to-term rule links one term to the next term in the sequence.

You can generate a sequence from a start number and a term-to-term rule.

**Example**

Generate the first five terms of the sequence with start number 7 and term-to-term rule 'add 4'.

7, 11, 15, 19, 23

$$7 + 4 = 11$$
$$11 + 4 = 15$$
$$15 + 4 = 19$$
$$19 + 4 = 23$$

You can use the term-to-term rule to work out missing terms in a sequence.

**Example**

Find the missing terms in these sequences.

**a**  3, 7, 11, ?, 19, ...

**b**  ?, 8, 11, 14, ...

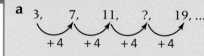

**a**    3,    7,    11,    ?,    19, ...
$$+4 \quad +4 \quad +4 \quad +4$$

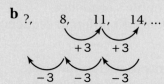

**b**    ?,    8,    11,    14, ...
$$+3 \quad +3$$
$$-3 \quad -3 \quad -3$$

The missing term is $11 + 4 = 15$.    The missing term is $8 - 3 = 5$.

Work backwards using the inverse operation.

- A **position-to-term** rule links a term to its position in the sequence.

The position-to-term rule is often called the **$n$th term**.
$n + 2$, $2n - 1$, $5n$, $4n + 3$ are all examples of $n$th terms.

1st term is in position 1,
2nd term is in position 2,
$n$th term is in position $n$.

**Example**

The $n$th term of a sequence is $2n + 1$.
Write the first three terms of the sequence.

Substitute the position number into $2n + 1$.
1st term        $n = 1$: $2 \times 1 + 1 = 3$
2nd term        $n = 2$: $2 \times 2 + 1 = 5$
3rd term        $n = 3$: $2 \times 3 + 1 = 7$

This topic is extended to the general term on page 424.

**1** Write the first five terms of these sequences.
  **a** start number 4      term-to-term rule 'add 2'
  **b** start number 7      term-to-term rule 'add 3'
  **c** start number 25     term-to-term rule 'subtract 2'
  **d** start number 30     term-to-term rule 'subtract 4'

**2** Find the missing terms in these sequences.
  **a** 3, 8, 13, ?, 23          **b** 18, 15, 12, ?, 6
  **c** ?, 9, 13, 17, 21         **d** ?, 16, 12, ?, 4

**3** Write the first five terms of the sequences with
  **a** start number 5      term-to-term rule 'multiply by 2'
  **b** start number 32     term-to-term rule 'divide by 2'
  **c** start number 3      term-to-term rule 'add consecutive odd
                            numbers'
  **d** start number 40     term-to-term rule 'subtract consecutive even
                            numbers'

**4** Generate the first five terms of these sequences.
  **a** start number $-5$   term-to-term rule 'add 2'
  **b** start number 7      term-to-term rule 'subtract 3'
  **c** start number 3      term-to-term rule 'multiply by $-1$'

**5** Generate the first five terms of the sequences with these $n$th terms.
  **a** $n + 1$     **b** $n + 3$     **c** $2n - 1$     **d** $2n + 3$
  **e** $3n - 1$    **f** $3n + 2$    **g** $4n + 3$     **h** $5n - 2$

**6** Find the missing terms in these sequences.
  **a** $-3$, 0, 3, ?, 9         **b** 12, ?, 2, $-3$, $-8$
  **c** 2, 3, 5, ?, 12           **d** ?, 12, 8, ?, $-6$

**7** Generate the first five terms of the sequence with $n$th term
  **a** $n - 1$     **b** $n - 3$     **c** $n^2$     **d** $-n + 3$

**8** Match each sequence in set A to an $n$th term in set B.
  **Set A:**

  | 5, 9, 13, 17, …  16, 14, 12, 10, …  1, 7, 13, 19, … |
  | 4, 7, 10, 13, …  21, 17, 13, 9, …   2, 8, 14, 20, … |

  **Set B:**

  | $6n - 4$   $4n + 1$   $25 - 4n$   $6n - 5$   $3n + 1$   $18 - 2n$ |

This spread will show you how to:

- Describe a sequence by giving its start number and term-to-term rule
- Describe a sequence by comparing it to a sequence of multiples

- You can describe a sequence by giving its start number and **term-to-term rule**.

WANTED
DEAD OR ALIVE
THE SEQUENCE
**2, 6, 10, 14**
Start number: 2
Term-to-Term Rule: +4

**Example**

Describe the sequence:     5, 11, 17, 23, 29, ...

5    11    17    23    29
  +6   +6   +6   +6

The sequence has start number 5 and term-to-term rule 'add 6'.

Some sequences have special names.
For example:
1, 3, 5, 7, 9, ... are 'the odd numbers'
2, 4, 6, 8, 10, ... are 'the even numbers' or 'the **multiples** of 2'
1, 4, 9, 16, 25, ... are 'the square numbers'.

- You can describe a sequence by comparing it to a sequence of multiples.

**Example**

**a** Write the first five terms of the sequence 'multiples of 3'.
**b** Here is a sequence
    2, 5, 8, 11, 14, ...
Describe this sequence in words by comparing it to the multiples of 3.

**a** 3, 6, 9, 12, 15
**b** Multiples of 3        3    6    9    12    15

                        −1   −1   −1   −1   −1

Term of sequence        2    5    8    11    14
The sequence is 'one less than the multiples of 3'.

Each term is one less than the corresponding term in the multiples of 3 sequence.

1 Describe each of these sequences in words, by giving the start number and the term-to-term rule.
   a 6, 7, 8, 9, 10, ...
   b 3, 7, 11, 15, 19, ...
   c 9, 15, 21, 27, 33, ...
   d 20, 17, 14, 11, 8, ...
   e 16, 14, 12, 10, 8, ...
   f 33, 28, 23, 18, 13, ...

2 Each set of numbers is a jumbled sequence of multiples.
   Write each sequence in the correct order.
   Write the name of each sequence in the form 'the multiples of _____'.
   a 20, 5, 10, 15, 25, ...
   b 21, 35, 7, 14, 28
   c 30, 6, 18, 24, 12, ...
   d 27, 9, 36, 18, 45

3 Write the first five terms of each of these sequences.
   a The multiples of 4
   b One more than the multiples of 4
   c One less than the multiples of 4
   d The multiples of 3
   e Two less than the multiples of 3
   f Four more than the multiples of 3

4 Describe each of your sequences from question 3 by giving the start number and term-to-term rule.

5 Describe these sequences by giving the start number and the term-to-term rule.
   a 10 000, 1000, 100, 10, 1, ...
   b 4, 8, 16, 32, 64, ...
   c 80, 40, 20, 10, 5, ...
   d 3, 9, 27, 81, 243, ...

6 Describe these sequences by giving the start number and the term-to-term rule.
   a −10, −4, 2, 8, 14, ...
   b 15, 11, 7, 3, −1
   c 100, 60, 20, −20, −60, ...
   d −5, 0, 10, 25, 45, ...

7 Describe these sequences in words by comparing them to the multiples of 4.
   a 6, 10, 14, 18, 22, ...
   b 1, 5, 9, 13, 17, ...

8 The $n$th term of a sequence is $2n$.
   Generate the first five terms of this sequence.
   Write two names for this sequence.

**Pattern sequences 1**

This spread will show you how to:

• Generate and describe sequences derived from patterns

**Keywords**

Pattern

These **patterns** are made from dots.

Pattern 1    Pattern 2    Pattern 3

To get from one pattern to the next in the sequence, you add two more dots.
The term-to-term rule is 'add 2'.
The numbers of dots in the patterns make a sequence

| Pattern number | 1 | 2 | 3 | 4 |
|---|---|---|---|---|
| Number of dots | 2 | 4 | 6 | 8 |

Pattern 4 is

The number of dots are the multiples of 2.
The number of dots in each pattern is

pattern number $\times$ 2

This is the position-to-term rule for the sequence.
The 10th pattern has $10 \times 2 = 20$ dots.

• You can use the term-to-term rule and position-to-term rule to work out the number of dots in other patterns.

**Example**

Here is a pattern made of tiles.

Pattern 1    Pattern 2    Pattern 3

a Copy and complete the table for the pattern sequence.

| Pattern number | 1 | 2 | 3 | 4 | 5 |
|---|---|---|---|---|---|
| Number of tiles | | | | | |

b Describe how the sequence grows.
c Work out the number of tiles in the 10th pattern.

..............................................................................

a

| Pattern number | 1 | 2 | 3 | 4 | 5 |
|---|---|---|---|---|---|
| Number of tiles | 4 | 7 | 10 | 13 | 16 |

b Add 3 blue tiles each time, one to each arm.
c Pattern 1: $3 = 1 \times 3$ blue + 1 pink
Pattern 2: $6 = 2 \times 3$ blue + 1 pink
Pattern 3: $9 = 3 \times 3$ blue + 1 pink
...
Pattern 10: $10 \times 3$ blue + 1 pink = 31 tiles

Count the tiles in patterns 1, 2 and 3.
Each time you add 3.
So pattern 4 has $10 + 3 = 13$ tiles.
Pattern 5 has $13 + 3 = 16$ tiles.

Write out how the pattern grows in 3s. This links the pattern number to the number of tiles.

**Unit 2**

**1** Draw the next pattern in each sequence.

**a**
  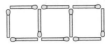
Pattern 1     Pattern 2        Pattern 3

**c**

Pattern 1     Pattern 2        Pattern 3

**b**
   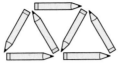
Pattern 1     Pattern 2        Pattern 3

**d**
 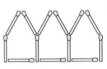
Pattern 1     Pattern 2        Pattern 3

**2** **a** Copy and complete this table for pattern **a** in question **1**.

| Pattern number | 1 | 2 | 3 | 4 | 5 |
|---|---|---|---|---|---|
| Number of matches | | | | | |

**b** Copy and complete this table for pattern **b** in question **1**.

| Pattern number | 1 | 2 | 3 | 4 | 5 |
|---|---|---|---|---|---|
| Number of pencils | | | | | |

**c** Copy and complete this table for pattern **c** in question **1**.

| Pattern number | 1 | 2 | 3 | 4 | 5 |
|---|---|---|---|---|---|
| Number of dots | | | | | |

**d** Copy and complete this table for pattern **d** in question **1**.

| Pattern number | 1 | 2 | 3 | 4 | 5 |
|---|---|---|---|---|---|
| Number of matches | | | | | |

**3** For each pattern
  **i** describe how the pattern grows
  **ii** copy and complete these statements.
    Pattern 1 has _____ + _____
    Pattern 2 has 2 × _____ + _____
    Pattern 3 has 3 × _____ + _____
    Pattern 10 has __ × _____ + _____

**a**

Pattern 1     Pattern 2     Pattern 3

**b**

Pattern 1     Pattern 2     Pattern 3

**4** Here are some patterns of dots.
  **a** Draw pattern number 4.
  **b** Copy and complete the table.
Pattern 1     Pattern 2     Pattern 3

| Pattern number | 1 | 2 | 3 | 4 | 5 | 10 |
|---|---|---|---|---|---|---|
| Number of dots | | | | | | |

  **c** Explain how you worked out the number of dots in pattern number 10.

This spread will show you how to:
• Generate and describe sequences derived from patterns

**Keywords**
Sequence
Term-to-term rule

Here is a **sequence** of patterns made from dots.

The next two patterns are:

○ ○ ○      ○ ○ ○ ○      ○ ○ ○ ○ ○      ○ ○ ○ ○ ○ ○      ○ ○ ○ ○ ○ ○ ○
○ ○        ○ ○ ○        ○ ○ ○ ○        ○ ○ ○ ○ ○        ○ ○ ○ ○ ○ ○

Pattern 1    Pattern 2    Pattern 3       Pattern 4          Pattern 5

The numbers of dots make a sequence.

| Pattern number | 1 | 2 | 3 | 4 | 5 |
|---|---|---|---|---|---|
| Number of dots | 5 | 7 | 9 | 11 | 13 |

The **term-to-term** rule is 'add 2'.

• You can use the term-to-term rule to work out the number of dots in the next pattern.

---

**Example**

Here is a sequence of patterns made from stars.

**a** Draw the next two patterns in the sequence.
**b** Describe how the patterns grow.
**c** Complete the table for the sequence.

| Pattern number | 1 | 2 | 3 | 4 | 5 |
|---|---|---|---|---|---|
| Number of stars | | | | | |

Pattern 1      Pattern 2      Pattern 3

**d** Work out the number of stars in the 6th and 7th patterns.
**e** Work out the number of stars in the 10th pattern.

**a**

Pattern 4              Pattern 5

**b** Add one star to each side
So add three stars each time.

**c**

| Pattern number | 1 | 2 | 3 | 4 | 5 |
|---|---|---|---|---|---|
| Number of stars | 3 | 6 | 9 | 12 | 15 |

**d** 6th pattern: $15 + 3 = 18$ stars.
7th pattern: $18 + 3 = 21$ stars.

**e** Number of stars = $3 \times$ pattern number.
Number of stars in pattern 10 = $3 \times 10$
$= 30.$

---

The relationship between the number of dots and the pattern number is the **position-to-term rule**.

The pattern number is the pattern's position in the sequence.

• You can use the position-to-term rule to work out the number of dots in any pattern.

**1** For each sequence
- draw pattern number 4 and pattern number 5
- copy and complete the table.

**a**

Pattern 1    Pattern 2    Pattern 3

| Pattern number | 1 | 2 | 3 | 4 | 5 |
|---|---|---|---|---|---|
| Number of dots | | | | | |

**b**

Pattern 1    Pattern 2    Pattern 3

| Pattern number | 1 | 2 | 3 | 4 | 5 |
|---|---|---|---|---|---|
| Number of square tiles | | | | | |

**2** For this sequence

Pattern 1    Pattern 2    Pattern 3

- draw pattern number 4 and pattern number 5
- describe how the pattern grows
- copy and complete the table.
- work out the number of dots in pattern number 6 and pattern number 7.

| Pattern number | 1 | 2 | 3 | 4 | 5 |
|---|---|---|---|---|---|
| Number of dots | | | | | |

**3** These patterns are made from square tiles.

Pattern 1    Pattern 2    Pattern 3

**a** Draw the 4th and 5th patterns in the sequence.
**b** Describe how the patterns grow.
**c** Copy and complete the table.
**d** Copy and complete:

| Pattern number | 1 | 2 | 3 | 4 | 5 |
|---|---|---|---|---|---|
| Number of tiles | | | | | |

   Number of tiles = ____ × pattern number

**e** Use your formula from **d** to work out the number of tiles in pattern number 10.

This spread will show you how to:

- Use position-to-term rules to work out any pattern or term in a sequence

**Keywords**
General term
*n*th term

A position-to-term rule links a term to its position in the sequence.

- The position-to-term rule is often called the *n*th term.

Another name for the *n*th term is the **general term**.

- You can work out the terms of a sequence by substituting the position numbers 1, 2, 3, 4, ... into the *n*th term.

The 1st term is in position 1. The 2nd term is in position 2. The *n*th term is in position *n*.

**Example**

Generate the first five terms of the sequences with these nth terms.

**a** $3n + 2$       **b** $n^2 + 3$

This topic is extended to finding the general term on page 424.

**a** $3n + 2$
  1st term substitute $n = 1$: $3 \times 1 + 2 = 3 + 2 \quad = 5$
  2nd term substitute $n = 2$: $3 \times 2 + 2 = 6 + 2 \quad = 8$
  3rd term substitute $n = 3$: $3 \times 3 + 2 = 9 + 2 \quad = 11$
  4th term substitute $n = 4$: $3 \times 4 + 2 = 12 + 2 \quad = 14$
  5th term substitute $n = 5$: $3 \times 5 + 2 = 15 + 2 \quad = 17$
  The first five terms are 5, 8, 11, 14, 17.

**b** $n^2 + 3$
  1st term:   $1^2 + 3 = 4$
  2nd term:   $2^2 + 3 = 4 + 3 \ = 7$
  3rd term:   $3^2 + 3 = 9 + 3 \ = 12$
  4th term:   $4^2 + 3 = 16 + 3 = 19$
  5th term:   $5^2 + 3 = 25 + 3 = 28$
  The first five terms are 4, 7, 12, 19, 28.

**Example**

Here is a sequence of patterns made from counters.

The general term for the sequence is

  $C = 3n - 1$

where $C$ is the number of counters and $n$ is the pattern number.
Which pattern in the sequence has 89 counters?

Pattern 1     Pattern 2     Pattern 3

For the pattern with 89 counters
    $89 = 3n - 1$
  $89 + 1 = 3n - 1 + 1$
    $90 = 3n$
  $90 \div 3 = 3n \div 3$
    $30 = n$          The 30th pattern has 89 counters.

Substitute 89 into the formula.
Solve the equation to find $n$.

Add 1 to both sides.
Divide both sides by 3.

**1** Generate the first five terms of the sequences with these $n$th terms.

  **a** $3n - 1$    **b** $2n + 3$    **c** $2n - 5$    **d** $6n + 2$

  **e** $4n + 5$    **f** $3 - 2n$    **g** $4n - 2$    **h** $-3n + 8$

**2** Write the first five terms of the sequences with these $n$th terms.

  **a** $n^2 + 1$    **b** $n^2 + 7$    **c** $n^2 - 4$    **d** $n^2 - 1$

  **e** $n^2 + 10$    **f** $3 - n^2$    **g** $n^2 - 2$    **h** $-n^2 + 1$

**3** Here is a sequence of beach hut patterns made from matchsticks. The formula for the number of matchsticks in a pattern is

  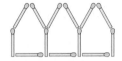

    $M = 4n + 1$

Pattern 1     Pattern 2     Pattern 3

where $M$ is the number of matchsticks and $n$ is the pattern number.

  **a** Work out the number of matchsticks in pattern number 9.

  **b** Work out the number of matchsticks in pattern number 10.

Trina has 40 matchsticks.

  **c** What is the pattern number of the largest pattern she can make?

  **d** How many matchsticks will she have left over?

**4** Here is a sequence of patterns made from tiles.

The general term for the sequence is

    $T = 3n + 1$

where $T$ is the number of tiles and $n$ is the pattern number.

  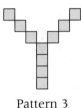

  **a** Work out the number of tiles in pattern number 15.

Pattern 1     Pattern 2     Pattern 3

  **b** Which pattern has 28 tiles?

  **c** Is there a pattern with 39 tiles? Explain your answer.

  **d** Which is the largest pattern you could make with 39 tiles? How many tiles would you have left over?

**5** Here is a sequence of patterns made from 2p coins.

The formula for this sequence is

    $C = 3n + 1$

where $C$ is the number of 2p coins and $n$ is the pattern number.

 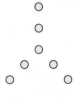 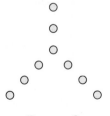

  **a** How many 2p coins are there in the 5th pattern?

  **b** What is the value of the 5th pattern?

  **c** Which pattern has twenty-two 2p coins?

Pattern 1     Pattern 2     Pattern 3

  **d** What is the value of the pattern in part **c**?

  **e** Which pattern has value 68p?

# Summary

## Check out
You should now be able to:

- Understand and use the vocabulary associated with sequences
- Generate sequences of numbers using a term-to-term rule
- Generate sequences of numbers using a position-to-term rule
- Identify which terms cannot be in a sequence
- Generate and describe sequences derived from diagrams

## Worked exam question
Here are the first 4 terms in a number sequence.

    124     122     120     118    .....

**a**  Write down the next term in this number sequence.     (1)

**b**  Write down the 7th term in this number sequence.     (1)

9 cannot be a term in this number sequence.

**c**  Explain why.     (1)

(Edexcel Limited 2009)

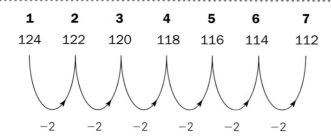

| 1 | 2 | 3 | 4 | 5 | 6 | 7 |
|---|---|---|---|---|---|---|
| 124 | 122 | 120 | 118 | 116 | 114 | 112 |

   −2    −2    −2    −2    −2    −2

**a**
116

**b**
112

**c**
Each term in the number sequence is an even number, but 9 is an odd number.

> Write a short explanation.

# Exam questions

**1** Here are some patterns made using sticks.

Pattern number 1     Pattern number 2     Pattern number 3

**a** Complete Pattern number 4. (1)

**b** Copy and complete the table. 

| Pattern number | 1 | 2 | 3 | 4 | 5 |
|---|---|---|---|---|---|
| Number of sticks | 3 | 5 | 7 | | |

(1)

**c** How many sticks are used in Pattern number 12? (1)

**2** Here are the first four terms of a number sequence.

　　　　7　　11　　15　　19

**a** Write down the next two terms of the number sequence. (2)

**b** Work out the 10th term of this number sequence. (2)

**3** Charlotte worked out the sum of some consecutive odd numbers starting with 1.
She put her results in a table.

| Sum of the first odd number | 1 | = 1 |
|---|---|---|
| Sum of the first 2 odd numbers | 1 + 3 | = 4 |
| Sum of the first 3 odd numbers | 1 + 3 + 5 | = 9 |
| Sum of the first 4 odd numbers | 1 + 3 + 5 + 7 | = 16 |
| Sum of the first 5 odd numbers | 1 + 3 + 5 + 7 + 9 | = 25 |
| Sum of the first 6 odd numbers | | |

**a** Copy and complete the bottom row of the table. (2)

**b** What is the special name for the numbers　　1, 4, 9, 16, 25? (1)

(Edexcel Limited 2007)

A03

**4** Here are the first three terms of a sequence.

　　1　　　2　　　4　　　☐　　　☐

Suggest what the next two terms could be.

Give **two** possible alternatives. (2)

Mathematics is used widely in sport, particularly when taking measurements and recording results.

Here are the results and reaction times (in alphabetical order) for the 100m Men's Final at the IAAF World Championships in Berlin in August 2009:

Use the photo to order Bailey and Thompson as well as Burns and Chambers. What degree of accuracy is shown here?

| Name | Nationality | Time (s) | Reaction (s) |
|---|---|---|---|
| Bailey | ANT | 9.93 | 0.129 |
| Bolt | JAM | 9.58 | 0.146 |
| Burns | TRI | 10.00 | 0.165 |
| Chambers | GBR | 10.00 | 0.123 |
| Gay | USA | 9.71 | 0.144 |
| Patton | USA | 9.84 | 0.149 |
| Powell | JAM | 9.93 | 0.134 |
| Thompson | TRI | 9.93 | 0.119 |

What degree of accuracy is reported for
a) the result times
b) the reaction times?

Draw a stem-and-leaf diagram to show the result times of this race.

Calculate the
a) range b) median c) mean
of the reported results, giving your answers to an appropriate level of accuracy.

Which average do you think best represents these results? Explain your answer.

Here are the results and reaction times for the 100m Women's Final at the same World Championships:

| Name | Nationality | Time (s) | Reaction (s) |
|---|---|---|---|
| Fraser | JAM | 10.73 | 0.146 |
| Stewart | JAM | 10.75 | 0.170 |
| Jeter | USA | 10.90 | 0.160 |
| Campbell-Brown | JAM | 10.95 | 0.135 |
| Williams | USA | 11.01 | 0.158 |
| Ferguson-McKenzie | BAH | 11.05 | 0.130 |
| Sturrup | BAH | 11.05 | 0.137 |
| Bailey | JAM | 11.16 | 0.173 |

Use diagrams and statistics to compare the Men's and Women's reported results.

## IAAF WORLD CHAMPIONSHIPS
### BERLIN, AUGUST 2009

NEWS          PHOTOS          VIDEO          AUDIO

By Date       By Event       Entry List      Medal Table      Placing Table      Entry Standards

Any reaction time quicker than 0.1 seconds is considered to be a false start.
How close was the fastest reaction time in the
a) Men's final                b) Women's final
to the false start limit?

Do you think that the limit of 0.1 seconds is a suitable value?
Explain your answer.
Find the range of the reaction times for both the Men's and Women's races.
Draw a scatter diagram to show result time against reaction time for
a) the Men's final          b) the Women's final.

Do you think there is any link between the reaction times of the athletes and the results of these races?
Explain your answer.
Recalculate the result times for the athletes in
a) the Men's race          b) the Women's race
assuming that all of the athletes had a reaction time of 0.1 seconds.
Use diagrams and statistics to show what affect this would have on the results of each race.

# Introduction

A fractal is a geometrical shape that can be split into parts so that each part is a smaller copy of the whole shape. Here is an example of the Von Koch Snowflake. The Von Koch Snowflake fractal is constructed from an equilateral triangle. On the middle third of each side is built another equilateral triangle and the process is repeated over and over again.

## What's the point?

Fractal geometry is a fairly new branch of mathematics that is finding new applications all the time. The von Koch snowflake can be used to model the reception of an antenna.

**Check in**

**1** State the sum of the three angles *x*, *y*, *z*.

**a** 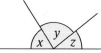    **b** 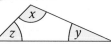    **c**

**2** Find the value of each unknown angle.

**a** 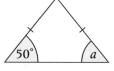    **b**

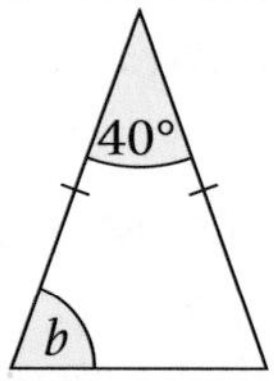

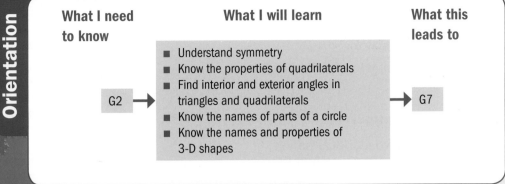

**What I need to know**

G2 →

**What I will learn**

- Understand symmetry
- Know the properties of quadrilaterals
- Find interior and exterior angles in triangles and quadrilaterals
- Know the names of parts of a circle
- Know the names and properties of 3-D shapes

**What this leads to**

→ G7

**Rich task**

A quadrilateral has been drawn on a 3 × 3 square dotty grid.

How many different quadrilaterals can you find?

This spread will show you how to:
- Recognise reflection symmetry of 2-D shapes

**Keywords**
Line of symmetry
Reflection
symmetry
Regular polygon

A shape has **reflection symmetry** if

- the shape divides into two identical halves
- you can fold the shape so that one half fits exactly on top of the other

The dotted line is the line of **symmetry**.

mirror

- a mirror reflects half the shape to give the completed shape.

- A line of symmetry divides the shape into two identical halves, each of which is the mirror image of the other.

You can find symmetry in nature.
This butterfly has one line of symmetry.

**Example**

**a** Add one extra square so that the shaded shape has 1 line of symmetry.
**b** Draw the line of symmetry.

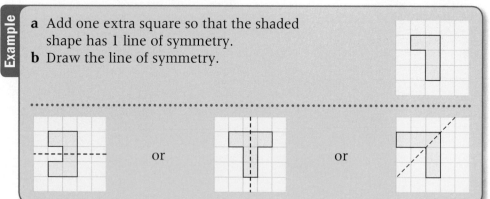

or      or

A shape can have more than one line of symmetry.

- A **regular polygon** with *n* sides has *n* lines of symmetry.

Regular polygons have equal sides and equal angles.

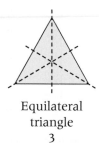   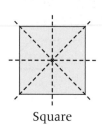      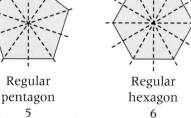

Equilateral triangle
3

Square
4

Regular pentagon
5

Regular hexagon
6

1  Copy these 2-D shapes and draw in the lines of symmetry.

a      b      c      d      e

f      g      h      i      j

2  State the number of lines of symmetry for each of these regular polygons.

a      b      c      d      e

   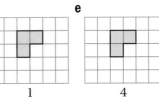

**A03 Problem**

3  Draw these shapes on square grid paper. Add one square to give a shape with the required number of lines of symmetry. Draw the lines of symmetry for the new shape.

a      b      c      d      e

 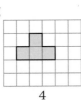  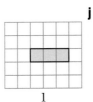 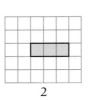

   2       1       2       1       4

f      g      h      i      j

   0       4       1       1       2

4  Draw these shapes on isometric paper. Add one triangle to give a shape with the required number of lines of symmetry. Draw the lines of symmetry for the new shape.

a   b   c   d  e 

    6       3       2       1       0

**Unit 2**

# Rotational symmetry

This spread will show you how to:
- Recognise rotational symmetry of 2-D shapes

**Keywords**
Order of rotational symmetry
Regular polygon
Rotational symmetry

- A shape has **rotational symmetry** if the shape looks like itself more than once in a full turn.

The **order of rotational symmetry** is the number of times a shape looks exactly like itself in a complete turn.

 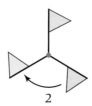 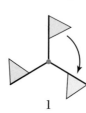 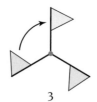

1        2        3

The order of rotational symmetry is 3.

---

**Example**

Add one extra square so that the shaded shape has rotational symmetry of order 2.

---

**Example**

Name these shapes. State the order of rotational symmetry for each one.

a       b       c       d

**a** rhombus    **b** arrowhead    **c** rectangle    **d** regular pentagon

2            1            2            5

---

- A **regular polygon** with *n* sides has rotational symmetry of order *n*.

regular heptagon    regular octagon    regular nonagon    regular decagon
order 7             order 8            order 9            order 10

Turn the page around to see the rotational symmetry.

**1** Copy these 2-D shapes and state the order of rotational symmetry for each shape.

a   b   c   d   e

f   g   h   i   j

**2** State the order of rotational symmetry for these regular polygons.

a   b   c   d   e

**A03 Problem**

**3** Draw these shapes on square grid paper. Add one square to each to give a shape with the given order of rotational symmetry.

a 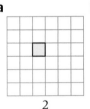  b   c 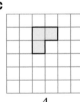  d 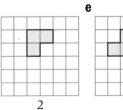  e

    2         2         4         2         4

f 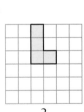  g 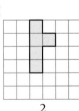  h 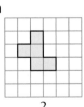  i 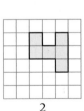  j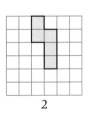

    2         2         2         2         2

**4** Draw these shapes on isometric paper. Add one triangle to give a shape with the given order of rotational symmetry.

a   b   c   d   e

    6         2         2         3         2

**Properties of quadrilaterals**

This spread will show you how to:
* Know the properties of quadrilaterals

**Keywords**
Diagonal
Parallel
Quadrilateral
Rotational
  symmetry

A **quadrilateral** is a 2-D shape with four sides and four angles.

You need to know the properties of these quadrilaterals.

| Square | Rhombus | Parallelogram | Rectangle |
|---|---|---|---|
| | | | |
| 4 equal angles<br>4 equal sides<br>2 sets parallel sides<br>4 lines of symmetry<br>Rotational symmetry of order 4 | 2 pairs equal angles<br>4 equal sides<br>2 sets parallel sides<br>2 lines of symmetry<br>Rotational symmetry of order 2 | 2 pairs equal angles<br>2 sets equal sides<br>2 sets parallel sides<br>0 lines of symmetry<br>Rotational symmetry of order 2 | 4 equal angles<br>2 sets equal sides<br>2 sets parallel sides<br>2 lines of symmetry<br>Rotational symmetry of order 2 |

The equal angles are colour coded.

| Trapezium | Isosceles trapezium | Kite | Arrowhead |
|---|---|---|---|
| | | | |
| Usually:<br>No equal angles<br>No equal sides<br>Always has:<br>1 set of parallel sides<br>0 lines of symmetry<br>Rotational symmetry of order 1 | 2 pairs equal angles<br>1 set equal sides<br>1 set parallel sides<br>1 line of symmetry<br>Rotational symmetry of order 1 | 1 pair equal angles<br>2 sets equal sides<br>No parallel sides<br>1 line of symmetry<br>Rotational symmetry of order 1 | 1 pair equal angles<br>2 sets equal sides<br>No parallel sides<br>1 reflex angle<br>1 line of symmetry<br>Rotational symmetry of order 1 |

**Example**

The diagonals on this rhombus are drawn.
Say whether each of these statements is true or false.

a The diagonals are of equal length.
b The diagonals are perpendicular.
c The diagonals are the lines of symmetry.
d The diagonals bisect each other.
e The diagonals bisect the angles.

Perpendicular lines cross at 90°.

a false     b true     c true     d true     e true

**A03** **Problem**

**1** Cut out four congruent (identical) right-angled triangles.
Arrange all four triangles to make
**a** square
**b** an isosceles trapezium
**c** a rectangle
**d** a parallelogram
**e** a rhombus.
Draw a sketch of each arrangement.

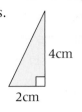

4cm

2cm

**Unit 2**

**2** Give the mathematical name of each coloured quadrilateral in the regular octagon.

**a** 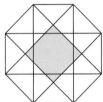  **b** 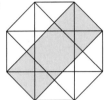  **c**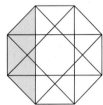

**d** 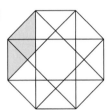  **e** 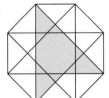  **f**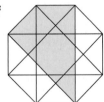

**3** On separate copies of this grid, plot and join up each set of points.
**a** (2, 3) (1, 0) (2, −3) (3, 0) (2, 3)
**b** (2, −3) (2, 3) (0, 1) (0, −1) (2, −3)
**c** (3, 2) (−2, 2) (−3, −1) (2, −1) (3, 2)
**d** (0, −1) (2, 2) (0, 3) (−2, 2) (0, −1)
**e** (2, 2) (−3, 3) (−1, 2) (−3, 1) (2, 2)
**f** (1, 1) (−1, 3) (−3, 1) (−1, −1) (1, 1)
**g** (−2, 3) (−3, 2) (1, −1) (2, 0) (−2, 3)
**h** (3, −3) (0, −1) (−2, −1) (−3, −3) (3, −3)
In each case, state the type of quadrilateral.

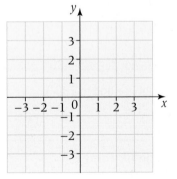

**4** **a** Copy this shape and reflect it in the dotted line.
**b** Give the mathematical name of the new shape.

**Properties of triangles and quadrilaterals**

This spread will show you how to:
- Use angle properties of equilateral, isosceles and right-angled triangles
- Use angle properties of quadrilaterals
- Find exterior angles in triangles and quadrilaterals

**Keywords**
Diagonal
Exterior
Interior
Quadrilateral
Triangle

- The angles in a triangle add to 180°.

A **quadrilateral** is a 2-D shape with 4 sides and 4 angles.

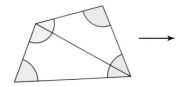 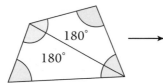 

You can draw a **diagonal** on a quadrilateral to form 2 triangles.

The angles in each triangle add to 180°.

$2 \times 180 = 360°$

This works for any quadrilateral.

- The angles in a quadrilateral add to 360°.

The angles inside a shape are called **interior** angles.

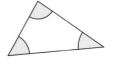 

You find the **exterior** angles by extending each side of the shape in the same direction.

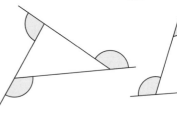

- Interior angle + exterior angle = 180°

  (angles on a straight line add to 180°)

  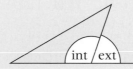 

  p.400

---

**Example**

Calculate the value of $x$ and $y$.
Give a reason for each answer.
..................................................

$125° + 110° + 58° = 293°$
$360° - 293° = 67°$
$x = 67°$ (angles in a quadrilateral add to 360°)
$180° - 67° = 113°$
$y = 113°$ (angles on a straight line add to 180°)

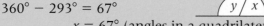

1 Give the mathematical name of each coloured shape in the regular hexagon.

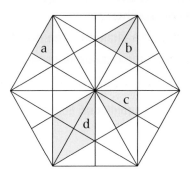

2 Calculate the value of the unknown angles.

**a**

**b**

**c**

3 Calculate the value of the unknown angles.

**a**

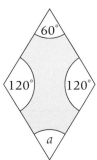

**b**

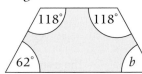

**c**

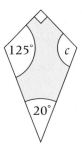

**d**

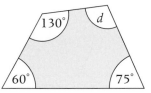

**e**

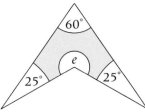

4 Calculate the value of the angles marked by a letter.

**a**

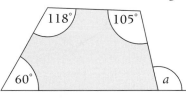

**b**

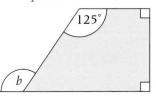

**c**

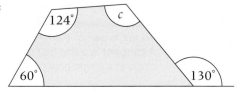

Unit 2

This spread will show you how to:

- Know the definition of a circle and the names of its parts
- Use a protractor and compasses to draw circles and sectors

**Keywords**

Arc
Centre
Chord
Circle
Circumference
Compasses
Diameter
Equidistant
Radius
Sector
Segment
Semicircle
Tangent

- A **circle** is a set of points **equidistant** from its **centre**.

Equidistant means 'the same distance from a fixed point'.

circumference

The **circumference** (C) is the distance around the circle.

radius

The **radius** (r) is the distance from the centre to the circumference.

p.402

**Radii** is the plural of radius.

diameter

The **diameter** (d) is the distance across the centre of the circle.

semi-circle

The diameter divides the circle into two **semicircles**.

**Example**

Draw a circle so that the line AB is the radius.

A———B

Put the point of the **compasses** at A or B and open the compasses to the length of AB. Draw the circle.

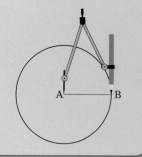

You also need to know these parts of a circle.

arc

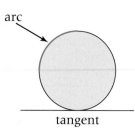

 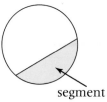  

chord

A **chord** is a line joining two points on the circumference.

segment

A **segment** is the region enclosed by a chord and an arc.

sector

A **sector** is the region enclosed by an arc and two radii.

tangent

An **arc** is part of the circumference. A **tangent** is a line that touches the circle at a single point.

**A03** **Problem**

**1 a** Draw two circles that intersect
at A and B.
**b** Draw the diameters AC and AD.
**c** Is CBD a straight line?

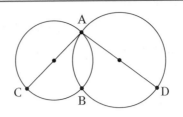

**Intersect** means
**cross.**

**2** Measure
**a** the diameter of the circle
**b** the radius of the circle.

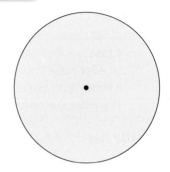

**3 a** Draw a circle with a radius of 4 cm.
**b** Draw a chord of length 5 cm inside the circle.

**4** Draw a circle with a diameter of 10 cm.

**5 a** Draw a 4 cm line AB.
**b** Draw a circle so that AB is the diameter.
**c** Find the radius of the circle.

A —————————————— B
4 cm

**6** Use a protractor and compasses to construct these sectors.

**a**

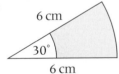

6 cm
30°
6 cm

**b**

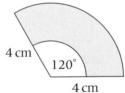

4 cm
120°
4 cm

**7** Two circles have the same centre.
One has a radius of 3.5 cm and the other has a radius of 2.5 cm.
Construct and colour this diagram for the two circles.

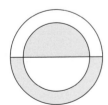

 **8** Explain why these circles are similar.

**Unit 2**

# 3-D shapes

This spread will show you how to:

- Understand the terms face, edge and vertex
- Know the names of general 3-D shapes

**Keywords**
Cube
Cuboid
Edge
Face
Prism
Pyramid
Solid
Three-
  dimensional
  (3-D)
Vertex

A **solid** is a **three-dimensional (3-D)** shape.

The three dimensions are length, width and height for a cuboid.

- In a 3-D shape
  - a **face** is a flat surface of the solid
  - an **edge** is the line where two faces meet
  - a **vertex** is a point at which two or more edges meet. The vertex is a corner of the shape.

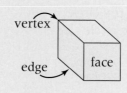
vertex    face    edge

The plural of vertex is vertices.

A **cube** has    6 faces that are squares
               12 edges
               8 vertices.

p.404

A **cuboid** has    6 faces that are rectangles
               12 edges
               8 vertices.

A **prism** has a constant cross-section.

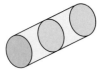 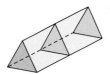 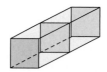

     cylinder        triangular prism      square-based prism

You name a prism by the shape of the cross-section.

A **pyramid** has faces that meet at a common point.

square-based pyramid    triangular-based pyramid      cone

A tetrahedron is a pyramid made from four triangles.

**Example**

For this solid, write

**a** its mathematical name    **b** the number of faces
**c** the number of edges    **d** the number of vertices.

..................................................................................................

**a** Pentagonal prism      **b** 7 faces
**c** 15 edges              **d** 10 vertices (corners)

**1** Decide whether these shapes are prisms, pyramids or neither of these.

a    b    c    d

e    f    g    h

i    j    k    l

m    n 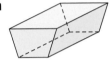   o

**2** This solid is made from eight isosceles triangles and one octagon.
For this solid, write
  **a** the mathematical name     **b** the number of faces
  **c** the number of edges      **d** the number of vertices.

**3 a** Copy and complete this table.

| Name of solid | Number of faces ($f$) | Number of edges ($e$) | Number of vertices ($v$) |
|---|---|---|---|
| pentagonal prism | 7 | 15 | 10 |
| cuboid | | | |
| pentagonal pyramid | | | |
| square-based pyramid | | | |
| cube | | | |
| hexagonal prism | | | |
| tetrahedron | | | |
| triangular prism | | | |
| hexagonal pyramid | | | |
| octagonal-based prism | | | |

  **b** Write a relationship between $f$, $e$ and $v$.

This spread will show you how to:

● Calculate the volume of cuboids

**Keywords**
Cube
Cubic centimetre (cm³)
Cubic metre (m³)
Cuboid
Volume

● The **volume** of a 3-D shape is the amount of space it takes up.

You measure volume using **cubes**.

1 cm
1 cm
1 cm

One **cubic centimetre** is 1 cm³.

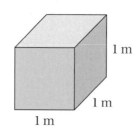

1 m
1 m
1 m

One **cubic metre** is 1 m³.

The ³ in cm³ shows there are 3 dimensions.

**Example**

Find the volume of these shapes made from centimetre cubes.
State the units of your answers.

**a**     **b**

......

**a** Volume
= 5 cm³

**b** Volume
= 6 cm³

The volume of a **cuboid** can be found by counting the number of layers.

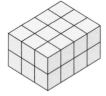    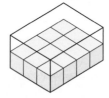    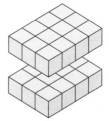

On the bottom layer, there are
3 × 4 = 12 cubes.

For 2 layers, there are
2 × 12 = 24 cubes.

● Volume of a cuboid = length × width × height

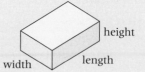

height
width
length

**Example**

Calculate the volume of this cuboid.
State the units of your answer.
......
Volume = 2 × 4 × 10
= 80 m³

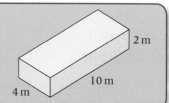

2 m
10 m
4 m

**p.404** ▶

The units are cubic metres or m³.

1 **a** Calculate the volume, for each solid.
Each cube represents 1 cm³.

i   ii   iii   iv

v   vi   vii

**b** All these solids fit together to make a cube.
Find the volume of the cube.

**c** What are the dimensions of the cube?

2 Calculate the volume, in cm³, of each cuboid.

a   b   c   d   e

f   g   h   i   j

3 Calculate the volume of each cuboid. State the units of your answers.

a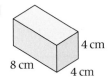
10 cm  2 cm  3 cm

b
5 m  5 m  5 m

c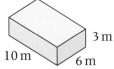
3 m  10 m  6 m

d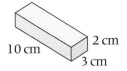
4 cm  8 cm  4 cm

e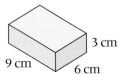
3 cm  9 cm  6 cm

f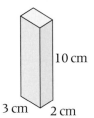
10 cm  3 cm  2 cm

4 A **prism** has a constant cross-section.
The cross-section of this prism is an L-shape.

> • Volume of a prism = area of cross-section × length

Calculate the volume of this prism.

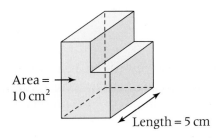
Area = 10 cm²
Length = 5 cm

**3-D shapes and isometric paper**

This spread will show you how to:
- Use 2-D representations of 3-D shapes
- Calculate the surface area and volume of cuboids

**Keywords**
3-D
Congruent
Cube
Cuboid
Isometric
Surface area
Volume

You can draw some **3-D** shapes using **isometric** paper.

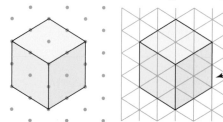

3-D means 3-dimensional.

The paper must be this way round.

The equal edges of the cube are shown by lines of equal length.

---

**Example**

Add one cube to shape B so that it is congruent to shape A.

**A**     **B**

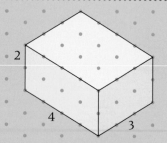

**Congruent** shapes are identical in size and shape. You will learn more about congruence on page 398.

---

- **Surface area** of a cuboid is the total area of its faces.

- **Volume** of cuboid = length × width × height

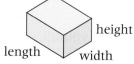 height

length    width

 p.404

---

**Example**

**a** On isometric paper, draw a cuboid with dimensions 2 cm by 3 cm by 4 cm.
**b** Calculate the surface area of the cuboid. State the units of your answer.
**c** Calculate the volume of the cuboid. State the units of your answer.

**a**

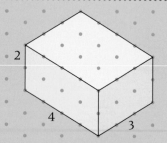

2

4    3

**b** Area of the 4 cm by 3 cm rectangle = 4 × 3 = 12 cm$^2$
Area of the 3 cm by 2 cm rectangle = 3 × 2 =   6 cm$^2$
Area of the 2 cm by 4 cm rectangle = 2 × 4 =   8 cm$^2$
26 cm$^2$

Surface area = 26 × 2 = 52 cm$^2$
**c** Volume = 2 × 3 × 4 = 24 cm$^3$

There are three hidden faces you must account for when finding the total surface area. Opposite faces are congruent.

**1** Draw these solids after the shaded cube is removed.

**a**

**b**

**c**

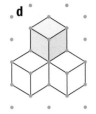
**d**

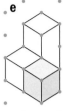
**e**

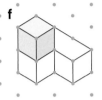
**f**

**g**

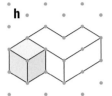
**h**

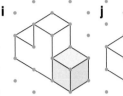
**i**

**j**

**2 a** State the dimensions of this cuboid.
 **b** Calculate the surface area of the cuboid.
 **c** Calculate the volume of the cuboid.

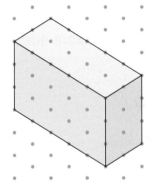

**3 a** Copy and complete the drawing of the
     1 cm by 2 cm by 5 cm cuboid on isometric paper.
 **b** Calculate the surface area of the cuboid.
 **c** Calculate the volume of the cuboid.

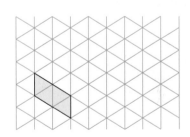

**4 a** On isometric paper, draw a cuboid with dimensions
     1 cm by 3 cm by 4 cm.
 **b** Calculate the surface area of the cuboid.
     State the units of your answer.
 **c** Calculate the volume of the cuboid.
     State the units of your answer.

**5** On isometric paper, draw a cube with
 a volume of 27 cm$^3$.

Volume
= 27 cm$^3$

A03 Problem

Unit 2

269

### Check out

You should now be able to:

- Recognise reflection symmetry and rotational symmetry of 2-D shapes
- Know the properties of special types of quadrilaterals
- Use angle properties of triangles and quadrilaterals
- Know the definition of a circle and the names of its parts
- Use a protractor and compasses to draw circles and sectors
- Know the terms face, edge and vertex
- Identify and name common 3-D shapes
- Find the volume of a cuboid

### Worked exam question

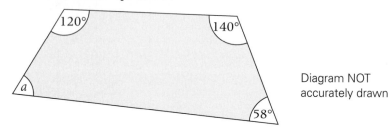

Diagram NOT accurately drawn

Work out the size of the angle $a$. (2)

(Edexcel Limited 2009)

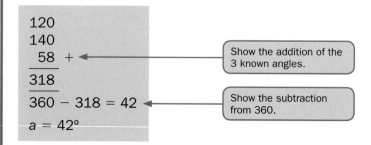

$$
\begin{array}{r}
120 \\
140 \\
58 \ + \\
\hline
318
\end{array}
$$

Show the addition of the 3 known angles.

$360 - 318 = 42$

Show the subtraction from 360.

$a = 42°$

## Exam questions

**1  a** Draw a circle with radius 4 cm and centre marked O.   (1)
**b** Here is a circle centre C.
Copy it and draw a diameter in the circle.

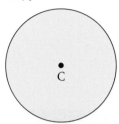

(1)

(Edexcel Limited 2009)

**2** Write down the mathematical name of each of these two 3-D shapes.

**a**    **b**    **c**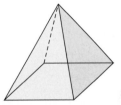

(3)

**3** The diagram shows a tetrahedron.

Diagram NOT
accurately drawn

Write down
**a** the number of faces
**b** the number of edges
**c** the number of vertices   (3)

**A03**

**4** The volume of a cuboid is 84 cm³.
Give **two** different answers for the
dimensions of this cuboid.

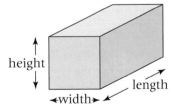

height

length

◄width►

Diagram NOT accurately drawn

271

# Introduction

When a sky diver jumps out of an aircraft, she immediately accelerates towards the earth under the force of gravity. She will continue to accelerate until she reaches terminal velocity (speed) at about 55 m/s. When the skydiver pulls her ripcord she will decelerate before reaching a new constant speed.

## What's the point?

A skydiver won't be drawing graphs or using a calculator before jumping – but she will need to make a mental calculation based on a formula in order to calculate the height at which to jump, and for how long she can freefall safely.

**Check in**

1   Simplify each of these expressions.
   **a** $x + x + x + x$      **b** $m \times m$
   **c** $4 \times p$      **d** $x \times 6$

2   Collect like terms for each expression.
   **a** $2p + q + 3p$      **b** $4x - 2y + x + 3y$
   **c** $m + 2n - 3p + 3n - 2m - p$

3   **a**   Draw a coordinate grid with $x$- and $y$-axes from $-5$ to $5$, using squared paper.
   **b**   Plot these coordinates on your grid.
      **i** $(0, 4)$    **ii** $(2, -5)$    **iii** $(-4, 1)$    **iv** $(-2, -1)$

A1 + 2 →

- Use formulae from mathematics and other subjects
- Write formulae to represent real-life situations
- Simplify formulae by collecting like terms
- Substitute numbers into formulae
- Draw, use and interpret conversion graphs
- Draw, use and interpret distance–time graphs

Nurses and electricians both use formulae in their everyday jobs.

**Rich task**

This L-shape is drawn on a 10 × 10 grid numbered from 1 to 100. It has 5 numbers inside it. We can call it $L_{35}$ because the largest number inside it is 35. The total of the numbers inside $L_{35}$ is 138. Find a connection between the L number and the total of the numbers inside the L shape.

| 1 | 2 | 3 | 4 | 5 | 6 | 7 | 8 | 9 | 10 |
|---|---|---|---|---|---|---|---|---|---|
| 11 | 12 | 13 | 14 | 15 | 16 | 17 | 18 | 19 | 20 |
| 21 | 22 | 23 | 24 | 25 | 26 | 27 | 28 | 29 | 30 |
| 31 | 32 | 33 | 34 | 35 | 36 | 37 | 38 | 39 | 40 |
| 41 | 42 | 43 | 44 | 45 | 46 | 47 | 48 | 49 | 50 |
| 51 | 52 | 53 | 54 | 55 | 56 | 57 | 58 | 59 | 60 |
| 61 | 62 | 63 | 64 | 65 | 66 | 67 | 68 | 69 | 70 |
| 71 | 72 | 73 | 74 | 75 | 76 | 77 | 78 | 79 | 80 |
| 81 | 82 | 83 | 84 | 85 | 86 | 87 | 88 | 89 | 90 |
| 91 | 92 | 93 | 94 | 95 | 96 | 97 | 98 | 99 | 100 |

# Formulae in words

This spread will show you how to:

- Use formulae from mathematics and other subjects expressed initially in words
- Substitute numbers into formulae

Sarah takes a job as a shop assistant.

In her first week she works 10 hours.
In her second week she works 14 hours.

Sarah uses this **formula** to work out her pay

| Pay = number of hours worked × hourly rate |
|---|

First week:     Pay = 10 × £6.20 = £62
Second week: Pay = 14 × £6.20 = £86.80

Wanted
**Shop Assistant**
**Flexible Hours**
Hourly rate
£6.20

- You can **substitute** values into a formula given in words.

Replace the words
with numbers.

Sarah's formula has a one-step calculation.
Formulae can have two or more steps.

The plural of
formula is **formulae**.

**Example**

Jeremy works in telesales.

His hourly rate of pay is £5.80.
He gets a bonus for every sale he makes.

He uses this formula to work out his pay

| Pay = number of hours worked × hourly rate + bonus |
|---|

**a** In week 1 Jeremy works 18 hours and gets £24 bonus.
Work out his pay for the week.

**b** In week 2 Jeremy earns £140 and gets a £24 bonus.
How many hours does he work?

....................................................................

**a** Pay = 18 × £5.80 + £24
         = £104.40 + £24
         = £128.40

**b** Subtract the bonus: 140 − 24 = 116
£116 at £5.80 per hour: 116 ÷ 5.80 = 20
Jeremy works 20 hours.

BIDMAS
**M**ultiplication
before **A**ddition.

**1** Here is part of a hockey league table:

| | Number of matches played | Goals for | Goals against |
|---|---|---|---|
| Woodford | 15 | 32 | 13 |
| Chorton | 15 | 27 | 17 |
| Digley | 14 | 24 | 18 |

To find a team's goal difference you can use the formula:

Goal difference = goals for − goals against

Work out the goal difference for
**a** Woodford          **b** Chorton          **c** Digley

**2** A music shop has a one-day sale.
In the sale, every CD costs £9.99.
The total price for a number of CDs is worked out using the formula:

Total price = number of CDs × £9.99

Work out the total price for
**a** 10 CDs          **b** 4 CDs          **c** 7 CDs

**3** A group of volunteers are painting the village hall.
They use this formula to work out how much paint they need:

Number of cans of paint = area to be painted (square metres) ÷ 15

The area to be painted is 285 square metres.
How many cans of paint do they need?

**4** Mick works in an electrical shop and is paid £5.50 per hour.
He calculates his pay using the formula:

Pay = number of hours worked × hourly rate + commission on goods sold

One week Mick works 16 hours and earns £15 commission.
Work out his pay for the week.

**5** Super Snacks Catering Ltd. calculate their prices using this formula:

Price = cost per head × number of guests

For a buffet, their cost per head is £4.50.
**a** Work out the cost of a Super Snacks buffet for 75 guests.

Tasty Treats Catering Ltd. calculate their prices using this formula:

Price = basic charge £45 + cost per head + number of guests

For a buffet, their basic charge is £45 and their cost per head is £3.
**b** Work out the cost of a Tasty Treats buffet for 75 guests.
**c** Stephen is organising a buffet for 75 people.
   Which company should he choose?

**Writing formulae in words**

This spread will show you how to:

- Use formulae from mathematics and other subjects expressed in words
- Write formulae to represent real-life situations

**Keywords**
Formula

Katie makes and sells bead necklaces and bracelets.

For glass beads, the price is 22p per centimetre.
For a 30 cm glass bead necklace, the price is
$$30 \times 22p = 660p = £6.60.$$

For plastic beads, the price is 18p per centimetre.
For a 20 cm plastic bead bracelet, the price is
$$20 \times 18p = 360p = £3.60.$$

Katie writes a formula to work out the price of any necklace or bracelet:

Price = cost per cm × length in cm

To write a formula, you can try a few examples with numbers first, to see a pattern in the calculations.

**Example**

Here is a sequence of patterns made from sticks.

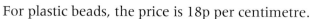

Pattern 1    Pattern 2    Pattern 3

**a** Write the number of blue sticks in
  **i** 1 square    **ii** 2 squares    **iii** 3 squares.
**b** Write a formula connecting the number of blue sticks with the number of squares.
**c** Write the number of red sticks in
  **i** 1 square    **ii** 2 squares    **iii** 3 squares.
**d** Use your answers to **b** and **d** to write a formula connecting the total number of sticks to the number of squares.
  Use your formula to find the number of sticks in 15 squares.

...................................................

**a**  **i** 1 square: 3 blue sticks
   **ii** 2 squares: 6 blue sticks
   **iii** 3 squares: 9 blue sticks
**b** Number of blue sticks = 3 × number of squares
**c**  **i** 1 square: 1 red stick
   **ii** 2 squares: 1 red stick
   **iii** 3 squares: 1 red stick
**d** Total number of sticks = number of blue sticks + number of red sticks
              = 3 × number of squares + 1
**e** In 15 squares
  Total number of sticks = 3 × 15 + 1
              = 45 + 1 = 46

**Functional Maths**

A02

Unit 2

**1** Plain ribbon costs 30p per metre.
Tartan ribbon costs 42p per metre.
  **a** How much does 2 m of plain ribbon cost?
  **b** How much does 3 m of tartan ribbon cost?
  **c** Write a formula connecting:

  | cost of ribbon |  | length of ribbon |

  | price per metre |

**2** Sareeta is making a row of coins in the High Street for charity.
She collects coins from the public and arranges them like this
on the pavement:

  **a** What is the value of each vertical
  column?
  **b** A 10 cm length includes four 10p pieces.
  What is the total value of a 10 cm length?
  **c** What is the total value of a 1 m length?
  Give your answer in pounds (£).
  **d** Copy and complete:
  Total value of row = _____ × length of row in metres

10 cm

**3** Employees in a factory are paid by the hour.
Under 18s and adults are paid different hourly rates.
Write a formula for any employee, connecting:

  | number of hours worked |  | hourly rate |

  | pay |

**4** To fix a car, Tony charges £20 per hour for labour. He also charges
the cost of any parts used.
Write a formula connecting:

  | cost of the repair |  | cost of parts |

  | number of hours worked |

  | hourly rate for labour |

This spread will show you how to:
- Use letter symbols to represent quantities in formulae
- Use the rules of algebra to simplify a formula written in symbols

**Keywords**
Symbol
Variable

- You can use letter **symbols** to represent quantities in a formula.

The formula to work out the area of a rectangle is

$$\boxed{\text{Area} = \text{length} \times \text{width}}$$

length

width [    ]

You can write this using letter symbols as

$$A = l \times w$$
or $$A = lw$$

where $A$ is the area, $l$ is the length and $w$ is the width.

You can use this formula to calculate the area of any rectangle.

When you write a formula, you need to use a different letter symbol for each variable.

In algebra you do not write the × sign.

$l$, $w$ and $A$ are called **variables**. $l$ and $w$ can take **any** values. The value of $A$ is determined by the values of $l$ and $w$.

---

**Example**

Write these formulae using letter symbols.
Explain what each letter symbol represents.

**a** goal difference = goals for − goals against
**b** taxi fare = basic charge + distance in miles × 0.2
**c** speed = distance ÷ time

..................................................

**a** $D = F - A$
  $D$ = goal difference, $F$ = goals for, $A$ = goals against
**b** $F = b + d \times 0.2$
  $F = b + 0.2d$
  $F$ = taxi fare, $b$ = basic charge, $d$ = distance in miles
**c** $s = d \div t$
  $s = \dfrac{d}{t}$
  where $s$ = speed, $d$ = distance and $t$ = time.

Write the number first and leave out the × sign.
$d \times 0.2 = 0.2d$

In algebra, write division $a \div b$ as $\dfrac{a}{b}$

---

**Example**

Recordable CDs come in packs of five.

**a** Write a formula in words for working out the cost of one CD.
**b** Write your formula using letter symbols.

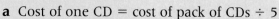

..................................................

**a** Cost of one CD = cost of pack of CDs ÷ 5
**b** $C = \dfrac{p}{5}$
  where $C$ = cost of one CD, $p$ = cost of pack of five CDs.

**1** Write these formulae using letter symbols.
Explain what each letter symbol represents.
  **a** Repair cost = labour cost + parts cost
  **b** Cost of electric cable = price per metre × length in metres
  **c** Monthly cost = annual cost ÷ 12
  **d** Cost of apples = price per kg × number of kg
  **e** Distance in metres = distance in km × 1000
  **f** Length in metres = length in centimetres ÷ 100

**2** A mobile phone bill is calculated by adding the cost of calls
made and the cost of texts sent.
  **a** Write a formula to calculate a mobile phone bill in words.
  **b** Write your formula from part **a** using algebra.
Explain what each letter symbol represents.

**3** In a school hall, chairs are arranged in rows.
There are 15 chairs in each row.
  **a** Write a formula to work out the number of chairs in the hall.
  **b** Write you formula in algebra.
    Explain what each letter symbol represents.
  **c** Use your formula to work out the number of chairs in the hall
    when there are 13 rows of chairs.

**4** Eggs are packed in boxes of six.
  **a** How many boxes are needed for 18 eggs?
  **b** Write a formula in words to work out the
    number of boxes needed for any number of eggs.
  **c** Write your formula using letter symbols.
  **d** Use your formula to work out the number of boxes needed for
    **i** 132 eggs        **ii** 75 eggs.

**5** In a café, each table has four chairs.
Write a formula connecting the number of tables and the
number of chairs. Use *t* for the number of tables and *c* for
the number of chairs.

**6** In a library, each shelf holds the same number of books.
Write a formula, using letter symbols, connecting the
number of books and the number of shelves.
Explain what each letter symbol represents.

**7** Duvets cost £30 each and pillows cost £4.50 each.
Write a formula for the cost of *m* duvets and *n* pillows.

**More formulae**

This spread will show you how to:
- Use the rules of algebra to simplify a formula written in symbols
- Simplify formulae by collecting like terms

You can use the rules of algebra to simplify a formula written in letter symbols.

$$a + a = 2a$$
$$3 \times b = 3b$$
$$m \times m = m^2$$

**Example**

**a** Write a formula in words for the area of a square.
**b** Write your formula using letter symbols. Give your formula in its simplest form.

length

**a** Area = length × length
**b** $A = l \times l$
   $A = l^2$

- You can simplify a formula by collecting **like terms**.

Like terms have exactly the same letter.

**Example**

Write a formula for the perimeter of this rectangle.
Simplify your formula as much as possible.

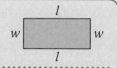

Perimeter $P = l + w + l + w$
         $= l + l + w + w$
   $P = 2l + 2w$

A formula may connect quantities in different units.
You need to explain which units to use for each variable.

**Example**

A plasterer charges a basic fee, plus £2 for each square metre of plaster.
Write a formula to work out the plasterer's charge in pounds.

Charge in pounds =

   basic fee in pounds + £2 × area of plaster in square metres

   $C = F + 2A$      where $C$ = charge in £
                     $F$ = basic fee in £
                     $A$ = area in m$^2$

The rate per square metre (£2) is in pounds – the charge needs to be in pounds so the basic fee needs to be in pounds.

**1** Write a formula for the perimeter of this equilateral triangle. Simplify your formula as much as possible.

**2** Write a formula for the perimeter of this square. Write your formula in its simplest form.

Look back at your answers to questions **1** and **2**.

**3** Write a formula for the perimeter of a polygon with *n* sides, where each side has length *z*.

**4** A taxi charges a basic fee and an extra £1 per mile.
Write a formula for the cost of a taxi ride in pounds.
Explain what each letter represents, and the units to use for each.

**5** To hire a carpet cleaner you pay a fixed amount per day and the cost of the shampoo.
Write a formula for the cost of hiring the carpet cleaner in pounds.
Explain what each letter represents, and the units to use for each.

**6** To make a cover for a square cushion, you need two squares of fabric.
Write a formula for the area of fabric (in square metres) needed for a square cushion of side *k* metres.

**7** The formula to work out average speed is

$$s = \frac{d}{t}$$

where *s* = speed in miles per hour, *d* = distance in miles, *t* = time in hours.
Ben uses the formula to calculate his average speed when he travels 120 km in 2 hours.

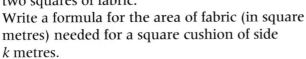

$d = 120\,\text{km}$
$t = 2\,\text{hours}$
$s = \frac{120}{2} = 60$

What are the units for Ben's average speed?

**8** *p* magazines are packed in a bundle.
  **a** Write an expression for the number of magazines in *m* bundles.
  *q* bundles are packed into one box.
  **b** Write a formula to work out the number of magazines in a lorry load of *n* boxes.

This spread will show you how to:
- Substitute numbers into formulae
- Solve simple equations

- In a formula, the letters represent quantities.

For example, in the formula for the perimeter of a rectangle
$$P = 2l + 2w$$
$l$ represents the length and $w$ represents the width of the rectangle.

p.162

If you know the values of $l$ and $w$, you can **substitute** the values of $l$ and $w$ into the formula.
Then you work out the calculation.

This means you write the formula replacing $l$ and $w$ with their number values.

**Example**

Use the formula
$$P = 2l + 2w$$
to work out

a the perimeter of a rectangular field with length 20 m and width 8 m
b the perimeter of a table mat with length 25 cm and width 30.

· · · · · · · · · · · · · · · · · · · · · · · · · · · · · · · · · · · · · · · · · · · · · · · · · · · · · · ·

a $l = 20$ m and $w = 8$ m
$P = 2l + 2w$
$P = 2 \times 20 + 2 \times 8$
$\quad = 40 + 16$
$P = 56$ m

b $l = 25$ cm and $w = 30$ cm
$P = 2l + 2w$
$P = 2 \times 25 + 2 \times 30$
$\quad = 50 + 60$
$\quad = 110$ cm

$2l$ means $2 \times l$ multiplication before addition.
In part **a**, $l$ and $w$ are in metres, so $P$ is also in metres.

You can calculate a quantity from a formula by substituting quantities you know.
Sometimes when you substitute values into a formula you end up with an equation to solve.

In part **b**, $l$ and $w$ are in centimetres, so $P$ is also in centimetres.

**Example**

The formula
$$v = u + at$$
is used in science.
Find the value of $t$ when $v = 16$, $u = 0$ and $a = 4$.

· · · · · · · · · · · · · · · · · · · · · · · · · · · · · · · · · · · · · · · · · · · · · · · · · · · · · · ·

$v = u + at$
$16 = 0 + 4t$       Substitute the values given
$16 = 4t$
$16 \div 4 = 4t \div 4$       Solve by dividing both sides by 4
$4 = t$
The value of $t$ is 4.

**1** Here is a formula
$$p = 5m$$
Work out the value of $p$ when
**a** $m = 4$      **b** $m = 3$      **c** $m = 10$      **d** $m = 2.5$

**2** Here is a formula
$$y = ax$$
Work out the value of $y$ when
**a** $x = 3$ and $a = 2$      **b** $x = 7$ and $a = 4$      **c** $x = 4.5$ and $a = 3$
Work out the value of $x$ when
**d** $y = 10$ and $a = 2$      **e** $y = 25$ and $a = 10$

**3** Use the formula
$$P = 2l + 2w$$
where $P$ is perimeter,
$l$ is length and $w$ is width,
to work out the perimeter
of each rectangle.

**a**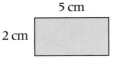

**b**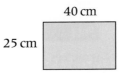

Be careful with
the units.

**c**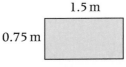

**d**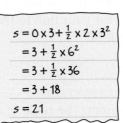

**4** For each formula, work out the value of $y$ when $x = 4$ and $c = 6$.
**a** $y = 3x + c$    **b** $y = 4x - c$      **c** $y = \dfrac{4c}{x}$      **d** $y = cx + 10$
**e** $y = x^2$      **f** $y = c^2$        **g** $y = x^3$      **h** $y = 2x^2 + c$

**5** Use the formula
$$s = \frac{d}{t}$$
where $s$ = average speed, $d$ = distance and $t$ = time
to work out the average speed when

Be careful with
the units.

**a** $d = 150$ miles, $t = 3$ hours      **b** $d = 190$ km, $t = 2$ hours
**c** $d = 500$ metres, $t = 10$ seconds      **d** $d = 60$ km, $t = 0.5$ hours

 **6** Jan uses the formula
$$s = ut + \tfrac{1}{2}at^2$$
to calculate $s$ when $u = 0$, $t = 3$ and $a = 2$
Her working is shown on the right.

Jan's answer is **wrong**.
Work out the correct value of $s$.
Explain which **two** mistakes Jan has made in her working.

$s = 0 \times 3 + \frac{1}{2} \times 2 \times 3^2$
$= 3 + \frac{1}{2} \times 6^2$
$= 3 + \frac{1}{2} \times 36$
$= 3 + 18$
$s = 21$

This spread will show you how to:
- Use and interpret conversion graphs
- Draw conversion graphs

Joe is comparing data on heights of trees.
Some of the data is in feet and some is in metres.
He draws a conversion graph to help him convert
from feet to metres easily.

From a ruler, Joe sees that 1 foot ≈ 30 cm = 0.3 m.

He uses this **conversion** to draw a **table of values**.

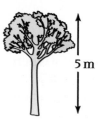

1 foot is
approximately
equal to 30 cm.

| Metres | 0 | 0.3 | 3.0 |
|--------|---|-----|-----|
| Feet   | 0 | 1   | 10  |

0 feet = 0 metres

1 foot = 0.3 m
↓ × 10   ↓ × 10
10 feet = 3 m

He writes the coordinate
pairs from the table.

(0, 0)  (0.3, 1)  (3, 10)

To plot a straight line
you only need to
plot two points.

If you plot three,
you can tell if you
have made a mistake.

3 points correct    1 point must be wrong

Joe plots the points on a coordinate
grid and joins them with a straight line.

- To draw a conversion graph
  - draw up a table of values with at
    least three values
  - plot the points from the table on a
    coordinate grid
  - join the points with a straight line
  - extend your line to the edges of
    the grid.

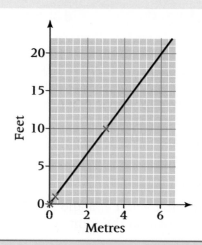

**Example**

Complete the table of values for a conversion graph for UK pounds
to US dollars.

| Pounds     | 0 | 1   | 10 |
|------------|---|-----|----|
| US dollars |   | 1.7 |    |

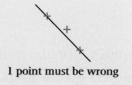

| Pounds     | 0 | 1   | 10 |
|------------|---|-----|----|
| US dollars | 0 | 1.7 | 17 |

1 pound = 1.7 dollars
↓ × 10        ↓ × 10
10 pounds = 17 dollars

0 pounds = 0 dollars

**1 a** Copy and complete this table of values for a grams-to-ounces conversion graph.

| Ounces | 0 | 1 | 10 |
|---|---|---|---|
| Grams | | 28 | |

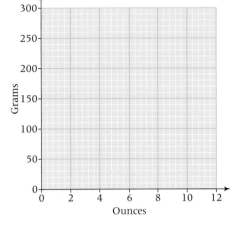

**b** Write three pairs of coordinates for the conversion graph.
Write them in this order
(number of ounces, number of grams)

**c** Copy these axes onto graph paper.

**d** Plot the points on the coordinate grid.
Join the points with a straight line.
Extend your line to the edge of the grid.

**e** Use your graph to convert
  **i** 4 ounces to grams     **ii** 200 g to ounces.

**2 a** Copy and complete this table of values for a kilometres-to-miles conversion graph.

| Miles | | 5 | 10 |
|---|---|---|---|
| Kilometres | 0 | 8 | |

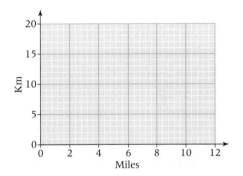

**b** Write three pairs of coordinates for the conversion graph.
Write them in this order
(number of miles, number of kilometres)

**c** Copy these axes onto graph paper.

**d** Plot the points on the coordinate grid and join the points with a straight line. Extend your line to the edge of the grid.

**e** Use your graph to convert
  **i** 6 miles to kilometres     **ii** 5000 metres to miles.

**3 a** Copy and complete this table of values for pounds to New Zealand dollars.

| Pounds | 0 | 1 | 10 |
|---|---|---|---|
| NZ dollars | | 2.4 | |

**b** Write three pairs of coordinates for the conversion graph.

**c** Draw the graph by copying the axes and plotting the points.

**d** Use your graph to convert
  **i** £8 to NZ dollars     **ii** 12 NZ dollars to pounds.

**e** Use your graph to work out which is more
  **i** £6 or 12 NZ dollars?     **ii** 18 NZ dollars or £7?

**Distance–time graphs**

This spread will show you how to:
- Draw, use and interpret distance–time graphs

**Keywords**
Distance
Horizontal
Time
Vertical

You can plot a graph for a journey.

- You plot **time** on the **horizontal** axis and **distance** on the **vertical** axis.

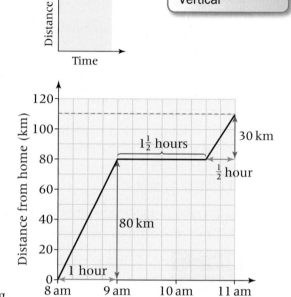

Shaun is a salesman.

- He leaves home at 8 am.
- He drives 80 km to his first meeting. This takes 1 hour.
- He arrives at 9 am.
- His meeting lasts $1\frac{1}{2}$ hours.
- At 10.30 am he sets off again.
- He drives 30 km to his next appointment. This takes $\frac{1}{2}$ hour.
- At 11 am he is 110 km from home.

While Shaun is in a meeting, he is not travelling. His distance from home does not change. The line on the graph is **horizontal**.

- A horizontal line on a distance-time graph shows a break in the journey.

**Example**

The graph shows Tristan's trip to the cinema and back again.

a What time did Tristan leave home?
b How far is the cinema from his home?
c How long was he at the cinema for?
d How long did he spend travelling home?

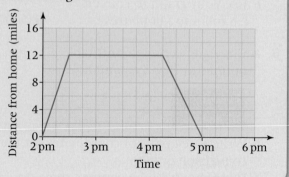

..............................................................

a He left home at 2 pm.
b 12 miles
c From 2.30 to 4.15 = $1\frac{3}{4}$ hours
d $\frac{3}{4}$ hour

On a journey going away from home, your distance from home is increasing. The graph slopes up.

On a journey back home, your distance from home is decreasing. The graph slopes down.

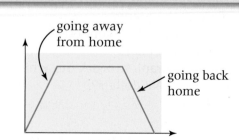

**1** Shona runs a corner shop.
The graph shows her trip from the shop to
the cash and carry.
  **a** What time did she set off to the cash and carry?
  **b** What time did she arrive at the cash and carry?
  **c** How long did the journey to the cash
     and carry take?
  **d** How long did she spend at the cash and carry?
  **e** How long did the journey home from the
     cash and carry take?
  **f** How far is the cash and carry from Shona's shop?
  **g** How many kilometres did she travel in total?

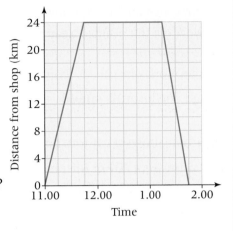

**2** The graph shows a train journey.
  **a** How many stations did the train stop at?
  **b** How far did the train travel before it stopped
     for the first time?
  **c** How far did the train travel in total?
  **d** How long did the whole journey take?
  **e** At one station stop, the train had to wait for
     a connection.
     Which stop do you think this was?
     How long did it wait for?

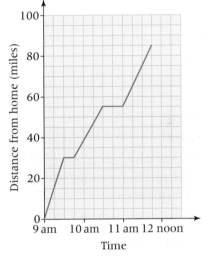

**3** The graph shows Luke's trip to the shop.
  **a** How far is the shop from Luke's home?
  **b** How many minutes did it take Luke to walk to
     the shop?
  **c** How many minutes did he spend in the shop?
  **d** What time did he leave the shop?
  **e** Luke bought a magazine, and read it as he
     walked home.
     It took him 30 minutes to walk home.
     What time did he arrive home?
  **f** Copy the graph onto graph paper.
     Follow these steps to complete the graph for
     Luke's trip.
     **i** Mark the time that Luke arrived home on
        the time (horizontal) axis.
     **ii** Join this point to the graph where he left
        the shop.

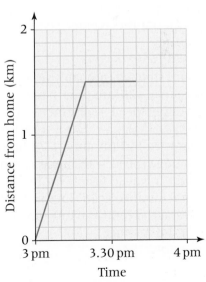

This spread will show you how to:
- Draw, use and interpret distance–time graphs
- Work out the average speed for a journey from a distance–time graph

You can work out speeds from a distance–time graph.

You use the formula **speed** $= \dfrac{\text{distance}}{\text{time}}$

This graph shows a car journey.

The car travels 120 km (distance) in 2 hours (time).

speed $= \dfrac{\text{distance}}{\text{time}} = \dfrac{120\,\text{km}}{2\,\text{hours}} = 60\,\text{km per hour}$

In real life, a car does not travel at exactly the same speed for 2 hours. It may have to slow down for junctions or traffic.

The **average speed** is 60 km per hour.

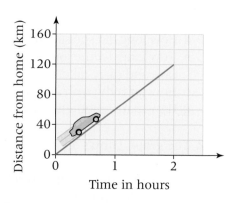

- Average speed $= \dfrac{\text{total distance}}{\text{total time}}$

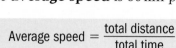

The graph shows a train journey.

**a** Explain what could have happened at 2 pm.
**b** Work out the average speed for the first part of the journey.
**c** Work out the average speed for the second part of the journey.
**d** For which part of the journey was the train travelling fastest?
**e** Work out the average speed for the whole journey.

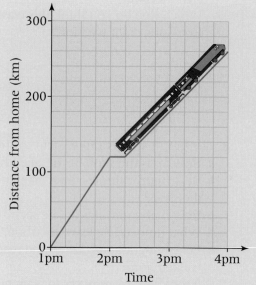

......................................................

**a** Train stopped, probably at a station.
**b** Distance 120 km, time 1 hour.
  Average speed = distance ÷ time
  $= 120 ÷ 1 = 120\,\text{km per hour}$
**c** Distance 140 km, time 1.75 hours.
  Average speed = distance ÷ time $= 140 ÷ 1.75 = 80\,\text{km per hour}$
**d** Train travelled fastest for first part.
**e** Total distance is 260 km, total time is 3 hours.
  Average speed for whole journey
  $= \dfrac{\text{total distance}}{\text{total time}} = \dfrac{260}{3} = 86.6666\,\text{km per hour}$
  $= 87\,\text{km per hour (to the nearest km)}$

For speed in km per hour, the distance must be in km and the time must be in hours.

**1** For each graph work out the average speed.

**a**

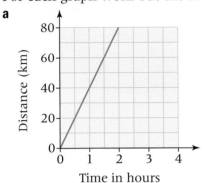

**b**

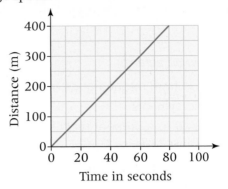

For part **a**, use km per hour.
For part **b**, use metres per second.

**2** For each graph, work out
- the average speed for each part of the journey
- the average speed for the whole journey.

**a**

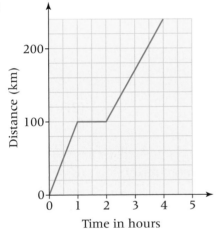

**b**

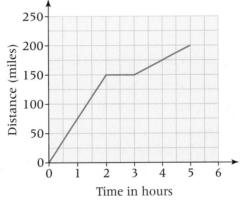

**3** The graph shows Amit's car journey to Wales.

**a** What distance does he travel in the first part of the journey?

**b** What is the time taken for the first part of the journey? Write your answer in hours, as a decimal.

**c** Use your answers from **a** and **b** to work out his average speed in km per hour for the first part of the journey.

**d** Work out Amit's average speed in km per hour for the second part of the journey.

**e** Work out his average speed in km per hour for the whole journey.

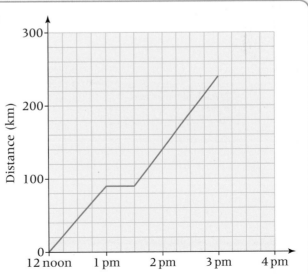

Unit 2

A02 Functional Maths

# Summary

## Check out
You should now be able to:

- Use formulae from mathematics and other subjects expressed in words and symbols
- Write formulae to represent real-life situations
- Substitute numbers into formulae
- Draw and interpret conversion graphs
- Draw and interpret distance-time graphs
- Work out the average speed from a distance-time graph

## Worked exam question
You can use this rule to work out the total charge for hiring a cement mixer.

> Total charge = £30 plus £7 for each hour of hire

On Monday, Sally hired a cement mixer for 4 hours.

**a** Work out Sally's total charge. (2)

On Tuesday, Tom hired a cement mixer.
Tom's total charge was £51.

**b** Work out for how many hours Tom hired the cement mixer. (3)

(Edexcel Limited 2008)

...............................................................................................

**a**
$$30 + 7 \times 4 = 30 + 28$$
$$= £58$$

Show this calculation.

**b**
$$51 - 30 = 21$$
$$21 \div 7 = 3 \text{ hours}$$

Show these calculations. You will get **multi-step** questions like this in your exams.

Check that the answer is correct.
$$30 + 7 \times 3 = 30 + 21$$
$$= 51$$

## Exam questions

**1** $P = 3n$
 $n = 6$
 **a** Work out the value of $P$. (1)
 $Q = 2c + d$
 $c = 3$
 $d = 2$
 **b** Work out the value of $Q$. (2)

(Edexcel Limited 2008)

**2** The Johnson family drove to Legoland.
 They stayed for a few hours.
 Then they drove home.
 Here is the distance-time graph for their complete journey.

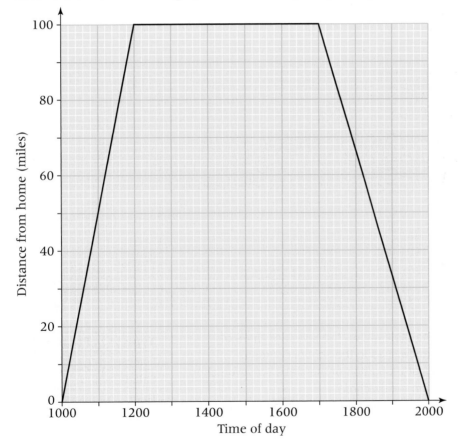

**a** What is the distance from the Johnsons' home to Legoland? (1)
 **b** For how many hours did they stay at Legoland? (1)
 **c** Work out their average speed on their journey home from Legoland.
 Give your answer in miles per hour. (2)

# Introduction

People come in all shapes and sizes, but for hundreds of years artists and scientists have shown great interest in the average proportions of the human body. A classic example is Leonordo da Vinci's Vitruvian Man.

**What's the point?**

By understanding human proportions, artists can understand better how to represent the human form. Also, inventors can design objects that conform to these proportions.

1 The table shows the favourite types of sandwiches in the school canteen.
What proportion of the class surveyed chose ham sandwiches?
Write your answer in its simplest form.

| Type | Frequency |
|------|-----------|
| Cheese | 12 |
| Salad | 8 |
| Ham | 10 |
| **Total** | 30 |

2 10 litres of white paint cost £12.
Work out the cost of 20 litres of paint.

3 Bart works for 4 hours. He gets paid £20.
How much does he get paid per hour?

4 The exchange rate for pounds into Australian dollars is £1 = AU$2.
How many Australian Dollars would you get for £5?

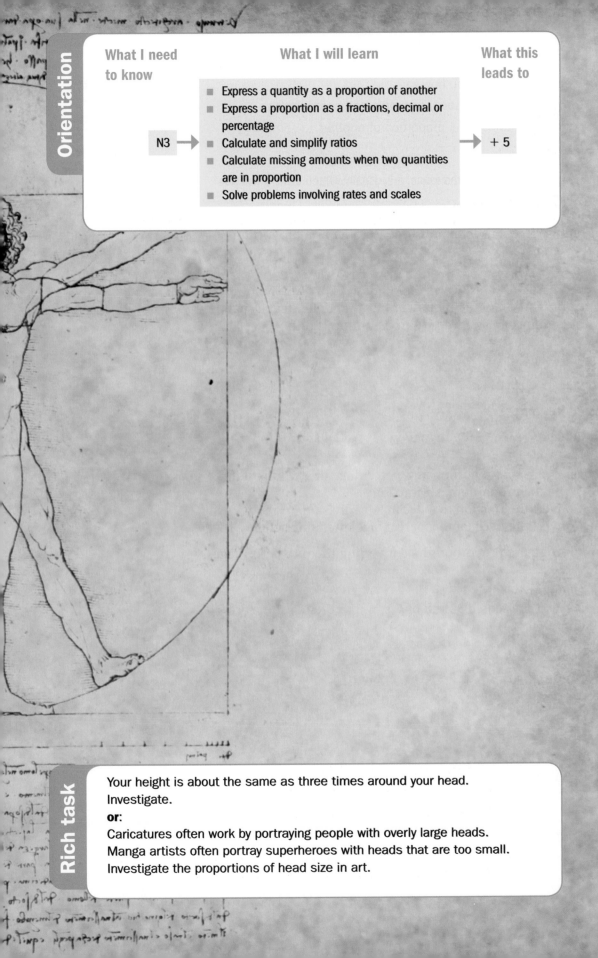

| What I need to know | What I will learn | What this leads to |
|---|---|---|
| N3 → | ■ Express a quantity as a proportion of another<br>■ Express a proportion as a fractions, decimal or percentage<br>■ Calculate and simplify ratios<br>■ Calculate missing amounts when two quantities are in proportion<br>■ Solve problems involving rates and scales | → + 5 |

**Rich task**

Your height is about the same as three times around your head.
Investigate.

**or:**

Caricatures often work by portraying people with overly large heads.
Manga artists often portray superheroes with heads that are too small.
Investigate the proportions of head size in art.

This spread will show you how to:

- Convert between fractions, decimals and percentages
- Express a quantity as a proportion of another

**Keywords**

Decimal
Equivalent
Fraction
Percentage
Proportion

- A **proportion** is a part of the whole. It is usually written using a **fraction** or a **percentage**.

You can use fractions to express one number as a proportion of another number.

> **Example**
>
> Steven has £40 in his wallet. He spends £30 on a new shirt.
> What proportion of the money in his wallet did Steven spend?
> Give your answer as a fraction in its simplest form.
>
> ..........................................................................................................
>
> Steven had £40 (the whole).
>
> Steven spent £30.
>
> Fraction spent $= \frac{£30}{£40} = \frac{30}{40} = \frac{3}{4}$.
>
> So Steven spent $\frac{3}{4}$ of the money in his wallet.

Cancel by the common factor 10.

You can express a proportion as a percentage of a whole in three steps:
1. Write the proportion as a fraction.
2. Convert the fraction to a decimal by division.
3. Convert the decimal to a percentage by multiplying by 100.

You can compare proportions by converting them to percentages.

> **Example**
>
> Skye took two tests.
> In German she scored 35 out of 50, and in French she scored 60 out of 80.
> In which test did she do the best?
>
> ..........................................................................................................
>
> **German**
>
> 35 out of 50 $= \frac{35}{50}$
>
> $= 35 \div 50$
>
> $= 0.7$
>
> $= 70\%$
>
> **French**
>
> 60 out of 80 $= \frac{60}{80}$
>
> $= 60 \div 80$
>
> $= 0.75$
>
> $= 75\%$
>
> Skye did better in French.

**Unit 2**

1 Write the proportion of each of these shapes that is shaded.
Write each of your answers as a fraction in its simplest form.

a 　　b 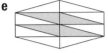　　c

d 　　e 　　f

**A02 Functional Maths**

2 Give your answers to each of these questions as
fractions in their simplest form.
   a There are 20 students in a class. 16 are boys and 4 are girls.
     What proportion of the class are　**i** boys　**ii** girls?
   b Tina has 12 T-shirts and 8 blouses. What proportion of her
     clothes are　**i** T-shirts　**ii** blouses?
   c Joachim earns £600 a week. He pays £180 of his money each
     week in tax. He saves £100 each week. What proportion of
     his weekly wage does Joachim　**i** pay in tax　**ii** save?

3 Write each of your answers as a percentage.
   a In a class there are 40 students. 25 of the students have
     brown hair. What proportion of the class have brown hair?
   b In a survey of 80 people, 35 said they enjoyed school meals.
     What proportion of the people said they enjoyed school meals?
   c At a rugby club there are 38 members. 15 players have been
     picked for the first team. What proportion of the members
     have been picked for the first team?

Give your answer
to one decimal
place.

4 Put these in order of size starting with the smallest first.

Convert them all
to percentages.

   a 72%　　$\frac{3}{4}$　　　0.74
   b 0.29　　31%　　$\frac{3}{10}$
   c 0.8　　83%　　$\frac{7}{8}$　　0.78
   d $\frac{2}{5}$　　0.39　　41%　　$\frac{3}{7}$
   e $\frac{8}{10}$　　$\frac{3}{4}$　　83%　　0.84
   f 28%　　$\frac{3}{11}$　　0.3　　$\frac{7}{24}$

**A02 Functional Maths**

5 Sunita took three tests. In Maths she scored 48 out of 60, in
English she scored 39 out of 50 and in Science she scored 55
out of 70. In which subject did she do
   a the best
   b the worst?

This spread will show you how to:

- Simplify a ratio
- Calculate missing amounts when two quantities are in direct proportion

**Keywords**
Direct proportion
Ratio

You can compare the size of two objects using a **ratio**.

**Example**

Henry the snake is only 30 cm long.
George the snake is 90 cm long.
Express this as a ratio.

The ratio of Henry's length
compared to George's length

= Henry's length : George's length
= 30 cm : 90 cm
= 30 : 90

You can simplify a ratio by dividing both parts of the ratio by the
same number.

**Example**

Express the ratio 30 : 90 in
its simplest form.

$$\div 10 \left( \begin{array}{c} 30 : 90 \\ = 3 : \ 9 \\ = 1 : \ 3 \end{array} \right) \div 10$$
$$\div 3 \qquad\qquad \div 3$$

The ratio 1 : 3
means that 90 is
three times bigger
than 30.

When a ratio cannot be simplified any further it is said to be in its
simplest form.

- When two quantities are in **direct proportion**, if one of the quantities changes,
  the other quantity changes by the same proportion.

You can use direct proportion to solve simple problems.

**Example**

Four pizzas cost £2.60.
Each pizza costs the same.
What is the cost of 12 pizzas?

$$\times 3 \left( \begin{array}{l} 4 \text{ pizzas cost} \qquad £2.60 \\ 12 \text{ pizzas cost } 3 \times £2.60 \\ \qquad\qquad = £7.80 \end{array} \right) \times 3$$

You will not
be assessed
formally on direct
proportion, but
the technique is
very useful for
real-life problems.

**Example**

15 boxes of chocolates cost £22.50.
Each box of chocolates costs
the same.
What is the cost of three boxes
of chocolates?

$$\div 5 \left( \begin{array}{l} 15 \text{ boxes cost} \qquad £22.50 \\ 3 \text{ boxes cost } £22.50 \div 5 \\ \qquad\qquad = £4.50 \end{array} \right) \div 5$$

1 Write each of these ratios in its simplest form.
   **a** 2 : 6      **b** 15 : 5      **c** 6 : 18
   **d** 4 : 28     **e** 5 : 50      **f** 30 : 6
   **g** 24 : 8     **h** 2 : 30      **i** 7 : 56

2 Write the number of blue squares to the number of red squares as a
   ratio in its simplest form for each of these shapes.

   **a**    **b**    **c**

3 How many times bigger than
   **a** 15 is 60     **b** 3 is 21      **c** 12 is 72
   **d** 20 is 180    **e** 18 is 36     **f** 9 is 45
   **g** 16 is 80     **h** 6 is 72      **i** 20 is 240
   **j** 25 is 625    **k** 10 is 15     **l** 36 is 90?

4 Copy and complete this table for working out the cost of
   buying carpet.

   | Area of carpet (m²) | Cost (£) |
   | --- | --- |
   | 6 m² | £39.00 |
   | 12 m² | |
   | 18 m² | |
   | 30 m² | |
   | 60 m² | |
   | 3 m² | |

5 Copy and complete this table for converting inches and centimetres.

   | Inches (in) | Centimetres (cm) |
   | --- | --- |
   | 6 | 15 |
   | 3 | |
   | | 30 |
   | | 45 |
   | 60 | |
   | 1 | |

6 **a** 5 pizzas cost £12.50. What is the cost of 10 pizzas?
   **b** 12 boxes of eggs cost £12. What is the cost of 4 boxes of eggs?
   **c** 3 packets of seeds cost £4.50. What is the cost of 9 packets of seeds?
   **d** 2 boxes of cornflakes cost £4.40. What is the cost of 8 boxes of cornflakes?
   **e** 4 tennis balls cost £1.80. What is the cost of 8 tennis balls?
   **f** 5 chocolate bars cost £3.00. What is the cost of 15 chocolate bars?
   **g** 7 bags of wood cost £27.93. What is the cost of 14 bags of wood?

This spread will show you how to:

- Calculate missing amounts when two quantities are in proportion using the unitary method

**Keywords**
Ratio
Unitary method

You can find the value of one unit of a quantity using division.

**Example**

Three bags of crisps cost 93 pence. What is the price of 1 bag of crisps?

Total cost of crisps = 93 pence
Number of bags of crisps = 3

$$\text{The price of 1 bag of crisps} = \frac{\text{total cost of crisps}}{\text{number of bags of crisps}}$$

= 93 ÷ 3
= 31 pence

- You can use the **unitary method** to solve proportion problems. In this method you find the value of 1 unit of a quantity.

**Example**

Here is a recipe for blackcurrant squash for 5 people.

Blackcurrant squash
(for 5 people)

400 g of blackcurrants
1200 ml of water
100 g sugar
250 ml blackcurrant juice

Work out the number of grams of blackcurrants needed to make squash for 8 people.

The recipe is for 5 people. First find the number of grams of blackcurrants needed for 1 person. Then multiply this by 8.

Number of people    Grams of blackcurrants

÷5 ( 5              400 ) ÷5
      1              80
×8 (                     ) ×8
      8              640

So for 8 people you need 640 g blackcurrants.

**Example**

15 boxes of chocolates cost £22.50. Each box of chocolates costs the same. What is the cost of 2 boxes of chocolates?

Number of boxes      Cost

÷15 ( 15             £22.50 ) ÷15
       1             £1.50
×2 (                        ) ×2
       2             £3.00

So 2 boxes of chocolates will cost £3.

**1** **a** 2 pizzas cost £6.00. What is the cost of 1 pizza?
   **b** 4 sweets cost 20p. What is the cost of 1 sweet?
   **c** 10 packets of seeds cost £18. What is the cost of 1 packet of seeds?
   **d** 4 tennis balls cost £2. What is the cost of 1 tennis ball?
   **e** There are 48 biscuits in 3 packets. How many biscuits are there in 1 packet?
   **f** 10 kg of apples cost £9.00. What is the cost of 1 kg of apples?
   **g** There are 320 MB of memory on 5 identical memory sticks. How much memory is there on each stick?

**2** **a** There are 24 inches in 2 feet. How many inches are there in 1 foot?
   **b** There are 2000 ml in 2 litres. How many ml are there in 1 litre?
   **c** There are 24 pints in 3 gallons. How many pints are there in 1 gallon?
   **d** There are 120 hours in 5 days. How many hours are there in 1 day?

**3** **a** Vince works for 4 hours. He gets paid £24. How much money is he paid each hour?
   **b** On average Barry fits 36 radiators in 3 days. How many radiators does he fit each day?
   **c** An athlete runs 240 metres in 30 seconds. How far does she run in 1 second?
   **d** Rashid drives his car 250 miles and uses 10 gallons of petrol. On average, how far does the car travel on each gallon of petrol?

**4** **a** A recipe for cake uses 400 g of sugar for 5 people. What weight of sugar is needed for
   **i** 1 person    **ii** 8 people    **iii** 12 people
   **iv** 14 people   **v** 30 people?
   **b** A recipe for three bean chilli uses 840 g of beans for 7 people. What weight of beans is needed for
   **i** 3 people    **ii** 6 people    **iii** 17 people
   **iv** 24 people   **v** 100 people?
   **c** Frank works for 8 hours a day and earns £128. He is paid the same amount each hour. How much will he get paid for working
   **i** 40 hours    **ii** 35 hours    **iii** 168 hours
   **iv** 10 days     **v** 3 hours     **vi** $\frac{1}{2}$ hour?

This spread will show you how to:

● Calculate with rates and scales

**Keywords**
Rate
Ratio
Scale

● You can express a **ratio** in the form 1 : *n* using division. This is often called a **scale**.

**Example**

A photograph is 8 cm tall. An enlargement of the same photograph is 24 cm tall. What is the ratio of the height of the original to the height of the enlargement? Express your answer as a scale in the form 1 : *n*.

 8 cm

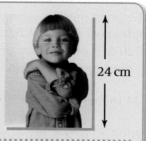 24 cm

Ratio of height of original : height of enlargement
= 8 cm : 24 cm
= 8 : 24

$\dfrac{\text{enlargement height}}{\text{original height}} = \dfrac{24}{8} = 3$

Scale = ratio of height of original : height of enlargement = 1 : 3

You will study more about enlargements in geometry on page 364.

● A rate is a way of comparing two quantities.

You can solve problems involving scales or rates by multiplying or dividing by the scale or rate.

**Example**

**a** Bill goes for a walk. On his map he travels 40 cm. The scale of his map is 1 : 2000. How far does he really walk?

**b** Sarah travels in her car. The petrol consumption of her car is 10 miles per litre. She travels 290 miles. How many litres of petrol does she use?

Petrol consumption is a **rate**.

**a** Map scale

$\overset{\times 2000}{\frown}$

$1 \ = \ 2000$

$\underset{\div 2000}{\smile}$

40 cm = 40 × 2000 cm
= 80 000 cm
= 800 m
Bill walks 800 m.

Multiply by the scale.

**b** Petrol consumption

$\overset{\div 10}{\frown}$

10 miles = 1 litre

$\underset{\times 10}{\smile}$

290 miles = 290 ÷ 10 litres
= 29 litres
Sarah uses 29 litres of petrol.

Divide by the rate.

1 Express each of these ratios as a ratio in the form 1 : *n* (a scale).
   
   **a** 2 : 6　　　**b** 3 : 12　　　**c** 10 : 20　　　**d** 8 : 40
   
   **e** 3 : 6　　　**f** 5 : 15　　　**g** 4 : 20　　　**h** 12 : 36
   
   **i** 30 : 60　　**j** 9 : 45　　　**k** 45 : 90　　　**l** 20 : 120

**A02 Functional Maths**

2 In each of these questions work out the ratio and then express this as a ratio in the form 1 : *n* (a scale).

   **a** A photograph is 6 cm wide. An enlargement of the same photograph is 30 cm wide. What is the ratio of the width of the original to the width of the enlargement?

   **b** On a model plane the wing span is 2 m. In real life the wing span of the plane is 40 m. What is the ratio of the model wing span to the wing span of the real plane?

3 Work out the hourly rate for each of these people.

   **a** Wilf works for 3 hours. He gets paid £21.
      What is his hourly rate of pay?

   **b** Aaron works for 10 hours. He is paid £55.
      What is his hourly rate of pay?

   **c** Gary is a plumber. On average he fits 8 radiator valves every 4 hours. What is his hourly rate of fitting radiator valves?

> Work out how many pounds per hour.

> Work out how many radiators he fits each hour.

4 **a** Kerry has a plan of her house. On her plan she walks 40 cm. The scale of her plan is 1 : 20. How far does she really walk?

   **b** John makes a scale drawing of his kitchen. On his scale drawing the cooker is 6 cm wide. The drawing has a scale of 1 : 10. What is the real width of the cooker?

   **c** Gustav builds a model plane. The scale is 1 : 25. On his model the wing span is 40 cm. What is the real wing span of the plane?

5 Here is the nutritional information for a 500 g serving of pizza. Copy and complete the nutritional amount for every 100 g of pizza.

| Typical values | Amount in a 500 g serving | Amount per 100 g |
|---|---|---|
| Energy | 1500 kcal | |
| Protein | 40 g | |
| Carbohydrate | 150 g | |
| Fat | 44 g | |
| Fibre | 20 g | |

**Unit 2**

# Conversion and exchange rates

This spread will show you how to:

- Calculate conversion and exchange rates
- Solve problems using conversion and exchange rates

- A **conversion rate** is a way of converting between two different units of measurement.

**Example**

May was driving her car on holiday.
The conversion rate for miles into kilometres is 1 mile = 1.6 kilometres.

**a** May travelled 300 miles in the UK. Work out the number of kilometres she travelled in the UK.

**b** May then travelled 1280 km in France. Work out the number of miles she travelled in France.

Conversion rate

$$\overset{\times 1.6}{\underset{\div 1.6}{1 \text{ mile} = 1.6 \text{ kilometres}}}$$

**Examiner's tip**
You are expected to remember the conversion from miles to km in the exam.

**a** 300 miles = 300 × 1.6 kilometres
  = 480 kilometres
May travelled 480 km in the UK.

**b** 1280 kilometres = 1280 ÷ 1.6 miles
  = 800 miles
May travelled 800 miles in France.

- An **exchange rate** is a way of comparing two currencies. It tells you how many units of one currency there are compared to one unit of another currency.

You can solve problems involving currency by multiplying or dividing by the exchange rate.

**Example**

Steve went to Austria.

**a** He changed £500 into euros. The exchange rate was £1 = €1.50. Work out the number of euros Steve got.

**b** He had €120 left at the end of the holiday. He changed them back into pounds. How many pounds did he get?

Exchange rate

$$\overset{\times 1.5}{\underset{\div 1.5}{£1 = €1.50}}$$

**a** £500 = 500 × 1.5
  = €750
Steve got €750.

**b** €120 = 120 ÷ 1.5
  = £80
Steve got £80.

**A02 Functional Maths**

**Unit 2**

**1 a** There are 48 inches in 4 feet. How many inches are there in 1 foot?
**b** There are 30 cl in 3 litres. How many cl are there in 1 litre?
**c** There are 40 pints in 5 gallons.
How many pints are there in 1 gallon?
**d** There are 25 cm in 10 inches.
How many centimetres are there in 1 inch?

**2 a** There are 1800 Rwandan francs in £2.
How many Rwandan francs are there in £1?
**b** There are 50 Canadian dollars in £25.
How many Canadian dollars are there in £1?
**c** There are 16 000 Belarussian rubles in £4.
How many Belarussian rubles are there in £1?
**d** There are 75 Ethiopian birrs in £5.
How many Ethiopian birrs are there in £1?

**3 a** David went to France. He changed £500 into €750.
What was the exchange rate for pounds into euros?
**b** Juan lives in Spain. He changes €400 into AUS$1000.
What was the exchange rate for euros into Australian dollars?
**c** There are approximately 50 squatches in 20 morcks.
What is the conversion rate for changing squatches into morcks?

> **DID YOU KNOW?**
>
>
>
> The Chinese first used paper money in the 7th century. Paper money was not printed in the UK until the 17th century.

**4** Each of these people change amounts of money from pounds into euros. The exchange rate is £1 = €1.60.
Work out the number of euros each person receives.

| Person | Amount (£) | Exchange rate (£1 = €1.60) | Amount (€) |
|---|---|---|---|
| Basil | £10 | £1 = €1.6 | |
| Peter | £200 | £1 = €1.6 | |
| Clark | £80 | £1 = €1.6 | |
| Kathy | £150 | £1 = €1.6 | |
| Harry | £2300 | £1 = €1.6 | |
| Rudolph | £265 | £1 = €1.6 | |

**5** Use the fact that **1 mile = 1.6 km** to answer each of these questions.

> In reality, 1 mile is only **roughly** equal to 1 kilometre.

**a** Convert these distances into kilometres.
 **i** 10 miles **ii** 50 miles **iii** 230 miles **iv** 48 miles
**b** Convert these distances into miles.
 **i** 32 km **ii** 640 km **iii** 512 km **iv** 1352 km

This spread will show you how to:

- Use a ratio to compare the size of two objects
- Use ratio notation and scales and express a ratio in its simplest form
- Divide a quantity in a given ratio

You can compare the size of two objects using a **ratio**.

**Example**

**a** Morrissey the kitten is 25 cm tall. Honey the puppy is 75 cm tall. What is the ratio of Morrissey's height compared to Honey's height? Express your answer in its simplest form.

**b** Loopy the dog is 100 cm (1 m) tall. Compare his height to Honey the puppy. Express your answer in its simplest form.

····································································

**a** Morrissey's height : Honey's height

$$= 25\,\text{cm} : 75\,\text{cm}$$
$$= 25 : 75$$
$$= 1 : 3$$

Honey is 3 times taller than Morrissey.

**b** Honey's height: Loopy's height

$$= 75 : 100$$
$$= 3 : 4$$

Honey's height is $\frac{3}{4}$ of Loopy's height.

Loopy's height is $\frac{4}{3} \times$ Honey's height.

You can simplify a ratio by dividing both parts of the ratio by the same number.

You can divide a quantity in a given ratio.

**Example**

Anne and Parvez share £200 in the ratio 3 : 7. How much money do they each receive?

··············································································

Anne receives 3 parts for every 7 parts that Parvez receives.

Total number of parts = 3 + 7 = 10 parts
Each part = £200 ÷ 10 = £20

Anne will receive 3 parts = 3 × £20 = £60
Parvez will receive 7 parts = 7 × £20 = £140

This topic is extended to dividing with harder ratios on page 416.

£200 is divided into 10 parts.

- A **scale** is a ratio expressed in the form 1 : $n$.

**Example**

A map has a scale of 1 : 20 000. A distance on the map is 4.5 cm. What is this distance in real life?

··············································································

Using the scale you can say
Distance in real life = 20 000 × distance on the map
$$= 20\,000 \times 4.5\,\text{cm}$$
$$= 90\,000\,\text{cm}$$
$$= 900\,\text{m}$$

1 Write each ratio in its simplest form.
   a 4 : 6      b 6 : 10      c 10 : 25      d 16 : 24
   e 25 : 45    f 50 : 60     g 46 : 58      h 200 : 250

2 Express these pairs of objects as ratios in their simplest form.
   a There are 40 boys and 55 girls in Year 11.
     What is the ratio of boys to girls in Year 11?
   b In a batch of apples there are 8 bad apples and 52 good
     apples. What is the ratio of good apples to bad apples?
   c In a crowd of football supporters there are 12 000 men and
     8000 women. What is the ratio of women to men?
   d Hugh has 50p. Gwen has £3. What is the ratio of Hugh's
     money to Gwen's money?

3 Solve these problems.
   a In a batch of concrete the ratio of sand to cement is 5 : 2.
     How much sand is needed to mix with 10 kg of cement?
   b In a school the ratio of teachers to students is 2 : 25. If there
     are 500 students at the school, how many teachers are there?
   c In a metal alloy the ratio of aluminium to zinc is 3 : 4. How
     much aluminium is needed to mix with 20 kg of zinc?
   d For his vegetable beds, Paul mixes some sand and compost
     in the ratio 3 : 4. How much compost does he mix with
     72 kg of sand?

Hint for part **a**:
Amount of sand =
$\frac{5}{2} \times$ amount of
cement

4 Use the scales to work out the measurements in each of these
  calculations.
   a A map has a scale of 1 : 500.
     i What is the distance in real life of a measurement of 10 cm on
       the map?
     ii What is the distance on the map of a measurement of 20 m in
       real life?
   b A map has a scale of 1 : 5000.
     i What is the distance in real life of a measurement of 4 cm on
       the map?
     ii What is the distance on the map of a measurement of 600 m in
       real life?

5 Solve these problems.
   a Divide £30 in the ratio 3 : 7.
   b Divide 250 kg in the ratio 7 : 3.
   c Divide 40 tonnes in the ratio 5 : 3.
   d Divide 135 litres in the ratio 5 : 4.

## Summary

### Check out

This spread will show you how to:

- Express a proportion as a fraction, decimal or percentage
- Solve problems involving proportion
- Use ratio notation and express a ratio in its simplest form
- Divide a quantity in a given ratio

### Worked exam question

Here are the ingredients needed to make 500 ml of custard.

> **Custard**
>
> **makes 500 ml**
>
> 400 ml of milk
> 3 large egg yolks
> 50 g sugar
> 2 teaspoons of cornflour

**a** Work out the amount of sugar needed to make 2000 ml
of custard. (2)

**b** Work out the amount of milk needed to make 750 ml
of custard. (2)

(Edexcel Limited 2005)

**a**

$$50 \text{ g} \times 4 = 200 \text{g}$$

OR

$$50 \text{ g} \div 500 \times 2000 = 200 \text{g}$$

> You should show your calculations whichever method you use.

**b**

$$\frac{1}{2} \text{ of } 400 \text{ ml} = 200 \text{ml}$$

$$400 \text{ ml} + 200 \text{ml} = 600 \text{ml}$$

OR

$$400 \text{ ml} \times 1.5 = 600 \text{ml}$$

OR

$$400 \text{ ml} \div 500 \times 750 = 600 \text{ ml}$$

## Exam questions

A02

**1** The total cost of these 2 pens is 60p.

Work out the total cost of 5 of these pens.
Give your answer in pounds. (3)

(Edexcel Limited 2008)

**2** The table can be used to convert between Euros (€) and Pounds (£).

| Euros (€) | Pounds (£) |
|---|---|
| 0.10 | 0.08 |
| 0.20 | 0.16 |
| 0.50 | 0.40 |
| 1 | 0.80 |
| 2 | 1.60 |
| 3 | 2.40 |
| 4 | 3.20 |

a Change €3 to pounds. (1)
b Change €2.50 to pounds. (2)
c Change £1 to euros. (2)

(Edexcel Limited 2005)

A02

**3** A coin is made from copper and nickel.
84% of its weight is copper.
16% of its weight is nickel.
Find the ratio of the weight of copper to the weight of nickel.
Give your ratio in its simplest form. (2)

(Edexcel Limited 2008)

A02

**4** Sidra and Gemma share £48 in the ratio 5 : 3
Work out how much more money Sidra gets than Gemma gets. (3)

(Edexcel Limited 2008)

# Functional Maths 6: Radio maths

Mathematics can be used to explain how radio transmission works.

FlexiscreenS3000

Radio transmitters use continuous sine waves to send and receive information such as music or speech.

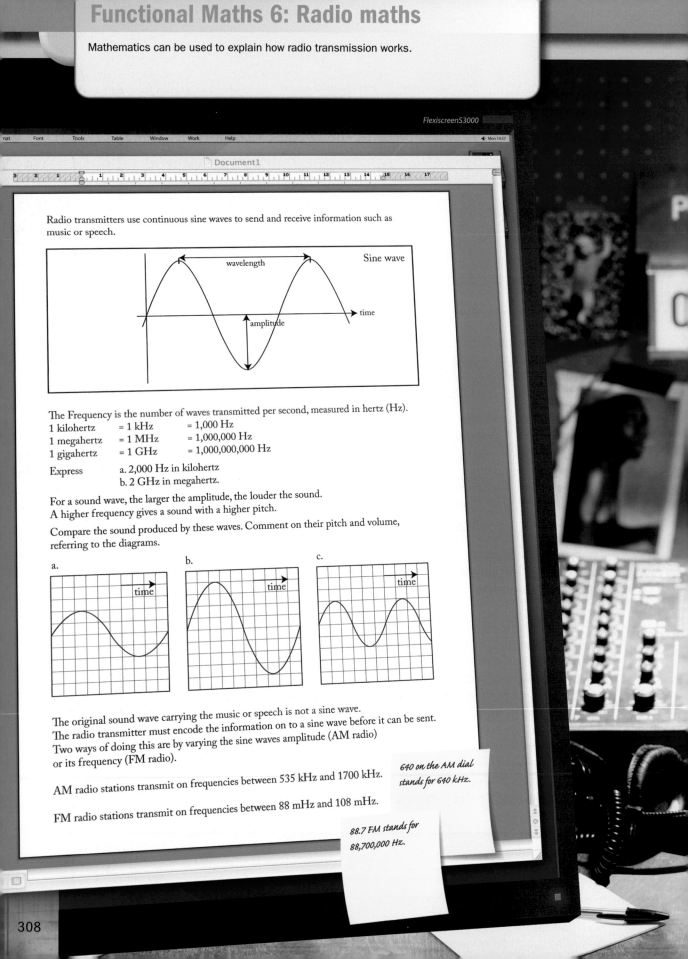

Sine wave

wavelength

time

amplitude

The Frequency is the number of waves transmitted per second, measured in hertz (Hz).

1 kilohertz = 1 kHz = 1,000 Hz
1 megahertz = 1 MHz = 1,000,000 Hz
1 gigahertz = 1 GHz = 1,000,000,000 Hz

Express      a. 2,000 Hz in kilohertz
              b. 2 GHz in megahertz.

For a sound wave, the larger the amplitude, the louder the sound.
A higher frequency gives a sound with a higher pitch.

Compare the sound produced by these waves. Comment on their pitch and volume, referring to the diagrams.

a.

time

b.

time

c.

time

The original sound wave carrying the music or speech is not a sine wave.
The radio transmitter must encode the information on to a sine wave before it can be sent.
Two ways of doing this are by varying the sine waves amplitude (AM radio) or its frequency (FM radio).

AM radio stations transmit on frequencies between 535 kHz and 1700 kHz.

*640 on the AM dial stands for 640 kHz.*

FM radio stations transmit on frequencies between 88 mHz and 108 mHz.

*88.7 FM stands for 88,700,000 Hz.*

Wave speed (m/s) = frequency (Hz) × wavelength (m)

Maths FM transmits on the frequency 100.0 FM with a wavelength of 3m.
a. What is the frequency of the radio station in
   i. mHz          ii. Hz?
b. Use the formula at the top of the page to calculate the speed of the waves that are being transmitted.
c. Rearrange the formula to give an equation for frequency in terms of wave speed and wavelength.
d. Use your answers from parts b and c to calculate the frequency (in Hz) of a radio station that transmits waves of wavelength 2.80m.
e. Is the radio station in part d on the AM or FM dial?
   Justify your answer and write down its AM or FM frequency.

**Mathematics can also be applied to plan and produce radio programmes.**

DJ Cool uses this wheel diagram to plan his hour-long show:

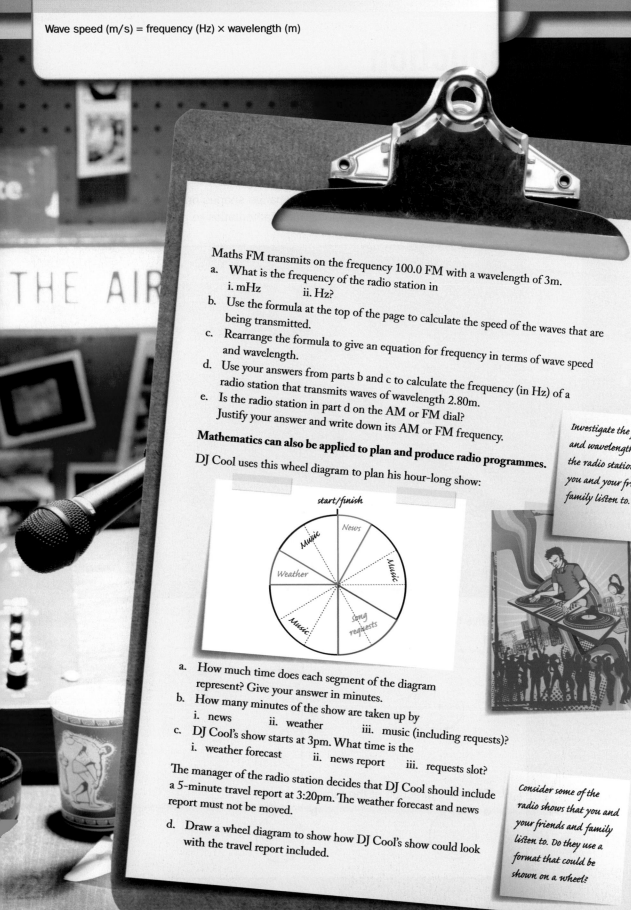

a. How much time does each segment of the diagram represent? Give your answer in minutes.
b. How many minutes of the show are taken up by
   i. news          ii. weather          iii. music (including requests)?
c. DJ Cool's show starts at 3pm. What time is the
   i. weather forecast          ii. news report          iii. requests slot?

The manager of the radio station decides that DJ Cool should include a 5-minute travel report at 3:20pm. The weather forecast and news report must not be moved.

d. Draw a wheel diagram to show how DJ Cool's show could look with the travel report included.

Investigate the frequency and wavelengths used by the radio stations that you and your friends and family listen to.

Consider some of the radio shows that you and your friends and family listen to. Do they use a format that could be shown on a wheel?

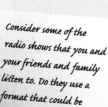

# Transformations

# Introduction

Transformations change points and shapes by moving them from one place to another. When you play a computer game your character is able to move around the screen because of mathematical transformations. Combinations of these transformations, often taking place in 3-D worlds, allow the characters to move in many different ways.

## What's the point?

Mathematicians use transformations not just to change shapes but also to change graphs and statistics. This helps them match the mathematics to real life situations.

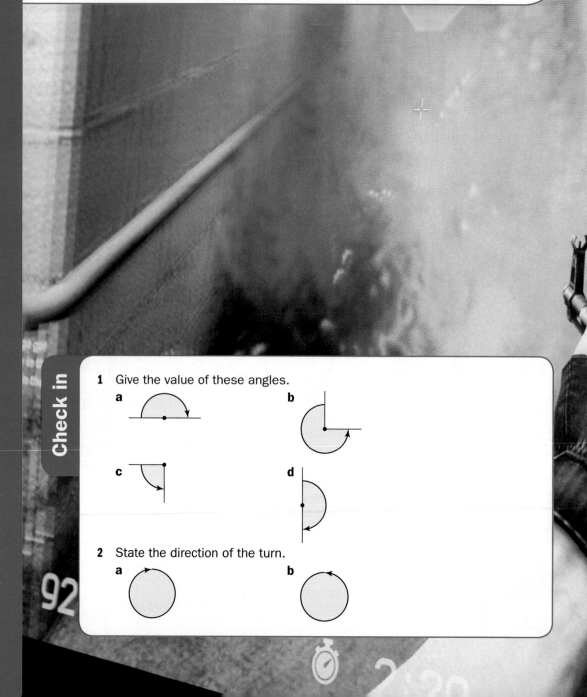

**Check in**

1 Give the value of these angles.

a          b

c          d

2 State the direction of the turn.

a          b

| What I need to know | What I will learn | What this leads to |
|---|---|---|

Key stage 3 →
- Plot and locate coordinates
- Transform shapes by reflection, rotation and translation

→ G5

G3 →
- Recognise reflection symmetry of 2-D shapes
- Recognise rotation symmetry of 2-D shapes

**Rich task**

A shape (object) is reflected in the line $y = x$.

To find the new coordinates of each vertex of the shape (image), simply swap the $x$ and $y$ coordinates around.

Investigate rules for finding the image coordinates for this and other transformations.

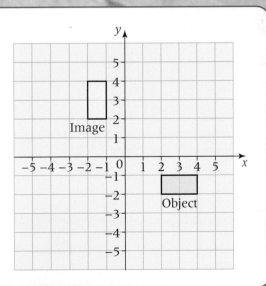

**Reflections 1**

This spread will show you how to:
- Recognise and visualise reflections
- Understand that reflections are specified by a mirror line
- Transform triangles and other shapes by reflection

A **transformation** can change the size and position of a shape.

p.358

- A **reflection** flips the shape over.

When you look at yourself in a mirror, you are seeing a reflection.

You specify a **mirror line** or reflection line to reflect the object.
To find the position of the reflection line you choose corresponding points on the object and the image.

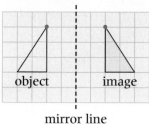

object     image

mirror line

Each dot is 2 units from the mirror line.

- The image is the same distance from the mirror line as the object.

**Example**

Draw the mirror line so that shape B is a reflection of shape A.

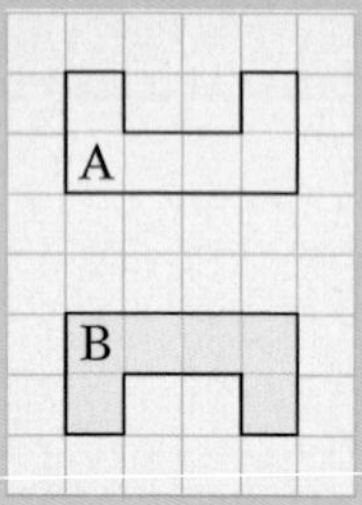

A

B

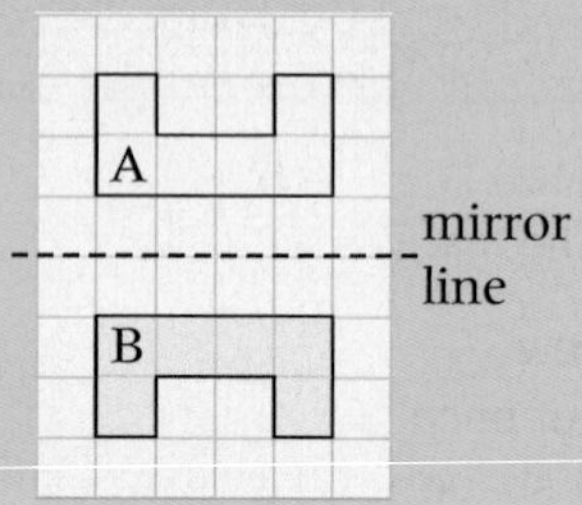

A

------- mirror line

B

You can rotate the page to make the mirror line vertical.

**Example**

Draw the reflection of the shape using the mirror line.

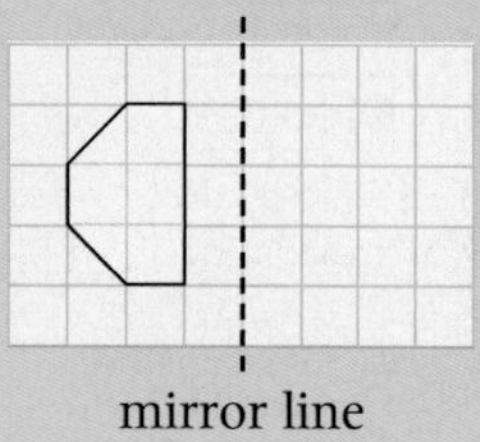

mirror line

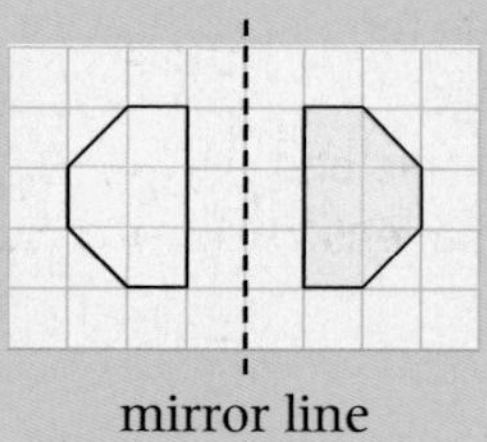

mirror line

**1** Copy the diagrams and draw the mirror lines.

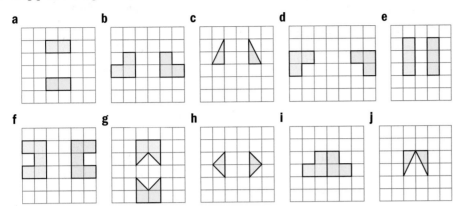

**2** Copy and complete each diagram to show the reflection of the shape in the mirror line.

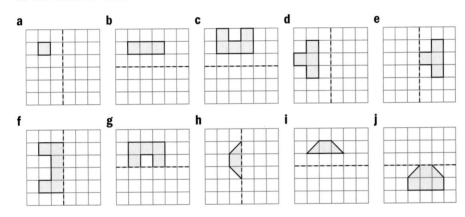

**3** Copy the diagrams.
Reflect the shapes in both mirror lines to create a pattern.

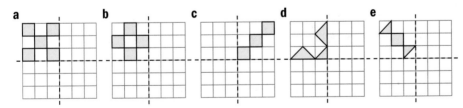

**4** Give the equation of the mirror line for each reflection.

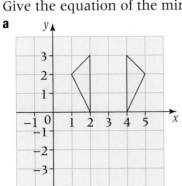
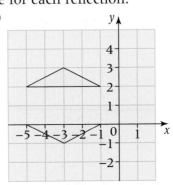

This spread will show you how to:
- Recognise and visualise rotations
- Understand that rotations are specified by a centre of rotation and an angle and direction of turn

**Keywords**
Anticlockwise
Centre of rotation
Clockwise
Degrees (°)
Rotation
Turn

- A **rotation** turns a shape.

To describe a rotation you give
- the **centre of rotation** – the point about which it **turns**
- the angle or measure of turn
- the direction of turn – either **clockwise** or **anticlockwise**.

p.360

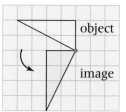

Clockwise

The dot is the centre of rotation.
The turn is 90° or $\frac{1}{4}$ of a turn.
The direction is anticlockwise.

The dot is the centre of rotation.
The turn is 180° or $\frac{1}{2}$ a turn.
The direction is either clockwise or anticlockwise.

Anticlockwise

**Example**

**a** Draw the position of the green triangle after a rotation of 90° clockwise about the dot (●).

**b** What rotation would return the triangle to its starting position?

**a**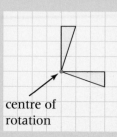

centre of rotation

**b** Rotation of 90° anticlockwise about the dot (●).

Use tracing paper to find the position of the blue triangle.

**1** State the angle and direction of turn for each of these rotations (green shape to blue shape).

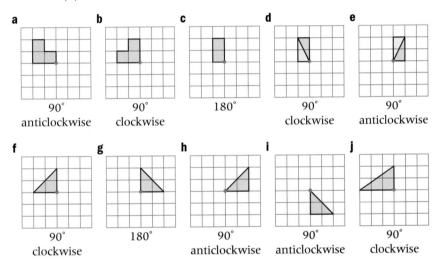

**2** Copy these shapes onto square grid paper.
Rotate the shapes through the given angle and direction about the dot (•).

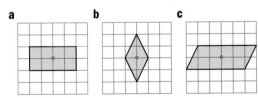

**3** Copy the shapes onto square grid paper.

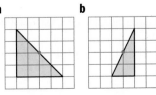

Rotate each shape through 180° about the dot (•).
Describe your results.

**4** Copy the triangles onto square grid paper.
Rotate each triangle through 180° about the dot (•).
Give the mathematical name of the new shape you have created.

This spread will show you how to:

- Recognise and visualise translations
- Understand that translations are specified by a distance and direction

p.362

**Keywords**
Left
Right
Slide
Translation

- A **translation** is a **sliding** movement.

To describe a translation you give:
- the distance moved **right** or **left**, then
- the distance moved **up** or **down**.

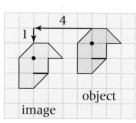

Translate the object 4 units left and 1 unit down.

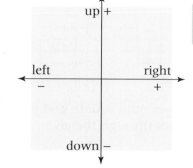

Right and up are positive directions.

You choose corresponding points on the object and image to work out the translation.

**Example**

Which triangles are translations of the black triangle?

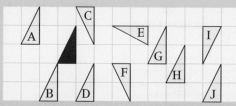

........................................................................................

A, B, D, G, H, J because they are all in the same orientation.

Same orientation means the same way up.

**Example**

**a** Give the coordinates of the point marked by a dot (•) in triangle A.

**b** Describe the transformation that moves triangle A to triangle B.

**c** Give the coordinates of the point in triangle B that corresponds to the dot (•) in triangle A.

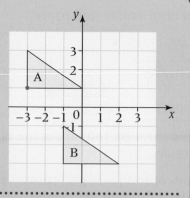

........................................................................................

**a** (−3, 1)
**b** Translation, 2 units right and 4 units down.
**c** (−1, −3)

1 Which shapes are translations of the green shape?

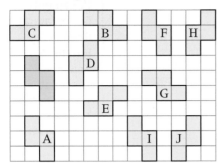

Unit 3

2 Describe these translations.

| | |
|---|---|
| **a** E to D | **b** E to C |
| **c** A to B | **d** A to C |
| **e** B to D | **f** C to A |
| **g** C to E | **h** B to A |
| **i** E to A | **j** A to E |

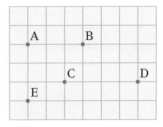

3 **a** Give the coordinates of point A.
   **b** Describe the transformation that moves the green shape to the blue shape.
   **c** Give the coordinates of the point in the blue shape that corresponds to point A in the green shape.

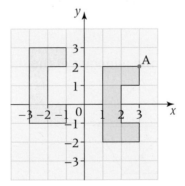

4 Describe these translations.

| | |
|---|---|
| **a** D to B | **b** A to B |
| **c** A to C | **d** D to E |
| **e** B to E | **f** B to C |
| **g** E to D | **h** E to A |
| **i** B to D | **j** B to A |
| **k** E to B | **l** A to D |
| **m** C to B | **n** E to C |
| **o** C to A | **p** A to E |
| **q** C to D | **r** D to C |
| **s** C to E | **t** D to A |

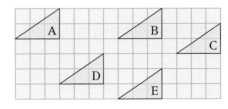

This spread will show you how to:
- Understand congruence and recognise congruent shapes
- Understand and create tessellations

**Keywords**
Congruent
Quadrilateral
Regular
Rotate
Scalene
Tessellation
Translate
Triangle

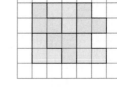

- **Congruent** shapes are exactly the same shape and size

You can make patterns with an L shape like this.

The L shapes fit together so that there are no gaps or overlaps. The L shape tessellates.

- A **tessellation** is a tiling pattern with no gaps.

 p.398

**Example**

Draw at least five more trapezium shapes on the grid to show how the shape tessellates.

   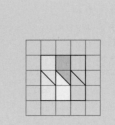

You are allowed to **rotate** or **translate** the shape.

- Any **triangle** tessellates.

Rotate the triangle about the midpoint of the sides.

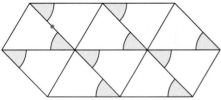

Even a **scalene** triangle tessellates.

- Any **quadrilateral** tessellates.

Rotate the quadrilateral about the midpoint of the sides.

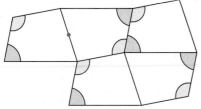

This means that all the special quadrilaterals also tessellate.

Only three regular shapes tessellate.

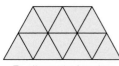      

Equilateral triangles        Squares        Hexagons

A **regular** shape has equal sides and equal angles.

1 Copy these shapes onto square grid paper.
Show how each shape tessellates, using rotations and translations.

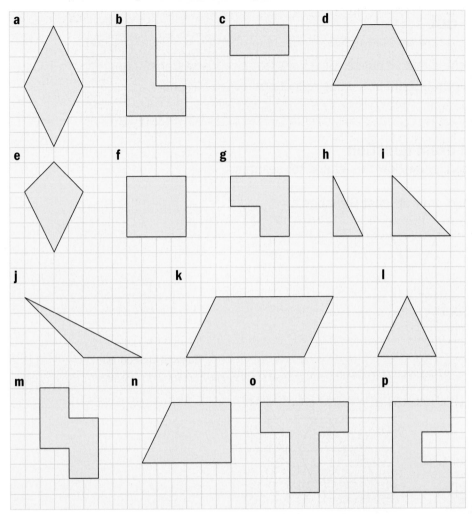

Unit 3

**2** Draw a 4 by 2 rectangle on square grid paper.

Remove the triangle and translate it to the new position as shown.

Remove a second triangle and translate it to the new position as shown.

Cut out the shape and tessellate it using translations.

AO3 Problem

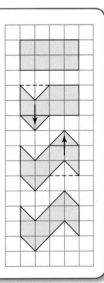

## Summary

### Check out
You should now be able to:

- Recognise and visualise reflections, rotations and translations
- Transform 2-D shapes using reflections, rotations and translations

### Worked exam question
On the grid, show how this shape tessellates.

You should draw at least 6 shapes.

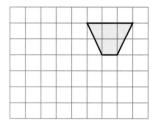

(2)
(Edexcel Limited 2007)

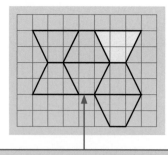

You must draw at least 6 more shapes, with no gaps between them.

# Exam questions

**1**

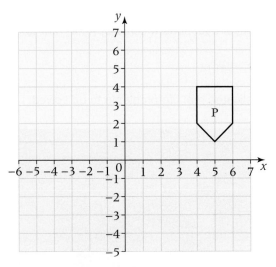

  **a** Reflect Shape **P** in the *y* axis.
     Label your new shape **Q**.                                        (2)
  **b** Translate Shape **P** by 6 squares left and 2 squares up.
     Label your new shape **R**.                                        (2)

**2**

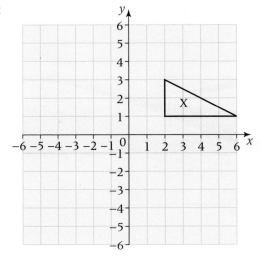

Triangle **X** has been drawn on the grid.
  **a** Reflect triangle **X** in the *y*-axis.
     Label the new triangle **A**.                                    (1)
  **b** Rotate triangle **X** by a half turn, centre O.
     Label the new triangle **B**.                                    (2)

# Introduction

Formula 1 engineers use complex mathematical equations to predict the effect on performance of their cars when they make technical modifications. Mathematicians turn problems in the real world into mathematical equations which they know how to solve.

## What's the point?
Learning how to solve equations allows complicated real life problems to be solved.

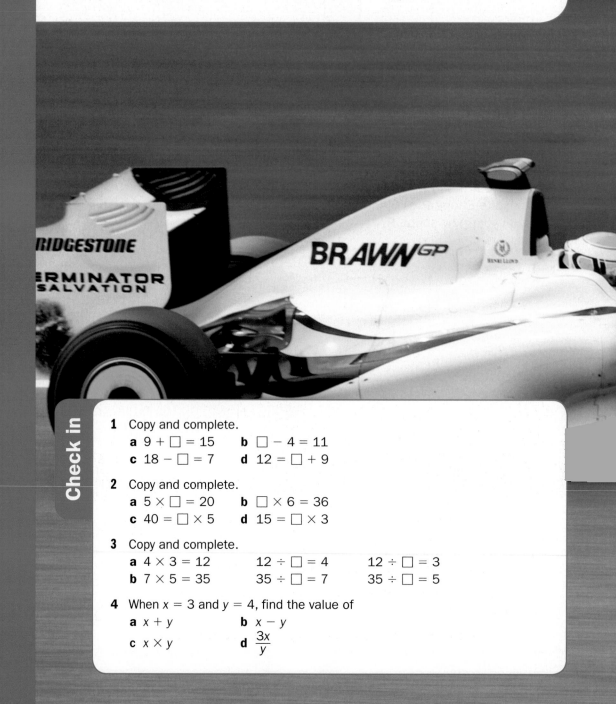

**Check in**

1 Copy and complete.
  **a** $9 + \square = 15$  **b** $\square - 4 = 11$
  **c** $18 - \square = 7$  **d** $12 = \square + 9$

2 Copy and complete.
  **a** $5 \times \square = 20$  **b** $\square \times 6 = 36$
  **c** $40 = \square \times 5$  **d** $15 = \square \times 3$

3 Copy and complete.
  **a** $4 \times 3 = 12$      $12 \div \square = 4$      $12 \div \square = 3$
  **b** $7 \times 5 = 35$      $35 \div \square = 7$      $35 \div \square = 5$

4 When $x = 3$ and $y = 4$, find the value of
  **a** $x + y$         **b** $x - y$
  **c** $x \times y$       **d** $\dfrac{3x}{y}$

| What I need to know | What I will learn | What this leads to |

A1 →
N2 →

■ Understand and use inverse operations
■ Solve equations with whole number coefficients
■ Write equations for word problems
■ Check a solution by substitution

→ A6

**Rich task**

This grid of numbers uses each of the numbers from 1 to 9.

Every row, column, and diagonal adds up to 15. It is called a magic square.

| 4 | 9 | 2 |
| 3 | 5 | 7 |
| 8 | 1 | 6 |

Using the numbers from 1 to 9 invent your own magic square.

**Function machines 2**

This spread will show you how to:
- Add subtract, multiply and divide any number
- Use inverse operations

- You can write **calculations** using function machines.

A function machine has

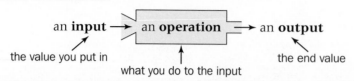

**Example**

Work out the outputs for these function machines.

a  2 → +5 →

b  12 → ÷3 →

a  2 → +5 → 7

b  12 → ÷3 → 4

- Every operation has an **inverse** operation.
  The inverse operation 'undoes' the operation.

- You can work backwards through a function
  machine using inverse operations.

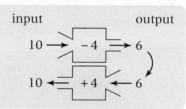

The inverse of 'add' is 'subtract'. The inverse of 'multiply' is 'divide'.

**Example**

Draw the inverse machines for these function machines.

a  3 → ×2 → 6     b  5 → +13 → 18     c  10 → ÷2 → 5

a  3 ← ÷2 ← 6     b  5 ← −13 ← 18     c  10 ← ×2 ← 5

- You can use function machines to solve 'think of a number' problems.

**Example**

I think of a number and
multiply it by 4.
My answer is 20.

What is my number?

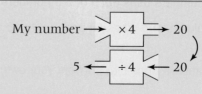

My number is 5.

324

**1** Work out the outputs for these function machines.

**a** 5 → ×4 →

**b** 8 → ×2 →

**c** 9 → +7 →

**d** 15 → −8 →

**e** 20 → ×3 →

**f** 18 → ÷3 →

**g** 14 → −6 →

**h** 19 → +12 →

**i** 27 → ÷9 →

**2** Copy each machine and write the outputs for the inputs given.

**a** input        output

8    ___
5    ___
3 → +7 → ___
0    ___
−1    ___

**b** input        output

4    ___
2    ___
1 → ×3 → ___
0    ___
−1    ___

**3** Copy and complete these function machines.

**a** 7 → ×? → 21

**b** 5 → ×? → 35

**c** 4 → ×? → 24

**d** 7 → −? → 2

**e** 6 → +? → 11

**f** 4 → +? → 17

**g** 12 → ÷? → 4

**h** 24 → ÷? → 6

**i** 12 → ×? → 60

**4** Write the inverse operation for each of these operations.

**a** ×2      **b** +4      **c** −3      **d** ÷6
**e** −7      **f** ×5      **g** ÷2      **h** +11

**5** Copy and complete the tables for these function machines.

**a** → ÷2 →

| Input | Output |
|-------|--------|
| 6 | |
| 10 | |
| 24 | |
| | 15 |

**b** → −4 →

| Input | Output |
|-------|--------|
| 5 | |
| 13 | |
| | 11 |
| 20 | |

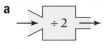

**6** Use function machines to solve these 'think of a number problems':

**a** I think of a number and add 12.
    The answer is 25. What number did I think of?

**b** I think of a number and divide it by 4.
    The answer is 5. What number did I think of?

# Solving equations

This spread will show you how to:

- Use letters to represent numbers in algebra
- Understand and use the vocabulary of algebra
- Set up and solve simple equations

**Keywords**
Equation
Expression
Solution
Solve

- An **expression** is made up of terms, containing letter symbols and numbers.

$3x + 2 \quad x - 4 \quad 2x \quad 4x + 1$
are all expressions.

- An **equation** includes letter and number terms and an equals sign.

$x + 2 = 5$ is an equation.

In an equation, the letter symbol represents one number value. You can work out the value of a letter in an equation using number facts.

For example, $x + 2 = 5$ and $3 + 2 = 5$. So $x = 3$ is the **solution** of the equation. Working out the value of the unknown is called solving the equation.

- You can use function machines to **solve** equations.

**Example**

Solve these equations.

**a** $x + 5 = 12$        **b** $y - 6 = 10$

**a**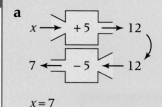

$x = 7$

**b**

$y = 16$

Draw the function machine for the equation.

Draw the inverse function machine.

- You can write an equation for a word problem and solve it.

**Example**

Tony had some pairs of socks.
For Christmas he got 4 more pairs of socks.
He counted all his socks and found he had 11 pairs altogether.
How many pairs of socks did he have to start with?

$n$ pairs + 4 pairs = 11 pairs     $n + 4 = 11$

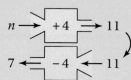

$n = 7$
Tony had 7 pairs of socks to start with.

Use the letter $n$ to represent the number of pairs of socks Tony started with.

Write an equation to represent the problem.

Use function machines to solve the equation.

**1** Use number facts to work out the missing numbers in these calculations.

   **a** $6 + \square = 10$      **b** $2 + \square = 7$      **c** $5 + \square = 8$

   **d** $3 + \square = 12$     **e** $6 + \square = 18$    **f** $7 = \square + 3$

   **g** $9 = 4 + \square$      **h** $14 = \square + 6$    **i** $19 = 13 + \square$

**2** Use number facts to work out the missing numbers in these calculations.

   **a** $8 - \square = 2$      **b** $12 - \square = 6$    **c** $10 - \square = 3$

   **d** $13 - \square = 2$     **e** $15 - \square = 8$    **f** $8 = 10 - \square$

   **g** $5 = \square - 10$     **h** $7 = \square - 5$     **i** $20 = \square - 6$

**3** Copy and complete these function machines to solve these equations.

   **a** $x + 3 = 6$         **b** $a - 8 = 5$         **c** $b + 4 = 3$

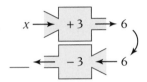 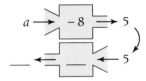 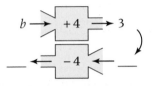

**4** For each function machine, draw the inverse function machine and find the value of the unknown.

   **a** $a \rightarrow \boxed{+8} \rightarrow 15$    **b** $b \rightarrow \boxed{+6} \rightarrow 23$    **c** $c \rightarrow \boxed{+7} \rightarrow 12$

   **d** $d \rightarrow \boxed{+11} \rightarrow 20$   **e** $e \rightarrow \boxed{+15} \rightarrow 48$   **f** $f \rightarrow \boxed{+13} \rightarrow 21$

   **g** $g \rightarrow \boxed{+27} \rightarrow 40$   **h** $h \rightarrow \boxed{+40} \rightarrow 100$   **i** $i \rightarrow \boxed{-5} \rightarrow 3$

   **j** $j \rightarrow \boxed{-8} \rightarrow 4$    **k** $k \rightarrow \boxed{-3} \rightarrow 9$    **l** $l \rightarrow \boxed{-13} \rightarrow 9$

   **m** $m \rightarrow \boxed{-25} \rightarrow 6$   **n** $n \rightarrow \boxed{-10} \rightarrow 90$   **o** $o \rightarrow \boxed{-15} \rightarrow 15$

**5** Use function machines to solve these equations.

   **a** $x + 3 = 7$      **b** $y + 6 = 10$     **c** $n - 1 = 6$

   **d** $m + 9 = 14$     **e** $r - 3 = 10$     **f** $9 + v = 0$

   **g** $y - 2 = 7$      **h** $x - 4 = 3$      **i** $z - 6 = 2$

   **j** $m - 5 = 9$      **k** $z + 2 = 15$     **l** $p - 7 = 9$

   **m** $q - 4 = 8$      **n** $n + 4 = 11$     **o** $a + 16 = 27$

Unit 3

This spread will show you how to:
- Solve equations with whole numbers, including those involving multiplication and division

**Keywords**
Equation

- You can use function machines to solve equations involving multiplication and division.

The equation $3x = 12$ means
'$x$ multiplied by $3 = 12$'.

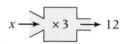

$x \longrightarrow \boxed{\times 3} \longrightarrow 12$

Solve the equation using
an inverse machine.

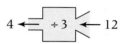

$4 \longleftarrow \boxed{\div 3} \longleftarrow 12$

$x = 4$

The equation $\dfrac{y}{4} = 6$ means
'$y$ divided by $4 = 6$'.

$y \longrightarrow \boxed{\div 4} \longrightarrow 6$

Solve the equation using
an inverse machine.

$24 \longleftarrow \boxed{\times 4} \longleftarrow 6$

$y = 24$

---

**Example**

Solve these equations using number facts.

**a** $3s = 12$

**b** $\dfrac{t}{2} = 5$

---

**a** $3 \times s = 12$ and $3 \times 4 = 12$
So $s = 4$

**b** $t \div 2 = 5$ and $10 \div 2 = 5$
So $t = 10$

---

**Example**

Solve these equations using function machines.

**a** $6m = 30$

**b** $\dfrac{n}{7} = 3$

---

**a**

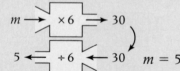

$m \longrightarrow \boxed{\times 6} \longrightarrow 30$

$5 \longleftarrow \boxed{\div 6} \longleftarrow 30$ $\quad m = 5$

**b**

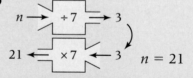

$n \longrightarrow \boxed{\div 7} \longrightarrow 3$

$21 \longleftarrow \boxed{\times 7} \longleftarrow 3$ $\quad n = 21$

---

**Example**

A pizza is cut into $m$ slices. Ali and Kate share the pizza equally
between them.

**a** Write an expression for the number of slices they have each.

**b** Ali and Kate have 6 slices each. Use your answer to part a to write
an equation.

**c** Solve your equation to find the value of $m$.

---

**a** $\dfrac{m}{2}$

**b** $\dfrac{m}{2} = 6$

**c**

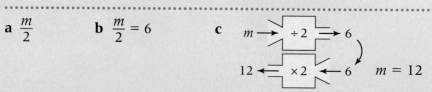

$m \longrightarrow \boxed{\div 2} \longrightarrow 6$

$12 \longleftarrow \boxed{\times 2} \longleftarrow 6$ $\quad m = 12$

$\dfrac{m}{2}$ means '$m$
divided by 2'.

1 Use number facts to find the missing numbers.

   **a** $3 \times \square = 15$    **b** $4 \times \square = 20$    **c** $5 \times \square = 25$    **d** $2 \times \square = 16$

   **e** $8 \times \square = 32$    **f** $4 \times \square = 24$    **g** $6 \times \square = 30$    **h** $\square \times 3 = 12$

   **i** $\square \times 5 = 30$    **j** $\square \times 8 = 24$    **k** $\square \div 2 = 4$    **l** $\square \div 5 = 5$

   **m** $\square \div 3 = 5$    **n** $\square \div 4 = 6$    **o** $6 \times \square = 18$    **p** $18 \div \square = 6$

   **q** $20 \div \square = 5$    **r** $\square \times 7 = 35$    **s** $\square \div 7 = 7$    **t** $\square \times \square = 36$

2 Copy and complete these function machines and their inverses to
find the value of the unknowns.

**a** 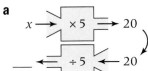    **b** 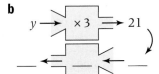    **c**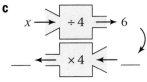

**A03 Problem**

3 Match each function machine in set A with an equation in set B.

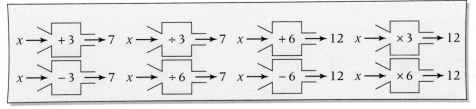

**Set A**

**Set B**

$3x=12$      $6x=12$      $x-6=12$      $x+6=12$

$\frac{x}{3}=7$      $x+3=7$      $x-3=7$      $\frac{x}{6}=7$

4 Draw function machines for these equations and use inverse
machines to solve them.

   **a** $4x = 20$    **b** $3y = 15$    **c** $5z = 30$    **d** $2r = 12$

   **e** $4s = 28$    **f** $3t = 18$    **g** $2v = 22$    **h** $2w = 18$

   **i** $\frac{x}{3} = 5$    **j** $\frac{y}{2} = 24$    **k** $\frac{z}{5} = 5$    **l** $\frac{r}{3} = 8$

**A03 Problem**

5 Maisie has 5 boxes of pencils.
     Each box contains $n$ pencils.

   **a** Write an expression for the number of pencils Maisie has.

   **b** Maisie counts the pencils. She has 40 in total.
      Use your expression from part **a** to write an equation.

   **c** Solve your equation to find $n$, the number of pencils in a box.

**Unit 3**

# The balance method

This spread will show you how to:

- Use the balance method to solve equations

**Keywords**
Balance
Inverse

In this set of scales, the two sides **balance**.

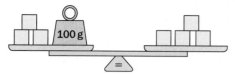

Add 2 boxes to each side.

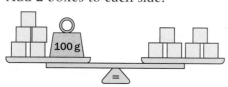

Still balanced.

Take 3 boxes from each side.

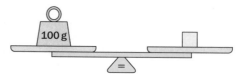

Still balanced.    1 box = 100 g

If you add or subtract (take away) the **same amount** from both sides, the scales still balance.

- The two sides of an equation balance.

Start with the equation
$x + 5 = 11$

Subtract 5 from each side
$x + 5 - 5 = 11 - 5$

The solution is $x = 6$.

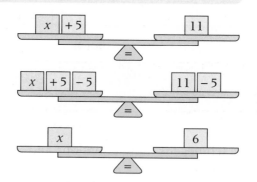

The **inverse** of +5 is −5.
Use the inverse operation to get $x$ on its own.

- You can use the **balance method** to solve an equation.
  You do the same to each side to keep the equation balanced.

**Example**

Use the balance method to solve these equations.
**a** $m + 4 = 15$          **b** $n - 3 = 8$

.................................................................................................

**a**      $m + 4 = 15$          **b**      $n - 3 = 8$
  $m + 4 - 4 = 15 - 4$          $n - 3 + 3 = 8 + 3$
          $m = 11$                      $n = 11$

In **a** the inverse of +4 is −4. Subtract 4 from both sides.

In **b** the inverse of −3 is +3. Add 3 to both sides.

**1** For each of these diagrams work out the weight of one box.

**a**

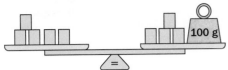

**b**

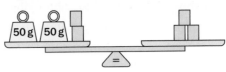

**c**

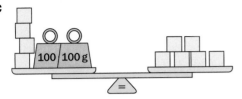

**d**

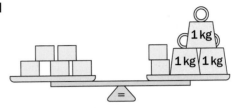

**2** Copy and complete these balances to solve the equations.

**a** $x + 6 = 19$          **b** $x - 4 = 8$

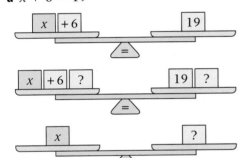

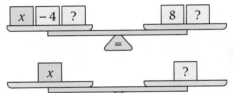

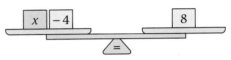

**3** Copy and complete to solve these equations.

**a**                    $m + 7 = 13$          The inverse of $+7$ is ___

Subtract 7 from both sides:

$m + 7$ ___ $= 13$ _____

$m =$ _____

**b**                    $n - 9 = 17$          The inverse of $-9$ is ___

Add ____ to both sides:

$n - 9$ ____ $= 17$ ____

$n =$ _____

**4** Solve these equations using the balance method.

**a** $x + 5 = 8$     **b** $x + 3 = 14$     **c** $x + 8 = 13$     **d** $x + 3 = 18$
**e** $x + 9 = 0$     **f** $5 + x = 11$     **g** $x - 4 = 7$     **h** $x - 9 = 6$

**5** Match each equation in set A to its solution in set B.

Set A:

$13 - x = 10$   $x - 4 = -3$   $x + 5 = 7$
$x + 17 = 21$   $x + 8 = 14$   $x + 6 = 15$
$x - 7 = 1$   $x - 3 = 4$   $22 + x = 27$

Set B:

$x = 1$   $x = 2$   $x = 3$
$x = 4$   $x = 5$   $x = 6$
$x = 7$   $x = 8$   $x = 9$

Unit 3

A03 Problem

**More solving equations**

This spread will show you how to:
- Use the balance method to solve equations
- Check a solution is correct by substituting it back into the equation

**Keywords**
Balance
Substituting

These scales are **balanced**.

3 boxes weigh 300 g.

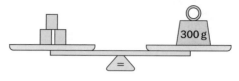

p.372

Double (×2) both sides.

Divide both sides by 3.

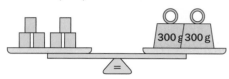 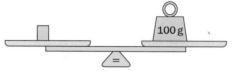

The scales still balance.          The scales still balance.
6 boxes weigh 600 g.              1 box weighs 100 g.

- You can solve equations using the balance method.
  To keep an equation balanced
  - You can add or subtract the same amount from both sides
  - You can multiply or divide both sides by the same number.

**Example**

Solve these equations using the balance method.

**a** $3x = 15$                    **b** $\dfrac{x}{4} = 5$

. . . . . . . . . . . . . . . . . . . . . . . . . . . . . . . . . . . . . . . . . . . . . . . . . . . . .

**a** $3x = 15$                    **b** $\dfrac{x}{4} = 5$

Divide both sides by 3:          Multiply both sides by 4:

$3x \div 3 = 15 \div 3$              $\dfrac{x}{4} \times 4 = 5 \times 4$

$\quad x = 5$                        $\quad x = 20$

$x$ is multiplied by 3. The inverse of ×3 is ÷3.

$\dfrac{x}{4} = x \div 4$. The inverse of ÷4 is × 4.

- You can check that a solution is correct by **substituting** it back into the equation.

**Example**

Daisy solves the equation $\dfrac{x}{7} = 4$.

Her solution is $x = 28$. Is she correct?

. . . . . . . . . . . . . . . . . . . . . . . . . . . . . . . . . . . . . . . . . . . . . . . . . . . . .

Substitute $x = 28$ into $\dfrac{x}{7}$:      $\dfrac{28}{7} = 28 \div 7 = 4$

$\qquad\qquad$ So $x = 28$ is correct

The correct value of $x$ will give the answer 4.

**1** For each of these diagrams work out the weight of one box.

**a**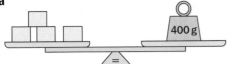

**b**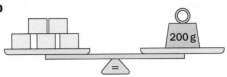

**c**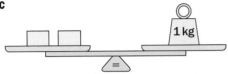

**d**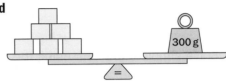

**2** Copy and complete to solve these equations.

**a**
$$6m = 24 \qquad \text{The inverse of} \times 6 \text{ is } \_\_\_\_$$

Divide both sides by \_\_\_:

$$6m \div \_\_\_ = 24 \div \_\_\_$$
$$m = \_\_\_\_$$

**b**
$$\frac{n}{5} = 1 \qquad \text{The inverse of} \div 5 \text{ is } \_\_\_\_$$

Multiply both sides by \_\_\_:

$$\frac{n}{5} \times \_\_\_ = 11 \times \_\_\_$$
$$n = \_\_\_\_$$

**3** Solve these equations using the balance method.

**a** $5x = 15$     **b** $3x = 21$     **c** $6x = 18$     **d** $4x = 36$
**e** $28 = 4x$     **f** $7x = 28$     **g** $50 = 25x$     **h** $4x = 10$

**4** Use the balance method to solve these equations.

**a** $\frac{s}{5} = 5$     **b** $\frac{t}{12} = 3$     **c** $\frac{u}{2} = 4$     **d** $\frac{v}{7} = 3$
**e** $\frac{v}{5} = 9$     **f** $\frac{w}{3} = 8$     **g** $10 = \frac{x}{5}$     **h** $3 = \frac{y}{9}$

**5** Solve these equations.
Check your answers using substitution.

**a** $a + 7 = 11$   **b** $g - 7 = 8$     **c** $\frac{c}{4} = 9$     **d** $d - 5 = -2$

**e** $3e = 21$     **f** $9 + f = 5$     **g** $4g = 0$     **h** $\frac{h}{4} = 2.5$

**6** Tom and Anya both solve the equation $7x = 56$.

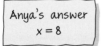

Tom's answer
x = 9

Anya's answer
x = 8

Who is correct? Explain how you worked it out.

A03 Problem

# Summary

## Check out
You should now be able to:

- Use letters to represent numbers in algebra
- Set up simple equations
- Solve simple equations using inverse operations
- Solve simple equations using the balance method
- Check a solution is correct by substituting it back into the equation

## Worked exam question

**a** Solve $2y = 8$ (1)

**b** Solve $t - 4 = 7$ (1)

(Edexcel Limited 2007)

**a**

Check in the original equation:
$2 \times y = 8$
$2 \times 4 = 8$
$8 = 8$

$$2y = 8$$
$$2y \div 2 = 8 \div 2$$
$$y = 4$$

Divide both sides by 2

**b**

Check in the original equation:
$t - 4 = 7$
$11 - 4 = 7$
$7 = 7$

$$t - 4 = 7$$
$$t - 4 + 4 = 7 + 4$$
$$t = 11$$

Add 4 to both sides.

# Exam questions

**1** The diagram shows a mathematical rule.

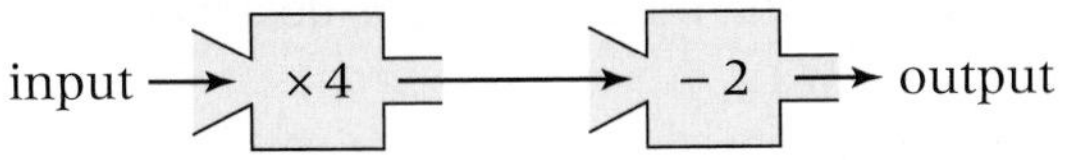

input → [ × 4 ] → [ − 2 ] → output

It multiplies a number by 4 and then subtracts 2.

**a** Copy and complete the diagram.

8 → [ × 4 ] → [ − 2 ] → ....................

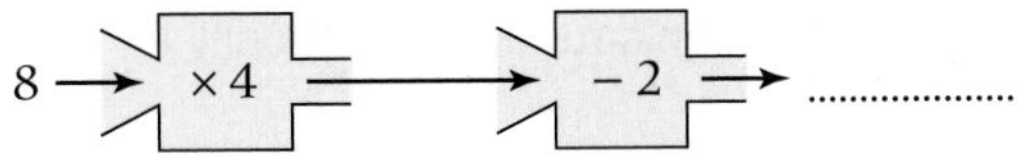

(1)

**b** Copy and complete the diagram.

.................... → [ × 4 ] → [ − 2 ] → 14

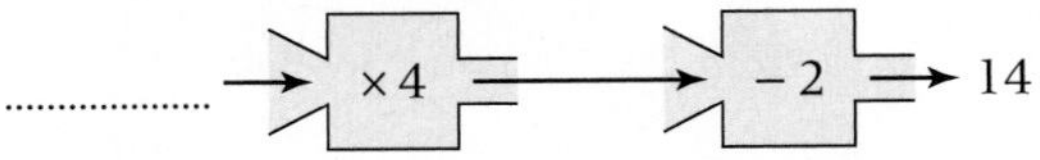

(1)

**c** Copy and complete the diagram.

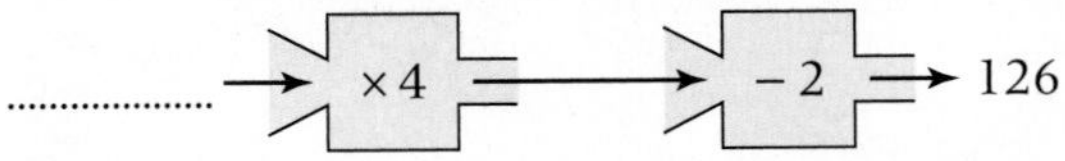

.................... → [ × 4 ] → [ − 2 ] → 126

(1)

**A03**

**2** Iman thinks of a number.

He multiplies the number by 3.
He then adds 19.

His answer is 61.

What number did Iman first think of? (2)

(Edexcel Limited 2005)

**3 a** Solve $2x = 12$ (1)

  **b** Solve $y - 1 = 9$ (1)

  **c** Solve $\frac{x}{3} = 8$ (1)

# Introduction

The decimal system is based on the number 10, and is the universal number system used throughout the world. It is what the metric system of measurement is based on, as well as most countries' money systems including the euro. In the UK, decimalisation of the money system occurred on 15th February 1971.

### What's the point?

A common number system allows different countries to appreciate and understand each others' measurements, quantities and calculations. In a world that is shrinking through enhanced travel and communication, the ability to communicate mathematically is increasingly important.

**Check in**

1 Calculate $5 \times 3 + 4 \times 8$

2 Calculate
   **a** $13 \div 10$     **b** $0.03 \times 10$

3 Round each of these numbers to 2 decimal places.
   **a** 3.5624     **b** 8.0392     **c** 0.0551

| What I need to know | What I will learn | What this leads to |
|---|---|---|
| N2 + 4 → | ■ Use approximation to estimate answers to decimal calculations<br>■ Use mental methods for decimal calculations<br>■ Use written methods for decimal calculations<br>■ Use calculators to carry out more complex calculations | → +1 |

**Rich task**

Try to make the numbers 1 to 20 using up to four 4s and any of the operations $+$, $-$, $\times$ or $\div$. You may also use brackets and square roots, and 4 can appear as an index.

For example, $\dfrac{44 - 4}{4} = 10$

This spread will show you how to:

- Multiply and divide by powers of 10 and by decimals between 0 and 1
- Use checking procedures, including approximation to estimate the answer to multiplication and division problems

**Keywords**

Approximate
Estimate

- You can multiply or divide a number by a power of 10. Move the digits of the number to the left or to the right.

$\times 10$
or $\div 0.1$

1.8 $\longrightarrow$ 18

$\div 10$
or $\times 0.1$

$\times 100$
or $\div 0.01$

12.4 $\longrightarrow$ 1240

$\div 100$
or $\times 0.01$

$\times 0.1$ is the same as $\div 10$.
$\times 0.01$ is the same as $\div 100$.

$\div 0.1$ is the same as $\times 10$.
$\div 0.01$ is the same as $\times 100$.

- You can multiply and divide by any decimal between 0 and 1 using mental methods.

**Example**

Calculate **a** $12 \times 0.3$ **b** $3.6 \div 0.04$ **c** $2 \div 0.05$

**a** $12 \times 0.3 = 12 \times 3 \times 0.1$
$= 36 \times 0.1$
$= 36 \div 10$
$= 3.6$

**b** $36 \div 0.04 = 36 \div (4 \times 0.01)$
$= 36 \div 4 \div 0.01$
$= 9 \div 0.01$
$= 9 \times 100$
$= 900$

**c** $2 \div 0.05 = \dfrac{2}{0.05}$
$= \dfrac{200}{5} = 40$
$= 40$

- You can **estimate** the answer to a calculation by first rounding the numbers in the calculation.

**Example**

Estimate the answers to these calculations.

**a** $\dfrac{8.93 \times 28.69}{0.48 \times 6.12}$

**b** $\dfrac{17.4 \times 4.89^2}{0.385}$

A good strategy is to round each number in the calculation to 1 significant figure.

**a** $\dfrac{8.93 \times 28.69}{0.48 \times 6.12} \approx \dfrac{9 \times 30}{0.5 \times 6}$
$= \dfrac{270}{3} = 90$

**b** $\dfrac{17.4 \times 4.89^2}{0.385} \approx \dfrac{20 \times 5^2}{0.4}$
$= \dfrac{20 \times 25}{0.4} = \dfrac{500}{0.4}$
$= \dfrac{5000}{4} = 1250$

1  Round each of these numbers to the nearest **i** 1000  **ii** 100  **iii** 10.
   **a** 1548.9     **b** 5789.47     **c** 17 793.8 kg
   **d** €35 127.35  **e** 236 872

2  Round each of these numbers to **i** 3 dp  **ii** 2 dp  **iii** 1 dp
   **iv** the nearest whole number.
   **a** 4.3563     **b** 9.8573     **c** 0.9373     **d** 19.4963
   **e** 26.8083    **f** 19.9999    **g** 0.004896   **h** 3896.6567

3  Calculate these.
   **a** $3 \times 0.1$     **b** $15 \div 0.1$     **c** $8 \times 0.01$     **d** $2.8 \times 100$
   **e** $3.8 \div 0.1$     **f** $0.4 \times 0.1$    **g** $9.23 \div 0.1$     **h** $44.6 \div 0.01$

---

**A03 Problem**

**4** Here are five number cards.

| 0.1 | 10 | 0.01 | 1000 | $10^2$ |

Fill in the missing numbers in each of these statements using
one of these cards.
**a** $3.24 \times ? = 324$          **b** $14.7 \times ? = 0.147$
**c** $6.3 \div ? = 630$             **d** $2870 \div ? = 2.87$
**e** $0.43 \div ? = 4.3$            **f** $2.04 \div ? = 204$

---

5  Round each of these numbers to  **i** 3 sf  **ii** 2 sf  **iii** 1 sf.
   **a** 9.4837     **b** 27.73      **c** 46.73      **d** 387.63
   **e** 2.4058     **f** 4905.81    **g** 0.009 483  **h** 3489.7
   **i** 9.8765     **j** 25.1407    **k** 2314.17    **l** 237 415

6  Work out these calculations using a mental method.
   **a** $12 \times 0.2$    **b** $8 \times 0.07$    **c** $15 \div 0.3$
   **d** $3 \div 0.15$      **e** $1.2 \times 0.4$   **f** $28 \div 0.07$

7  Write a suitable estimate for each of these calculations.
   In each case clearly show how you estimated your answer.
   **a** $3.76 \times 4.22$                  **b** $17.39 \times 22.98$
   **c** $\dfrac{4.59 \times 7.9}{19.86}$     **d** $54.31 \div 8.8$

8  Write a suitable estimate for each of these calculations.
   In each case clearly show how you estimated your answer.

   **a** $\dfrac{29.91 \times 38.3}{3.1 \times 3.9}$       **b** $\dfrac{16.2 \times 0.48}{0.23 \times 31.88}$

   **c** $\{4.8^2 + (4.2 - 0.238)\}^2$                     **d** $\dfrac{63.8 \times 1.7^2}{1.78^2}$

   **e** $\sqrt{(2.03 \div 0.041)}$                        **f** $\sqrt{(27.6 \div 0.57)}$

This spread will show you how to:

- Use a range of mental methods for calculations with whole numbers and decimals

p.50

**Keywords**
Compensation
Mental method
Multiple
Partitioning
Place value

There are lots of **mental methods** you can use to help you work out calculations in your head.

You can use **place value**.

> **Example**
>
> Use the fact that $35 \times 147 = 5145$ to write the value of
>
> **a** $3.5 \times 1.47$     **b** $0.35 \times 147\,000$     **c** $51.45 \div 3.5$
>
> . . . . . . . . . . . . . . . . . . . . . . . . . . . . . . . . . . . . . . . . . . . . . . . . . . . . .
>
> **a** $3.5 \times 1.47 = (35 \div 10) \times (147 \div 100)$     **b** $0.35 \times 147\,000 = (35 \div 100) \times (147 \times 1000)$
> $\qquad = 35 \times 147 \div 1000$ $\qquad\qquad\qquad\qquad = 35 \times 147 \times 10$
> $\qquad = 5145 \div 1000$ $\qquad\qquad\qquad\qquad = 5145 \times 10$
> $\qquad = 5.145$ $\qquad\qquad\qquad\qquad = 51\,450$
>
> **c** $51.45 \div 3.5 = \dfrac{51.45}{3.5} = \dfrac{514.5}{35}$
> $\qquad\qquad = \dfrac{(5145 \div 10)}{35}$
> $\qquad\qquad = 147 \div 10$
> $\qquad\qquad = 14.7$

You can use **partitioning**.

> **Example**
>
> **a** Calculate $18.5 - 7.7$.     **b** Calculate $6.3 \times 12$.
>
> . . . . . . . . . . . . . . . . . . . . . . . . . . . . . . . . . . . . . . . . . . . . . . . . . . . .
>
> **a** $18.5 - 7.7 = 18.5 - 7 - 0.7$     **b**     $12 = 10 + 2$
> $\qquad\qquad\quad = 11.5 - 0.7$ $\qquad\qquad 6.3 \times 12 = (6.3 \times 10) + (6.3 \times 2)$
> $\qquad\qquad\quad = 10.8$ $\qquad\qquad\qquad\qquad\quad = 63 + 12.6$
> $\qquad\qquad\qquad\qquad\qquad\qquad\qquad\qquad\quad = 75.6$
>
> Split **12** into **10 + 2**. Then work out **10** $\times$ 6.3 and **2** $\times$ 6.3. Add your two answers together.

You can use **compensation**.

> **Example**
>
> **Calculate**    **a** $12.4 - 4.9$        **b** $23.2 \times 1.9$
>
> . . . . . . . . . . . . . . . . . . . . . . . . . . . . . . . . . . . . . . . . . . . . . . . . . . . .
>
> **a** $12.4 - 4.9 = 12.4 - 5 + 0.1$     **b**     $1.9 = 2 - 0.1$
> $\qquad\qquad\quad = 7.4 + 0.1$
> $\qquad\qquad\quad = 7.5$ $\qquad\qquad 23.2 \times 1.9 = (23.2 \times 2) - (23.2 \times 0.1)$
> $\qquad\qquad\qquad\qquad\qquad\qquad\qquad\qquad = 46.4 - 2.32$
> $\qquad\qquad\qquad\qquad\qquad\qquad\qquad\qquad = 44.08$
>
> Rewrite **1.9** as **2 − 0.1**. Work out $2 \times 23.2$ and **0.1** $\times$ 23.2. Subtract your two answers.

**1** Calculate these.
   **a** $9 \times 7$      **b** $121 \div 10$      **c** $2 \times 2.7$      **d** $48.4 \div 2$
   **e** $3.6 \times 100$   **f** $430 \div 100$    **g** $23.6 \times 10$     **h** $0.78 \div 100$

**2** Use an appropriate mental method to calculate these. Show the method you have used.
   **a** $1.4 \times 11$    **b** $21 \times 9$      **c** $5.3 \times 11$     **d** $41 \times 2.8$
   **e** $19 \times 7$      **f** $12 \times 5.3$     **g** $147 \div 3$        **h** $276 \div 4$
   **i** $3.2 \times 11$    **j** $31 \times 5.6$     **k** $14.9 \times 9$     **l** $25.3 \times 31$
   **m** $14 \times 8$      **n** $51 \div 1.5$       **o** $81 \div 4.5$       **p** $4.4 \times 4.5$

**3** Use the mental method of partitioning to work out each of these.
   **a** $19.5 - 7.6$       **b** $45.3 + 12.6 + 7.2$       **c** $132.6 - 21.4$
   **d** $7.2 \times 13$     **e** $8.4 \times 12$            **f** $11 \times 19.2$
   **g** $129 \div 3$        **h** $292 \div 4$

**4** Use the mental method of compensation to work out each of these.
   **a** $19.5 - 7.9$       **b** $48.4 - 12.8$       **c** $164.5 - 15.9$
   **d** $8.1 \times 19$     **e** $36 \times 3.9$      **f** $17 \times 5.9$

**5** Use an appropriate mental method to calculate each of these.
   **a** $27.6 + 21.7$ **b** $1623 - 897$    **c** $32 \times 2.1$    **d** $2.9 \times 23$

   **e** $19 \times 1.4$   **f** $9 \times 7.5$    **g** $2.4 \div 0.2$    **h** $\dfrac{30 \times 0.2}{0.15}$

**6** **a** Using the information that $69 \times 147 = 10\,143$, write the value of each of these.
      **i** $69 \times 1470$      **ii** $690 \times 1470$   **iii** $6.9 \times 147$
      **iv** $0.69 \times 14.7$    **v** $6.9 \times 0.147$   **vi** $690 \times 1.47$
      **vii** $0.069 \times 14.7$  **viii** $0.69 \times 0.147$
   **b** Using the information that $37 \times 177 = 6549$, write the value of each of these.
      **i** $3.7 \times 17.7$      **ii** $0.37 \times 1770$
      **iii** $654.9 \div 177$     **iv** $65.49 \div 3.7$

**7** **a** Using the information that $43 \times 217 = 9331$, write the value of each of these.
      **i** $4.3 \times 2170$      **ii** $0.43 \times 2.17$
      **iii** $933.1 \div 4.3$     **iv** $93.31 \div 0.217$
   **b** Using the information that $48 \times 164 = 7872$, write the value of each of these.
      **i** $4.8 \times 16.4$      **ii** $0.48 \times 16\,400$
      **iii** $787.2 \div 1640$    **iv** $78.72 \div 4.8$

This spread will show you how to:

- Use a range of written methods for calculations with whole numbers and decimals
- Use checking procedures, including approximation to estimate the answer to multiplication and division problems

p.176

**Keywords**
Dividend
Divisor
Estimate
Grid method
Standard method
Whole number

You can multiply decimals by replacing them with an equivalent **whole-number** calculation that is easier to work out.

**Example**

Carol is working out the area of carpet she needs for her floor. The floor is in a rectangle with a length of 4.8 m and a width of 3.12 m. What is the area of Carol's floor?

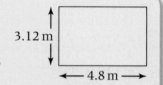
3.12 m

4.8 m

$4.8 \times 3.12 = (48 \div 10) \times (312 \div 100)$
$= 48 \times 312 \div 1000$

| ×  | 300                  | 10                | 2              |
|----|----------------------|-------------------|----------------|
| 40 | 40 × 300 = 12 000    | 40 × 10 = 400     | 40 × 2 = 80    |
| 8  | 8 × 300 = 2400       | 8 × 10 = 80       | 8 × 2 = 16     |

$48 \times 312 = 12\,000 + 400 + 80 + 2400 + 80 + 16 = 14\,976$
The area of Carol's floor is $4.8 \times 3.12 = 48 \times 312 \div 1000$
$= 14\,976 \div 1000$
$= 14.98\,\text{m}^2$ (2 decimal places)

Estimate the answer first.
$4.8 \times 3.12 \approx 5 \times 3$
$= 15\,\text{m}^2$

You can divide a number by a decimal by rewriting the calculation as an equivalent whole-number division.

**Example**

Mandy has a floor with an area of $91\,\text{m}^2$. She fills the floor with carpet tiles which have an area of $2.8\,\text{m}^2$.
How many tiles does she need to cover the floor?

$91 \div 2.8 = 910 \div 28$

```
   28) 910
      -840      28 × 30
       70
      -56       28 × 2
      14.0
     -14.0      28 × 0.5      30 + 2 + 0.5 = 32.5
        0
```

$910 \div 28 = 91 \div 2.8 = 32.5$
Mandy needs $91 \div 2.8 = 32.5$ tiles.

Estimate the answer first.
$9.1 + 2.8 \approx 90 \div 3$
$= 30$

1 Use a written method for each of these calculations.
   **a** 16.4 + 9.68
   **b** 27.3 + 5.41
   **c** 9.51 − 6.7
   **d** 24.3 + 7.69
   **e** 34.76 − 8.29
   **f** 38.29 − 24.8
   **g** 16.5 − 12.67 + 5.34
   **h** 78.7 − 14.92 + 16.66 − 12.9

2 Use an appropriate method of calculation to work out each of these.
   **a** 15 × 3.4
   **b** 5.6 × 18
   **c** 8.4 × 13
   **d** 23 × 7.6
   **e** 28 × 4.2
   **f** 9.7 × 49

3 Use an appropriate method of calculation to work out each of these.
   **a** 27.3 ÷ 7
   **b** 36.6 ÷ 6
   **c** 70.4 ÷ 8
   **d** 73.8 ÷ 6
   **e** 119.7 ÷ 9
   **f** 119.2 ÷ 8

4 Use a mental or written method to solve each of these problems.
   **a** Oliver sells tomatoes at the market. On Thursday he sells 78.6 kg; on Saturday he sells 83.38 kg. What mass of tomatoes has he sold during the two days?
   **b** A mobile phone without a battery weighs 188.16 g. When the battery is inserted the combined mass of the mobile phone and battery is 207.38 g. What is the mass of the battery?
   **c** A recycling box is full of things to be recycled.
      The empty box weighs 1.073 kg.

| | |
|---|---|
| Bottles | 12.45 kg |
| Cans | 1.675 kg |
| Paper | 8.7 kg |
| Plastic objects | ? kg |

      The total weight of the box and all the objects to be recycled is exactly 25 kg. What is the weight of the plastic objects?

5 Use an appropriate method of calculation to work out each of these.
   **a** 2.3 × 1.74
   **b** 1.6 × 2.75
   **c** 1.7 × 44.3
   **d** 2.5 × 5.88
   **e** 8.7 × 4.79
   **f** 38 × 4.78
   **g** 3.4 × 4.45
   **h** 0.54 × 8.28
   **i** 0.93 × 3.87

6 **a** Scooby buys 1.8 m of carpet. Each metre costs £1.85. How much does this cost in total?
   **b** Shaggy buys 7.8 kg of apples. Each kilogram of apples costs £1.45. How much money does Shaggy pay for the apples?
   **c** Brian is a gardener. He plants trees at a rate of 11.8 trees per hour.
      How many trees does he plant in 6.4 hours?
   **d** Clarke works as a car mechanic. He charges £31.70 per hour for his work. How much does he charge for working 2.5 hours?

Functional Maths

A02

Unit 3

This spread will show you how to:

- Use a fraction as an operator
- Multiply fractions
- Calculate a fraction of a fraction

Multiplying by $\frac{1}{5}$ is the same as dividing by 5.

For example, $3 \times \frac{1}{5} = \frac{3}{5}$    $3 \div 5 = \frac{3}{5}$

Multiplying by $\frac{1}{10}$ is the same as dividing by 10.

For example, $7 \times \frac{1}{10} = \frac{7}{10}$    $7 \div 10 = \frac{7}{10}$

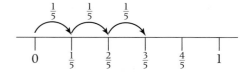

- You can multiply any **fraction** by a whole number using unit fractions.

**Example**

Calculate

**a** $\frac{2}{3} \times 8$    **b** $\frac{3}{5}$ of £220

**a** $\frac{2}{3} \times 8 = 8 \times 2 \times \frac{1}{3}$
$= 16 \times \frac{1}{3}$
$= \frac{16}{3}$
$= 5\frac{1}{3}$

**b** $\frac{3}{5}$ of £220 $= \frac{3}{5} \times 220$
$= 3 \times \frac{1}{5} \times 220$
$= 3 \times 220 \times \frac{1}{5}$
$= 660 \times \frac{1}{5}$
$= \frac{660}{5} = 132$

So $\frac{3}{5}$ of £220 is £132.

Remember: You can find a fraction of an amount by multiplying.

- You can multiply a fraction by another fraction by multiplying the **numerators** together and multiplying the **denominators** together.    $\frac{3}{4} \times \frac{7}{10} = \frac{3 \times 7}{4 \times 10} = \frac{21}{40}$

**Example**

Sarah saves $\frac{1}{3}$ of her weekly wage.

She puts $\frac{3}{4}$ of the money she saves into a pension.

What fraction of her weekly wage does Sarah put into a pension?

Sarah's pension is $\frac{3}{4}$ of the money she saves; she saves $\frac{1}{3}$ of her weekly wage.

Sarah's pension $= \frac{3}{4}$ of $\frac{1}{3}$ of her weekly wage.
$= \frac{3}{4} \times \frac{1}{3} = \frac{3 \times 1}{4 \times 3}$
$= \frac{3}{12} = \frac{1}{4}$ of her weekly wage

Savings    Pension

1  Calculate each of these, leaving your answer in its simplest form.

   **a** $3 \times \frac{1}{5}$          **b** $4 \times \frac{1}{7}$          **c** $11 \times \frac{1}{3}$

   **d** $18 \times \frac{1}{3}$          **e** $\frac{1}{7} \times 14$          **f** $\frac{1}{5} \times 20$

2  Calculate each of these, leaving your answer in its simplest form.

   **a** $4 \times \frac{1}{9}$          **b** $8 \times \frac{1}{3}$          **c** $9 \times \frac{1}{2}$

   **d** $10 \times \frac{1}{8}$          **e** $12 \times \frac{1}{6}$          **f** $\frac{1}{8} \times 13$

3  Calculate each of these amounts.

   **a** $\frac{1}{2}$ of 24 apples     **b** $\frac{1}{3}$ of 21 shops     **c** $\frac{1}{5}$ of 45 texts     **d** $\frac{1}{6}$ of 36 cups

4  Use an appropriate method for each of these calculations. The first
   question has been started for you using the multiplication method.

   **a** $\frac{3}{10}$ of €500 $= 3 \times \frac{1}{10} \times 500$

   $\qquad\qquad\quad = 3 \times 500 \times \frac{1}{10}$

   $\qquad\qquad\quad = 1500 \times \frac{1}{10}$   ($\times \frac{1}{10}$ is the same as $\div 10$)

   $\qquad\qquad\quad = \overline{\phantom{xx}10}$

   $\qquad\qquad\quad = €\underline{\phantom{xxx}}$

   **b** $\frac{3}{5}$ of £60          **c** $\frac{2}{3}$ of 120 kg          **d** $\frac{4}{5}$ of 250p

   **e** $\frac{7}{10}$ of 40 m          **f** $\frac{5}{6}$ of 54 cards          **g** $\frac{5}{12}$ of $84

5  Calculate each of these, leaving your answer in its simplest form.

   **a** $6 \times \frac{2}{3}$     **b** $9 \times \frac{1}{3}$     **c** $4 \times \frac{2}{3}$     **d** $\frac{2}{3} \times 12$

   **e** $4 \times \frac{3}{5}$     **f** $\frac{4}{5} \times 3$     **g** $\frac{2}{5} \times 10$     **h** $\frac{3}{8} \times 4$

6  Use a suitable method to calculate each of these amounts.
   Where appropriate round your answer to two decimal places.

   **a** $\frac{4}{15}$ of £390   **b** $\frac{7}{10}$ of 4500 m   **c** $\frac{3}{7}$ of 50 g   **d** $\frac{4}{9}$ of 639 mm

   **e** $\frac{7}{18}$ of 200 kg  **f** $\frac{3}{17}$ of 360°   **g** $\frac{2}{25}$ of 775 miles   **h** $\frac{7}{15}$ of 345 m²

   **i** $\frac{14}{15}$ of £70   **j** $\frac{5}{6}$ of 18 hours

7  Calculate each of these, leaving your answer in its simplest form.

   **a** $\frac{1}{5} \times \frac{2}{3}$     **b** $\frac{2}{5} \times \frac{3}{4}$     **c** $\frac{2}{7} \times \frac{3}{4}$     **d** $\frac{2}{7} \times \frac{2}{5}$

   **e** $\frac{5}{6} \times \frac{3}{4}$     **f** $\frac{3}{8} \times \frac{5}{9}$     **g** $\frac{3}{5} \times \frac{4}{9}$     **h** $\frac{5}{6} \times \frac{2}{5}$

   **i** $\frac{3}{7} \times \frac{5}{6}$     **j** $\left(\frac{2}{5}\right)^2$     **k** $\left(\frac{2}{3}\right)^2$     **l** $\left(\frac{4}{9}\right)^2$

**Calculator methods 1**

This spread will show you how to:
- Carry out more complex calculations using the functions of a calculator
- Give an answer to a given degree of accuracy

You can use a scientific calculator to carry out more complex calculations that involve decimals.

**Example**

Use your calculator to work out this calculation
$$3.46 + 2.9 \times 4.8$$
Give your answer to one decimal place.

·········································································

Estimate
$$3.46 + 2.9 \times 4.8 \approx 3 + 3 \times 5 \qquad \text{(using the order of operations)}$$
$$= 3 + 15 = 18$$

You type $\boxed{3}\boxed{\cdot}\boxed{4}\boxed{6}\boxed{+}\boxed{2}\boxed{\cdot}\boxed{9}\boxed{\times}\boxed{4}\boxed{\cdot}\boxed{8}\boxed{=}$

The calculator should display
$$\boxed{\begin{array}{l} 3.46+2.9\times4.8 \\ \textit{17.38} \end{array}}$$

So the answer is $17.38 = 17.4$ (1 decimal place)

A scientific calculator has algebraic logic, which means that it understands the **order of operations**.

In this case the calculator automatically works out the multiplication before the addition.

A scientific calculator has **bracket** keys.

**Example**

**a** Use your calculator to work out $(3.9 + 2.2)^2 \times 2.17$.
Write all the figures on your calculator display.
**b** Put brackets in this expression so that its value is 16.26.
$$1.4 + 3.9 \times 2.2 + 4.6$$

·········································································

**a** Estimate
$$(3.9 + 2.2)^2 \times 2.17 \approx (4 + 2)^2 \times 2 \qquad \text{(using the order of operations)}$$
$$= 6^2 \times 2$$
$$= 36 \times 2$$
$$= 72$$

You type $\boxed{(}\boxed{3}\boxed{\cdot}\boxed{9}\boxed{+}\boxed{2}\boxed{\cdot}\boxed{2}\boxed{)}\boxed{x^2}\boxed{\times}\boxed{2}\boxed{\cdot}\boxed{1}\boxed{7}\boxed{=}$

The calculator should display $\boxed{\begin{array}{l} (3.9+2.2)^2\times2.17 \\ \textit{80.7457} \end{array}} = 80.7457$

**a** $(1.4 + 3.9) \times 2.2 + 4.6$

The calculator should display $\boxed{\begin{array}{l} (1.4+3.9)\times2.2+4.6 \\ \textit{16.26} \end{array}}$

$$= 16.26 \quad \checkmark \text{ the correct answer}$$

1 Use your calculator to work out these.
In each case, first write an estimate for your answer.
Write the answer from your calculator to one decimal place.

   **a** $3.4 + 6.2 \times 2.7$

      Estimate $\qquad$ $3.4 + 6.2 \times 2.7 \approx 3 + 6 \times 3$

                                  $= 3 + 18$

                                    $= \underline{\quad}$

      Using the calculator $\qquad$ $3.4 + 6.2 \times 2.7 = \underline{\qquad}$

   **b** $1.98 \times 11.7 - 4.6$             **c** $7.8 + 19.3 \div 4.12$

   **d** $2.09 \times 2.87 + 3.25 \times 1.17$      **e** $13.67 \div 1.75 + 3.24$

   **f** $1.2 + 3.7 \times 0.5$

2 Use your calculator to work out each of these calculations.
Write all the figures on your calculator display.

   **a** $(2.3 + 5.6) \times 3^2$            **b** $2.3^2 \times (12.3 - 6.7)$

   **c** $(2.8^2 - 2.04) \div 2.79$       **d** $7.2 \times (4.3^2 + 7.4)$

   **e** $11.33 \div (6.2 + 8.3^2)$       **f** $(2.5^2 + 1.37) \times 2.5$

3 Calculate each of these, giving your answer to one decimal place.

   **a** $\dfrac{5.4 + 3.8}{4.5 - 2.9}$            **b** $\dfrac{3.8 - 1.67}{4.3 - 2.68}$

   **c** $\dfrac{12.4 + 5.8}{14.5 - 3.9}$         **d** $\dfrac{13.08 - 2.67}{2.13 + 2.68}$

> Hint for part **a**:
> Type the calculation as $(5.4 + 3.8) \div (4.5 - 2.9) =$

4 Put brackets into each of these expressions to make them correct.

   **a** $3.4 \times 2.3 + 1.6 = 13.26$      **b** $3.5 \times 2.3 - 1.04 = 4.41$

   **c** $2.6 + 6.5 \div 1.3 = 7$         **d** $1.4^2 - 1.2 \times 2.3 = 1.748$

   **e** $2.4^2 \div 1.8 \times 3.2 + 1.6 = 15.36$    **f** $3.2 + 5.3 \times 2.4 - 1.2 = 10.2$

5 Use your calculator to work out each of these. Write all the figures on your calculator display.

   **a** $\dfrac{462.3 \times 30.4}{(0.7 + 4.8)^2}$         **b** $\dfrac{13.58 \times (18.4 - 9.73)}{(37.2 + 24.6) \times 4.2}$

6 Here is a mathematical calculation.

   $\dfrac{50.1 + 29.8}{50.1 - 29.8}$

   **a** Write **approximate** values for 50.1 and 29.8 that you could use to estimate the value of the mathematical expression.

   **b** Work out an estimate for the mathematical calculation.

   **c** Use your calculator to work out the value of the calculation. Write all the figures on your calculator display.

Unit 3

347

This spread will show you how to:

- Use calculators to carry out more complex calculations
- Use checking procedures, including approximation to estimate the answer to multiplication and division problems
- Give answers to an appropriate degree of accuracy

**Keywords**

Appropriate degree of accuracy
Brackets
Order of operations

You can use the bracket keys on a scientific calculator to do calculations where the **order of operations** is not obvious.

**Example**

**a** Use a calculator to work out the value of

$$\frac{21.42 \times (12.4 - 6.35)}{(63.4 + 18.9) \times 2.83}$$

Write all the figures on the calculator display.

**b** Put brackets in this expression so that its value is 45.908.
8.2 + 3.4 × 2.7 − 4.3

Estimate
$$\frac{20 \times (12 - 6)}{(60 + 20) \times 3}$$
$$= \frac{120}{240} = 0.5$$

**a** Rewrite the calculation as (21.42 × (12.4 − 6.35)) ÷ ((63.4 + 18.9) × 2.83)
Type this into the calculator:

(21.42×(12.4-6.35))÷((63.4+18.9)×2.83) ⟹ (21.42×(12.4⊸
0.556401856

So the answer is 0.556 401 856.

**b** By inserting a pair of brackets:   (1.4 + 3.9 × 2.2) × 4.6
The calculator should display 45.908.   ✓ This is the correct answer.

You can solve multi-step problems using a calculator. You will need to give your answer to an **appropriate degree of accuracy**.

**Example**

The diagram shows a box in the shape of a cuboid.
**a** Work out the volume, in m³, of the box.
**b** Saleem builds boxes of different sizes.
He charges £7.89 for each m³ of a box's volume.
Work out Saleem's charge for building this box.

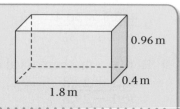

0.96 m
0.4 m
1.8 m

**a** Volume of a cuboid
= length × width × height

Volume ≈ 2 × 1 × 0.4 = 0.8 m³
Volume = 1.8 × 0.4 × 0.96
= 0.6912 m³
= 0.7 m³

**b** Saleem's charge
= cost for each m³ × number of m³

Estimate: Saleem's charge ≈ £8 × 0.8
= £6.40

Type:   Saleem's charge = £7.89 × 0.6912
= £5.453 568
= £5.45

**1** Put brackets into each of these expressions to make them correct.

　**a** $2.4 \times 4.3 + 3.7 = 19.2$　　　　　　**b** $6.8 \times 3.75 - 2.64 = 7.548$

　**c** $3.7 + 2.9 \div 1.2 = 5.5$　　　　　　　**d** $2.3 + 3.4^2 \times 2.7 = 37.422$

　**e** $5.3 + 3.9 \times 3.2 + 1.6 = 24.02$　**f** $3.2 + 6.4 \times 4.3 + 2.5 = 46.72$

**2** Use your calculator to work out each of these. Write all the figures on your calculator.

　**a** $\dfrac{165.4 \times 27.4}{(0.72 + 4.32)^2}$　　　　　　　　**b** $\dfrac{(32.6 + 43.1) \times 2.3^2}{173.7 \times (13.5 - 1.78)}$

　**c** $\dfrac{24.67 \times (35.3 - 8.29)}{(28.2 + 34.7) \times 3.3}$　　　　　**d** $\dfrac{1.45^2 \times 3.64 + 2.9}{3.47 - 0.32}$

　**e** $\dfrac{12.93 \times (33.2 - 8.34)}{(61.3 + 34.5) \times 2.9}$　　　　**f** $\dfrac{24.7 - (3.2 + 1.09)^2}{2.78^2 + 12.9 \times 3}$

**3** Work out each of these using your calculator. In each case give your answer to an appropriate degree of accuracy.

　**a** Véronique puts carpet in her bedroom. The bedroom is in the shape of a rectangle with a length of 4.23 m and a width of 3.6 m. The carpet costs £6.79 per m².

　　**i** Calculate the floor area of the bedroom.

　　**ii** Calculate the cost of the carpet which is required to cover the floor.

　**b** Calculate $\frac{1}{3}$ of £200.

**4** Barry sees a mobile phone offer.

**Vericheep Fone OFFER**

Monthly fee £12.99
FREE – 200 texts every month
FREE – 200 voice minutes every month

Extra text messages 3.2p each
Extra voice minutes 5.5p each

　Barry decides to see if the offer is a good idea for him.
　His current mobile phone offers him unlimited texts and voice minutes for £22.99 per month.

　**a** In February, Barry used 189 texts and 348 voice minutes. Calculate his bill using the new offer.

　**b** In March, Barry used 273 texts and 219 voice minutes. Calculate his bill using the new offer.

　**c** Explain if the new offer is a good idea for Barry.

A02 Functional Maths

Unit 3

This spread will show you how to:
- Solve percentage increase and decrease problems
- Calculate simple interest
- Use checking procedures involving estimation

**Keywords**
Decrease
Increase
Percentage
Simple interest

Banks and building societies pay **interest** on money in an account.
The interest is always written as a **percentage**.
4.5% interest means that the bank pays you an extra 4.5% of the
money you put into the bank account.

> **Example**
>
> Jamal puts £750 into a bank account. The bank pays interest of 4.5%
> on any money he keeps in the account for one year. Calculate the
> interest Jamal receives at the end of the year.
>
> ...................................................................
>
> Estimate:  4.5% of £750 ≈ 5% of £700
> $$= (10\% \text{ of } 700) \div 2$$
> $$= 70 \div 2 = £35$$
>
> Interest $= 4.5\%$ of £750 $= \frac{4.5}{100} \times 750$
> $$= 0.045 \times 750$$
> $$= 33.75$$
> $$= £33.75$$

Always estimate
your answers
when working
with a calculator.

People sometimes choose to have the interest they earn at the end of
each year paid out of their bank account. This is called **simple interest**.

- To calculate simple interest you multiply the interest earned at the end of the year
  by the number of years.

This topic is
extended to
compound
interest on
page 414.

> **Example**
>
> Calculate the simple interest on £3950 for
> **a** 4 years at an interest rate of 5%
> **b** 10 years at an interest rate of 8%.
>
> ...................................................................
>
> **a** Interest each year = 5% of £3950
> $$= \frac{5}{100} \times 3950$$
> $$= 0.05 \times 3950 = £197.50$$
> Total amount of simple interest after 4 years = 4 × £197.50
> $$= £790$$
>
> **b** Interest each year = 8% of £3950
> $$= \frac{8}{100} \times 3950$$
> $$= 0.08 \times 3950 = £316$$
> Total amount of simple interest after 10 years = 10 × £316
> $$= £3160$$

Don't forget to
estimate.
5% of £3950
≈ 5% of £4000
= 10% of
£4000 ÷ 2
= £400 ÷ 2
= £200

1 Calculate these amounts without using a calculator.
   **a** 10% of £5000    **b** 10% of $260      **c** 5% of £3900
   **d** 25% of €800     **e** 50% of £3.60     **f** 5% of $7500
   **g** 25% of £1240    **h** 20% of £780      **i** 15% of $8430
   **j** 1% of £560      **k** 15% of £230      **l** 25% of €1250

2 Calculate these percentages, giving your answer to two decimal places where appropriate.
   **a** 7% of £3200     **b** 12% of £3210     **c** 27% of €5400
   **d** 3.5% of £2200   **e** 0.3% of €4450    **f** 3.7% of £12 590

**A02  Functional Maths  Unit 3**

**3 a** Jane puts £3700 into a bank account. The bank pays interest of 4% on any money she keeps in the account for one year. Calculate the interest received by Jane at the end of the year.
   **b** Majid puts £30 000 into a savings account. The account pays interest of 8.1% on any money he keeps in the account for one year. Calculate the interest received by Majid at the end of the year.

4 Calculate the simple interest paid on £4580
   **a** at an interest rate of 4% for 3 years
   **b** at an interest rate of 11% for 5 years
   **c** at an interest rate of 4.6% for 4 years
   **d** at an interest rate of 8.5% for 3 years.

5 Calculate the simple interest paid on these amounts.
   **a** An amount of £4500 at an interest rate of 5% for 3 years
   **b** An amount of £8500 at an interest rate of 7% for 5 years
   **c** An amount of £320 at an interest rate of 2.5% for 8 years
   **d** An amount of £3900 at an interest rate of 7.5% for 11 years

6 Calculate these amounts.
   **a** Increase £250 by 10%       **b** Decrease £2830 by 20%
   **c** Increase £17 200 by 5%     **d** Decrease £3600 by 30%
   **e** Increase £3.60 by 17.5%    **f** Decrease £2500 by 20%

7 Calculate these amounts. Give your answer as appropriate to two decimal places.
   **a** Increase £740 by 8%        **b** Decrease £39 450 by 32%
   **c** Increase £107.80 by 5%     **d** Decrease $8230 by 34%
   **e** Increase $5900 by 4.5%.    **f** Decrease £2950 by 17.5%

# Summary

## Check out

You should now be able to:

- Use mental and written methods for calculations with whole numbers and decimals
- Multiply or divide by powers of 10
- Use rounding to estimate answers to calculations
- Use a calculator effectively and efficiently
- Multiply fractions
- Calculate simple interest

## Worked exam question

Nick takes 26 boxes out of his van.
The weight of each box is 32.9 kg.

**a** Work out the total weight of the 26 boxes. (3)

Then Nick fills the van with large wooden crates.
The weight of each crate is 69 kg.
The greatest weight the van can hold is 990 kg.

**b** Work out the greatest number of crates that the van can hold. (4)

(Edexcel Limited 2004)

**a**

$32.9 \times 26$    $32.9 \times 10 = 329$
                $32.9 \times 10 = 329$
                $32.9 \times 6 \ = \underline{197.4}$  ← $10 + 10 + 6 = 26$
                        $855.4\,\text{kg}$

OR            $329$
                  $\underline{26} \times$
   $329 \times 20$   $6580$
   $329 \times 6$    $\underline{1974}$
              $8554$         $855.4\,\text{kg}$

> The decimal point is put in after the calculation. An estimate is $30 \times 25 = 750$

**b**

$990 \div 69$

   $69)\,990$
    $\underline{-690}$    $69 \times 10$
     $300$
    $\underline{-276}$    $69 \times 4$
      $24$           14 remainder 24
Greatest number of crates is 14

> There are many other methods to answer this question, but you must show your working whichever method you choose.

> Remember to state the greatest number of crates that the van can hold.

# Exam questions

**1** Copy and complete this bill.

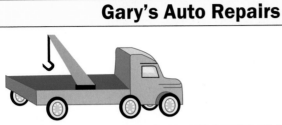

### Gary's Auto Repairs

| Description | Number | Cost of each item | Total |
|---|---|---|---|
| Spark plug | 4 | £2.50 | £10.00 |
| Wiper blade | 2 | £1.50 | £ .................... |
| Light bulb | 2 | £ .................... | £5.00 |
| Labour charge $1\frac{1}{2}$ hours at £16.00 an hour | | | £ .................... |
| | | **Total** | £ .................... |

(4)

(Edexcel Limited 2006)

**2** Margaret goes on holiday to Switzerland.
The exchange rate is £1 = 2.10 francs.

She changes £450 into francs.

How many francs should she get?

(2)

(Edexcel Limited 2005)

**3** Use your calculator to work out
$$(2.3 + 1.8)^2 \times 1.07$$
Write down all the figures on your calculator display.

(2)

(Edexcel Limited 2003)

**4** Work out an estimate for the value of
$$\frac{637}{3.2 \times 9.8}$$

(2)

(Edexcel Limited 2005)

One out of every two small businesses goes bust within its first two years of trading. Mathematics can be applied to reduce the risk of failure for a business as well as to maximise its profits.

A manager needs to know how much cash is coming into and going out of the business.

Accountants must set a suitable budget that includes realistic performance targets, and limits expenditure to what the business can afford.

## Example

Annie sells hand made cards at a monthly craft fair.

The production costs and selling price per card are:

| Cost of materials used | Production time | Wages paid | Selling price | Profit |
|---|---|---|---|---|
| £0.30 | 15 minutes | £1.00 | £2.55 | £1.25 |

This is Annie's cash flow budget for her first three craft fairs (some of the information is missing):

| | January (£) | February (£) | March (£) |
|---|---|---|---|
| TOTAL SALES INCOME | 56.10 | 71.40 | 63.75 |
| | | | |
| Materials used | 6.60 | 8.40 | 7.50 |
| Wages | | | |
| Craft fair fees | 10.00 | 10.00 | 10.00 |
| Advertising | 5.00 | 5.00 | 5.00 |
| TOTAL EXPENDITURE | 43.60 | | |
| | | | |
| NET CASH SURPLUS/DEFICIT | 12.50 | | |
| CASH BALANCE BROUGHT FORWARD | - | 12.50 | |
| CASH BALANCE TO CARRY FORWARD | 12.50 | | |

How many cards did Annie sell in each of the three months?

Use this information to calculate the wages paid for each month.

Calculate the total expenditure for each month. During which month were Annie's expenses highest?

The net surplus (profit) or net deficit (loss) is calculated using the formula Balance = Income − Expenditure
Copy the table and complete the missing values.

On separate copies of the table template, show how the cash flow could change if
a) the craft fair fees were increased to £15
b) the cost of the materials used per card increased to £0.40
c) the selling price per card was increased to £2.75.

Investigate how other changes to costs/income might affect Annie's cash flow.

The breakeven point is when a company's expenditure is equal to its income. If the company can operate at levels above the breakeven point, it will make a profit. If sales fall below this point, the company will make a loss.

For Annie's cards:

Fixed costs = craft fair fees (£10) + advertising (£5) = £15;

Variable cost per card = material costs (£0.30) + wages (£1) = £1.30 per card;

Total costs = fixed costs + variable costs

To calculate total variable cost, multiply: variable cost per card × number of cards

To calculate revenue, multiply: sales price per card × number of cards

If 20 cards are sold, revenue = £2.55 × 20 = £51

Variable costs and revenue increase in direct proportion with the number of cards produced.

Fixed costs: £15, Variable costs:
£1.30 per card, Sales price: £2.55 per card

What do you notice about the gradient and y-axis intercept of each line?

Make sure you understand where the plotted values come from. You may find it useful to draw up a table of values (showing number of cards, fixed costs, variable costs, total costs and revenue).

The fixed cost line is horizontal because the fixed costs do not change regardless of the number of cards produced.

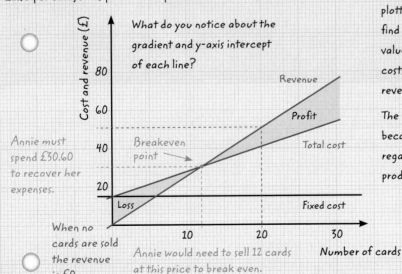

Annie must spend £30.60 to recover her expenses.

When no cards are sold the revenue is £0.

Annie would need to sell 12 cards at this price to break even.

Plot your own charts to show the breakeven point if

a) the craft fair fees were increased to £15

b) the cost of the materials used per card increased to £0.40

c) the selling price per card was increased to £2.75.

Investigate how other changes to costs/income could affect Annie's profit/loss.

# Introduction

Enlargements are mathematically similar to the original object – this means that the properties of the original shape, except the size, are retained. In practical terms when you enlarge a picture you want it to look like an exact copy of the original – just bigger!

## What's the point?

From giant billboard posters to making model planes, enlarging (or reducing) an object is a very visible part of the modern world. Whether you are using a map or zooming in on a computer page, you are making use of enlargements.

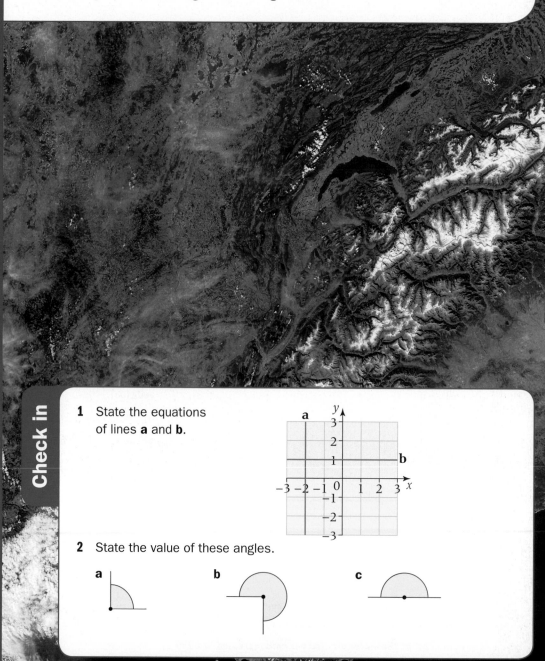

1   State the equations
    of lines **a** and **b**.

2   State the value of these angles.

    **a**          **b**          **c**

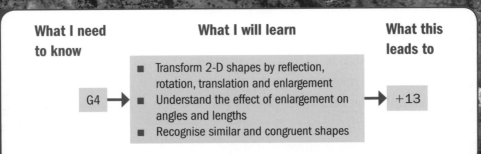

## Rich task

You can tessellate combinations of squares, hexagons and equilateral triangles.

Investigate which of the regular polygons tessellate, and which ones don't.

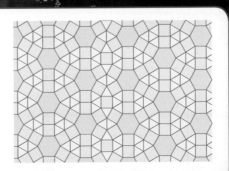

**Reflections 2**

This spread will show you how to:
- Recognise and visualise reflections
- Understand that reflections are specified by a mirror line

**Keywords**
Congruent
Equidistant
Mirror line
Reflection
Transformation

A **transformation** changes the position of a shape.

- A **reflection** flips the shape over.

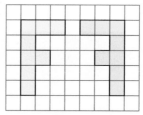

p.312 You specify the **mirror line** or reflection line.

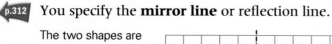

The two shapes are **congruent** – they are exactly the same size and the same shape.

image | object

mirror line

The object and image are **equidistant** from the mirror line.

Each dot is 1 unit from the mirror line.

**a** Draw the mirror line so that shape B is a reflection of shape A.

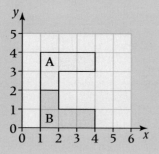

**b** Give the equation of the mirror line.

**a**

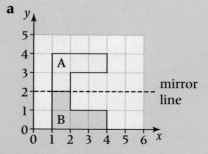

mirror line

**b** Each point on the mirror line has $y$-coordinate 2.
$y = 2$

You can rotate the page to make the mirror line vertical.

To reflect a shape, you choose a point on the object and find the position of the corresponding point in the image.

Reflect this pattern using the $y$-axis as the mirror line.

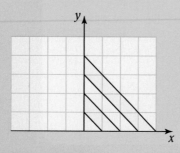

The equation of the $y$-axis is $x = 0$.

**1** Copy the diagrams on square grid paper. Reflect each shape in the mirror line. Give the mathematical name of each new shape you have made.

a 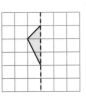　b 　c 　d 　e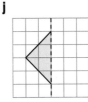

f 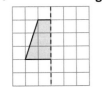　g 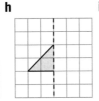　h 　i 　j

 Explain why it is impossible to draw a parallelogram using this method.

**2** Copy and complete the diagrams to show the reflections in both the *x*-axis and the *y*-axis.

a 　b 　c 　d

**3** Copy and complete the diagrams to show the reflection of each triangle in the mirror line *x* = 3.

a 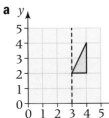　b 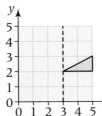　c 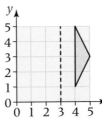　d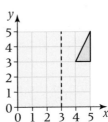

**4** Give the equation of the mirror line for each reflection.

a 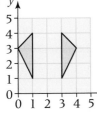　b 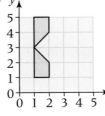　c 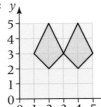　d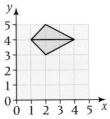

Unit 3

359

This spread will show you how to:

- Recognise and visualise rotations
- Understand that rotations are specified by a centre of rotation and an angle and direction of turn

**Keywords**
Anticlockwise
Centre of
    rotation
Clockwise
Congruent
Origin
Rotation
Transformation

 A **rotation** turns a shape.

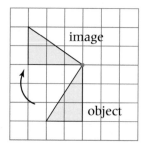

The turn is 90°. The direction is **clockwise**.

The dot is the **centre of rotation**.

The two shapes are **congruent**.

**Example**

Draw the pentagon after a rotation of 180° about the dot.

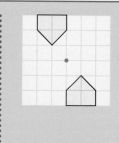

A rotation of 180° can be clockwise or anticlockwise.

You can use tracing paper to help rotate shapes.

- To describe a rotation you give
  - the centre of rotation – the point about which it turns
  - the angle of turn
  - the direction of turn – either clockwise or anticlockwise.

**Example**

a  Give the mathematical name of the green shape.

b  Draw the position of the green shape after a rotation of 90° clockwise about the origin.

The **origin** is the point (0, 0).

a  Kite

b

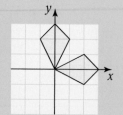

1 State the angle and direction of turn for each of these rotations, green shape to blue shape.

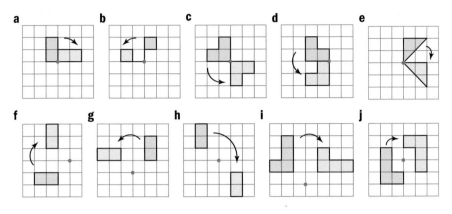

a     b     c     d     e

f     g     h     i     j

**DID YOU KNOW?**

The Earth takes $365\frac{1}{4}$ days to rotate once around the Sun. That extra quarter is the reason we have a 'leap year' once every 4 years!

**Unit 3**

2 Copy these shapes on square grid paper. Rotate each shape through the given angle and direction about the dot (•).

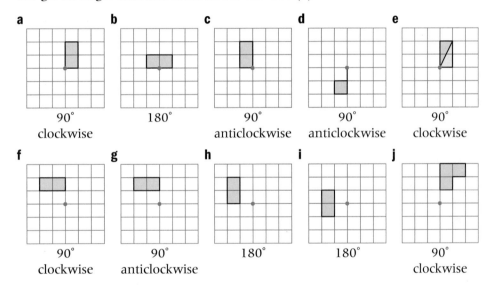

a     b     c     d     e

90°
clockwise     180°     90°
anticlockwise     90°
anticlockwise     90°
clockwise

f     g     h     i     j

90°
clockwise     90°
anticlockwise     180°     180°     90°
clockwise

3 a Plot and join the points (0, 0) (1, 2) (0, 4) and (−1, 2) on a copy of this grid.
   b Give the mathematical name of this shape.
   c Rotate the shape through 90° anticlockwise about the origin.
   d Give the coordinates of the rotated points.
   e Are the two shapes congruent?

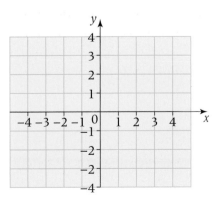

This spread will show you how to:
- Recognise and visualise translations
- Understand that translations are specified by a distance and direction

**Keywords**
Congruent
Slide
Translation

- A **translation** is a **sliding** movement.

You specify the distance moved
- right or left, then
- up or down.

Translate the object 5 units right and

1 unit up $\begin{pmatrix} 5 \\ 1 \end{pmatrix}$.

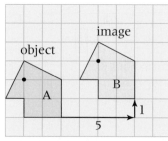

The two shapes are congruent.

You can write the translation in a column like this $\begin{pmatrix} \text{right} \\ \text{up} \end{pmatrix}$.

$\begin{pmatrix} 5 \\ 1 \end{pmatrix}$ means 5 right and 1 up.

Left and down are negative directions.

Shape B to shape A is $\begin{pmatrix} 5 \text{ left} \\ 1 \text{ down} \end{pmatrix}$ or $\begin{pmatrix} -5 \\ -1 \end{pmatrix}$.

Here are some other examples of translations.

2 units right and
1 unit down

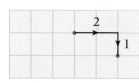

$\begin{pmatrix} 2 \\ -1 \end{pmatrix}$

4 units left and
1 unit down

$\begin{pmatrix} -4 \\ -1 \end{pmatrix}$

**Example**

Describe fully the transformation that moves the shaded triangle to

**a** shape A

**b** shape B.

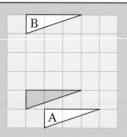

...........................................................

**a** A translation of 1 unit right and 1 unit down = $\begin{pmatrix} 1 \\ -1 \end{pmatrix}$.

**b** A translation of 0 units right and 4 units up = $\begin{pmatrix} 0 \\ 4 \end{pmatrix}$.

**1** Which of these shapes are translations of the green shape?

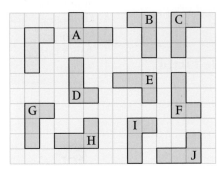

**2** Describe these translations.

| | |
|---|---|
| **a** A to B | **b** A to C |
| **c** A to D | **d** A to E |
| **e** B to C | **f** B to E |
| **g** C to E | **h** C to A |
| **i** D to C | **j** D to B |
| **k** B to A | **l** B to D |

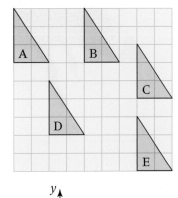

**3** **a** Give the coordinates of the point A.

**b** What is the mathematical name of the shape?

**c** Copy the diagram. Draw the shape after a translation of 4 units left and 3 units down.

**d** State whether the two shapes are congruent.

**e** Give the coordinates of the point A after the translation.

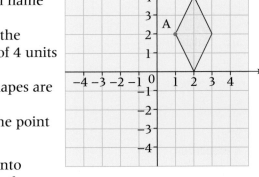

**4** Copy these quadrilaterals onto square grid paper. Translate the shapes and give the mathematical name of the new shape you have made.

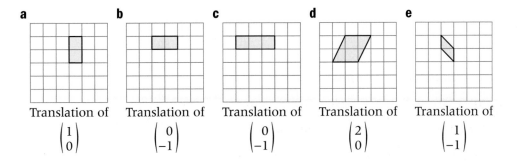

| a | b | c | d | e |
|---|---|---|---|---|
| Translation of $\begin{pmatrix} 1 \\ 0 \end{pmatrix}$ | Translation of $\begin{pmatrix} 0 \\ -1 \end{pmatrix}$ | Translation of $\begin{pmatrix} 0 \\ -1 \end{pmatrix}$ | Translation of $\begin{pmatrix} 2 \\ 0 \end{pmatrix}$ | Translation of $\begin{pmatrix} 1 \\ -1 \end{pmatrix}$ |

This spread will show you how to:

- Understand that enlargements are specified by a centre of enlargement and a scale factor

**Keywords**
Enlargement
Multiplier
Proportion
Scale factor
Similar

In an **enlargement** the lengths change by the same **scale factor**.

- The scale factor is the **multiplier** in an enlargement.

p.388

The two bees are **similar** – the same shape but different sizes.

3cm | 6cm

The bee has been enlarged by a scale factor of 2.

3 cm × 2 = 6 cm

The green rectangle is an enlargement of the yellow rectangle.

Corresponding lengths are multiplied by 2:

$$4 \times 2 = 8 \qquad 1 \times 2 = 2$$

The scale factor of this enlargement is 2.

- In an enlargement
  - the angles stay the same
  - the lengths increase in **proportion**.

**Example**

**a** Decide if these triangles are enlargements of the purple triangle. If so, calculate the scale factor.

**b** List the triangles that are similar to the purple triangle.

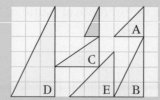

..............................................................

**a** A No, not an enlargement, as different shape.
  B Yes, enlargement. Each length is multiplied by 2. Scale factor 2.
  C No, not an enlargement, as a different shape.
  D Yes, enlargement. Each length is multiplied by 3. Scale factor 3.
  E No, not an enlargement, as a different shape.

**b** B and D are similar to the purple triangle.

1 **a** Decide if these rectangles are enlargements of the green rectangle. If so, calculate the scale factor.

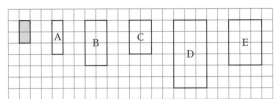

**b** List the rectangles that are similar to the green rectangle.

2 **a** Decide if these triangles are enlargements of the green triangle. If so, calculate the scale factor.

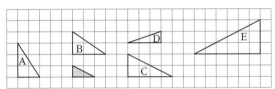

**b** List the triangles that are similar to the green triangle.

3 Find the kite that is similar to the green kite.

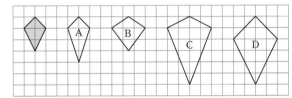

4 One rhombus is an enlargement of the green rhombus. State the letter of this shape and calculate the scale factor of the enlargement.

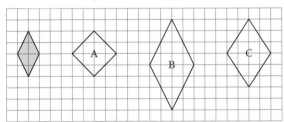

5 **a** Draw these triangles by plotting the coordinates on a copy of this grid.

| | | | |
|---|---|---|---|
| Green | (5, 5) | (7, 5) | (5, 6) |
| A | (6, 9) | (9, 9) | (6, 10) |
| B | (2, 7) | (8, 7) | (2, 10) |
| C | (8, 4) | (10, 4) | (8, 6) |
| D | (2, 2) | (10, 2) | (2, 6) |
| E | (1, 0) | (5, 0) | (1, 2) |

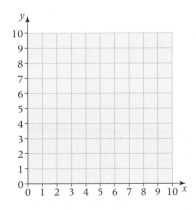

**b** State the triangles that are enlargements of the green triangle. Calculate the scale factor of the enlargement in each case.

Unit 3

365

**Enlarging shapes**

This spread will show you how to:

- Understand the effect of enlargement on the angles and lengths of shapes and how this relates to the scale factor of the enlargement
- Recognise similar shapes

- In an **enlargement**
  - the angles stay the same
  - the lengths increase in proportion.

The green triangle is an enlargement of the yellow triangle.

Corresponding lengths are multiplied by 3:
$2 \times 3 = 6$

The **scale factor** of this enlargement is 3.

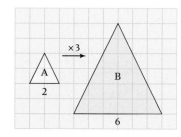

The two triangles are **similar** – the same shape but different sizes.

The scale factor of enlargement from B to A is $\frac{1}{3}$. You divide all the lengths by 3: $6 \div 3 = 2$.

- The scale factor is the multiplier in an enlargement.

**Example**

a Draw an enlargement of the yellow arrowhead with scale factor 2.

b Measure the length $x$. Measure the corresponding length $y$ in your enlargement.

c Measure the angle at A. Measure the corresponding angle in your enlargement.

a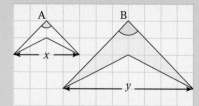

b $x = 4$ units
$y = 8$ units

c Angle A = 90°
Angle B = 90°

Check:
Scale factor is 2
$4 \times 2 = 8$.

Angles stay the same in enlargements.

**Example**

On the isometric paper draw an enlargement of the cuboid with scale factor 2.

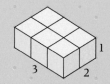

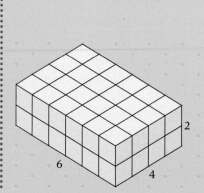

Check:
Scale factor is 2
$3 \times 2 = 6$
$2 \times 2 = 4$
$1 \times 2 = 2$

This topic is extended to similar shapes on page 432.

**1** Copy each diagram onto square grid paper. Enlarge each shape by the given scale factor.

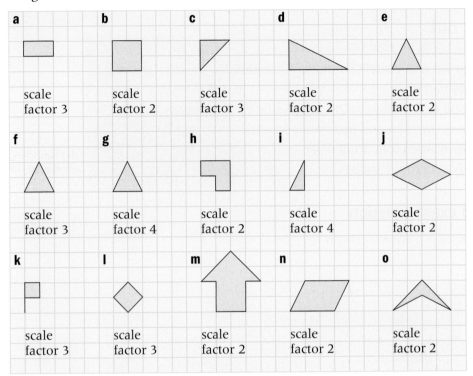

| a | b | c | d | e |
|---|---|---|---|---|
| scale factor 3 | scale factor 2 | scale factor 3 | scale factor 2 | scale factor 2 |

| f | g | h | i | j |
|---|---|---|---|---|
| scale factor 3 | scale factor 4 | scale factor 2 | scale factor 4 | scale factor 2 |

| k | l | m | n | o |
|---|---|---|---|---|
| scale factor 3 | scale factor 3 | scale factor 2 | scale factor 2 | scale factor 2 |

**2 a** Copy the 'L' shape onto square grid paper.
   **b** Calculate the perimeter of the shape.
   **c** Draw the shape after an enlargement of scale factor 3.
   **d** Calculate the perimeter of the enlarged shape.

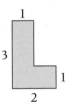

**3 a** Copy the triangle onto square grid paper.
   **b** Measure the shaded angle.
   **c** Draw the triangle after an enlargement of scale factor 2.
   **d** Measure the corresponding shaded angle in the enlargement.

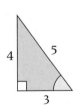

**4** Copy each diagram onto isometric paper.
   Enlarge each shape by the given scale factor.

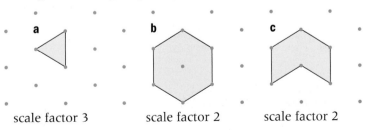

| a | b | c |
|---|---|---|
| scale factor 3 | scale factor 2 | scale factor 2 |

**Unit 3**

### Check out

You should now be able to:

- Recognise and visualise reflections, rotations, translations and enlargements
- Describe and transform 2-D shapes using reflections, rotations, translations and enlargements
- Identify shapes that are similar
- Identify congruent shapes

### Worked exam question

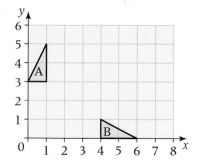

Triangle **A** and triangle **B** have been drawn on the grid.

**a** Reflect triangle **A** in the line $x = 3$.
   Label this image **C**. (2)

**b** Describe fully the single transformation which will map triangle **A** onto triangle **B**. (2)

**a**

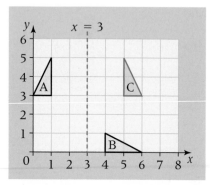

Draw the line of reflection $x = 3$.

**b** Rotation of 90° clockwise about (1, 0).

## Exam questions

**1**

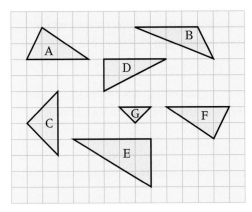

   **a** Write down the letter of an isosceles triangle.                             (1)
   **b** Write down the letters of two triangles which are congruent.      (1)

   Triangle **C** is an enlargement of triangle **G**.
   **c** Write down the scale factor of this enlargement.                  (1)

                                                         (Edexcel Limited 2007)

**2** A shape has been drawn on a grid of centimetre squares.
   **a** Work out the area of the shape.
      State the units of your answer.                                   (3)
   **b** On a copy of the grid, enlarge the shape with a scale factor of 2.

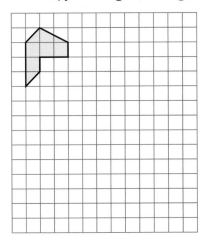

                                                         (2)
                                          (Edexcel Limited 2005)

# Introduction

Scientists are currently trying to understand and respond to the effects of global warming on the environment. These effects are modelled by complex mathematical functions, and involve a large amount of data on a wide range of variables.

## What's the point?

If we can understand the causes and effects of global warming, we can predict more accurately what is likely to happen, and begin to take steps to reduce its harmful effects. None of this would be possible without algebra.

1  State the inverse operation for each of these operations.
   **a** $+3$            **b** $-6$
   **c** $\times 5$            **d** $\div 4$

2  Simplify each of these expressions.
   **a** $x + x + y + y$    **b** $5 \times p + 2$
   **c** $\dfrac{m}{3 + 5}$

3  Calculate the value of each expression when $x = 4$ and $y = 3$.
   **a** $xy$            **b** $2x + y$
   **c** $\dfrac{3x}{y}$            **d** $x + 3y$

4  Solve each of these equations.
   **a** $4x + 2 = 10$    **b** $3x - 6 = 9$
   **c** $2y \times 4 = 16$    **d** $\dfrac{y}{7} = 1$

**Rich task**

In this diagram the equation $3x + 2 = 17$ has been changed in different ways, but all of these ways still give the same solution of $x = 5$.

$$3x + 4 = 19$$

$$3x + 1 = 16 \qquad 3x + 5 = 20$$

$$3x + 2 = 17$$

$$3x - 1 = 14 \qquad 3x + 3 = 18$$

$$3x = 15$$

Describe each change to the equation.

Continue each change for at least one more step.

Invent a new starting equation of your own.

# Solving simple equations

This spread will show you how to:

- Solve linear equations where the unknown appears on either side

**Keywords**
Balance method
Inverse
  operations
Solve

- You can **solve** equations using the **balance method**.

An equation remains balanced if you do the same to both sides.

You can

- add the same number to both sides

- subtract the same number from both sides

- multiply both sides by the same number

- divide both sides by the same number

- You use **inverse operations** to get the letter on its own on one side of the equation.

**Example**

Solve

**a** $x + 3 = 17$
**b** $y - 5 = 27$
**c** $3s = 24$
**d** $\frac{t}{5} = 4$

........................................................................................

**a**
$$x + 3 = 17$$
$$x + 3 - 3 = 17 - 3$$
$$x = 14$$

**b**
$$y - 5 = 27$$
$$y - 5 + 5 = 27 + 5$$
$$y = 32$$

**c**
$$3s = 24$$
$$3s + 3 = 24 + 3$$
$$s = 8$$

**d**
$$\frac{t}{5} = 4$$
$$5 \times \frac{t}{5} = 4 \times 5$$
$$t = 20$$

**Example**

Solve $15 - x = 18$

........................................................................................

$$15 - x = 18$$     subtract 15 from both sides
$$15 - 15 - x = 18 - 15$$
$$-x = 3$$
$$x = -3$$

**1** Work out the weight of one box on these balances.

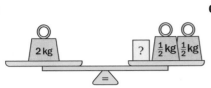

**2** Solve these equations using the balance method.

**a** $x + 4 = 12$    **b** $y - 6 = 15$    **c** $18 = z + 9$

**d** $r - 89 = 27$   **e** $75 = 40 + s$    **f** $11 - t = 5$

**3** Solve these equations.

**a** $8m = 40$    **b** $7n = 70$     **c** $25 = 5p$     **d** $42 = 6q$

**e** $9r = 72$    **f** $2t = 3$      **g** $15 = 2u$     **h** $4m = 48$

**4** Solve these equations.

**a** $\dfrac{m}{5} = 11$    **b** $\dfrac{n}{6} = 8$     **c** $15 = \dfrac{p}{2}$     **d** $9 = \dfrac{q}{7}$

**5** Solve these equations.

**a** $9 + r = 15$   **b** $11 - s = 14$    **c** $-15 = 3t$     **d** $\dfrac{u}{4} = -10$

**e** $v - 8 = -6$ **f** $6w = 8$        **g** $4 = \dfrac{x}{9}$     **h** $17 = 12 - y$

**A03 Problem**

**6 a** Use these numbers and symbols.

Write all the correct equations you can make.

**b** Use these numbers and symbols.

Write the different equations you can make.
Solve each equation to find the value of $x$.

**c** Use these numbers and symbols.

Write the different equations you can make.
Solve each equation to find the value of $x$.

The $x$ key is a symbol, not a multiply.

**Unit 3**

This spread will show you how to:
- Set up and solve equations with two steps

p.324

**Keywords**
Function machine
One-step
Order of operations
Two-step

- You can draw a **function machine** for an equation.

$x + 7 = 20$

$x \rightarrow \boxed{+7} \rightarrow 20$

- Some functions have two operations or steps.

In number calculations with two steps, you follow the order of operations.

In the calculation $3 \times 2 + 4 = 10$
You multiply first, then you add $6 + 4 = 10$

In algebra you follow the same order of operations.

The equation $3n + 4 = 10$
means $3 \times n + 4 = 10$

You multiply first, then you add.

So the function machine for $3n + 4 = 10$ is

$n \rightarrow \boxed{\times 3} \rightarrow \boxed{+4} \rightarrow 10$

BIDMAS helps you remember the order.

Draw a function box for each operation. Two operations need a two-step function machine.

- To draw a function machine for a two-step function, follow the order of operations.

**Example**

For each function machine, work out the outputs for the inputs given.

**a** input                    output   **b** input                    output

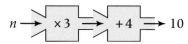

0
3 → $\boxed{\times 4} \rightarrow \boxed{-1} \rightarrow$
7

1
5 → $\boxed{\times 3} \rightarrow \boxed{+2} \rightarrow$
9

**a** $0 \times 4 - 1 = 0 - 1 = -1$
$3 \times 4 - 1 = 12 - 1 = 11$
$7 \times 4 - 1 = 28 - 1 = 27$

**b** $1 \times 3 + 2 = 3 + 2 = 5$
$5 \times 3 + 2 = 15 + 2 = 17$
$9 \times 3 + 2 = 27 + 2 = 29$

**Example**

Draw function machines for these equations.

**a** $4y + 2 = 26$          **b** $2x - 5 = 7$

**a**
$y \rightarrow \boxed{\times 4} \rightarrow \boxed{+2} \rightarrow 26$

**b**
$x \rightarrow \boxed{\times 2} \rightarrow \boxed{-5} \rightarrow 7$

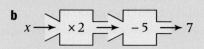

Multiplication then addition.          Multiplication then subtraction.

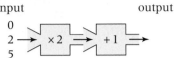

**1** Here are some number machines. Work out the output for each input given.

**a** input           output    **b** input           output

0
2 → ×2 → +1 →
5

1
4 → ×3 → −2 →
7

**c** input           output    **d** input           output

1
3 → ×4 → −3 →
5

4
6 → ×2 → +2 →
8

**2** Copy and complete the table of input and output values for each function machine.

**a**  →→ ×2 →→ −1 →

| Input | Output |
|-------|--------|
| 1 | |
| 3 | |
| 5 | |
| 7 | |
| 9 | |

**b**  → ×3 → +1 →

| Input | Output |
|-------|--------|
| 0 | |
| 2 | |
| 5 | |
| 7 | |
| 10 | |

**c** 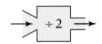 → ×2 → −5 →

| Input | Output |
|-------|--------|
| 20 | |
| 15 | |
| | 15 |
| 4 | |
| 1 | |

**3** Draw function machines for these expressions.

  **a** $3x - 1$     **b** $4n + 2$     **c** $5m - 3$     **d** $6p + 1$
  **e** $3y + 5$     **f** $7z - 2$     **g** $4s - 9$     **h** $8t + 3$

**4** A two-step function machine has input 4.

4 → [ ] → [ ] →

Use any **two** of these function machines

→ +5 →     → ×3 →     → −6 →     → ÷2 →

to make a two-step machine that gives the output
  **a** 3         **b** 7         **c** 17
Make as many different outputs as you can. Draw the function machines you use each time.

**5** Match each function machine to the expression it represents.
  **A** $3x - 2$    **B** $7x + 6$    **C** $2x + 4$    **D** $2x - 1$

**a** 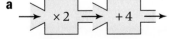 → ×2 → +4 →     **b** 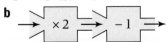 → ×2 → −1 →

**c** 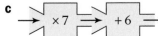 → ×7 → +6 →     **d** 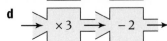 → ×3 → −2 →

**A03** **Problem**

This spread will show you how to:

- Set up and solve equations using inverse operations

**Keywords**

Inverse
  operation

You can draw a function machine for a 'think of a number' problem.

You can work out the unknown number using the **inverse** function machine.

---

**Example**

Solve this 'think of a number' problem using a function machine.
  I think of a number.
  Half my number is 8.
  What is my number?

........................................................................

Draw a function machine

Work backwards, using **inverse operations**.
The number is 16.

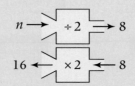

Use $n$ for the unknown number.

This is the inverse function machine.

---

- To draw an inverse function machine, work backwards through the function machine, using inverse operations.

---

**Example**

I think of a number. I double my number and add 3.
The answer is 17. What is my number?

........................................................................

Function machine

Inverse function machine

The number is 7.

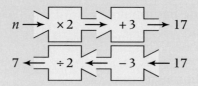

$17 - 3 = 14$
$14 \div 2 = 7$

---

You can use inverse function machines to solve equations.

---

**Example**

Solve these equations.
**a** $4x + 2 = 22$  **b** $3x - 5 = 13$

........................................................................

**a**

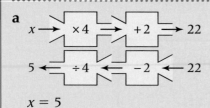

$x = 5$

**b**

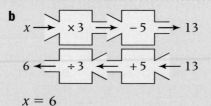

$x = 6$

Draw the function machine.
Draw the inverse machine.
$22 - 2 = 20$
$20 \div 4 = 5$

$13 + 5 = 18$
$18 \div 3 = 6$

**1** Draw the inverse function machine for each of these function machines.

**a**

**b**

**c**

**d**

**2** For each of these 'think of a number' problems
   - Draw a function machine.
   - Draw the inverse function machine.
   - Use your inverse machine to work out the number.

   **a** I think of a number. I double it and add 3. The answer is 13. What is my number?

   **b** I think of a number. I double it and subtract 6. The answer is 0. What is my number?

   **c** I think of a number. I multiply it by 3 and add 3. The answer is 15. What is my number?

   **d** I think of a number. I multiply it by 4 and subtract 2. The answer is 26. What is my number?

**3** Draw a function machine for each equation.
   Use the inverse function machine to solve the equation.
   **a** $3x + 4 = 16$ **b** $5x + 2 = 12$   **c** $4x + 3 = 19$   **d** $3x + 7 = 13$
   **e** $4x + 9 = 17$ **f** $8x + 5 = 21$   **g** $6x + 10 = 22$   **h** $9x + 3 = 30$

**4** Use function machines to solve these equations.
   **a** $4x - 3 = 9$     **b** $6x - 4 = 20$     **c** $3x - 5 = 25$
   **d** $5x - 7 = 8$     **e** $2x - 10 = 12$    **f** $7x - 2 = 19$
   **g** $4x - 8 = 16$    **h** $5x - 7 = 43$

**5** Solve these equations.
   **a** $2x + 7 = 5$     **b** $3x + 8 = 2$      **c** $4x + 15 = 3$
   **d** $2x - 5 = -9$    **e** $4x - 7 = -19$    **f** $2x + 3 = 8$
   **g** $4x + 2 = 0$     **h** $2x - 2 = 1$

**6** Match each equation in box A with its solution in box B.

There are four 'spare' solutions. Make up an equation with each of these spare solutions.

| Box A | Box B | |
|---|---|---|
| $2x + 6 = 9$ | $x = 1$ | $x = -1$ |
| $3x + 1 = 7$ | $x = 2$ | $x = -2$ |
| $3x + 15 = 6$ | $x = 3$ | $x = \frac{1}{2}$ |
| $4x - 3 = -5$ | | |
| $4x + 11 = 3$ | $x = 4$ | $x = \frac{3}{2}$ |
| $4x + 7 = 19$ | $x = 5$ | $x = -\frac{1}{2}$ |
| $5x - 12 = 13$ | $x = 6$ | $x = -\frac{2}{3}$ |
| $7x + 8 = 15$ | | |

Unit 3

A03 Problem

377

**The balance method for two-step equations**

This spread will show you how to:
- Solve equations using the balance method
- Check a solution to an equation by substituting it back into the equation

**Keywords**
Balance method
Substitution

You can work out the unknown weight on a balance by doing the same to both sides.

Take 3 weights off both sides

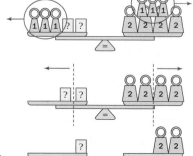

Divide both sides by 2

The unknown weight equals 4.

This topic is extended to equations with brackets and fractions on page 422.

You can work out the value of $x$ in the equation $2x + 3 = 7$ by doing the same to both sides.

Subtract 3 from both sides.

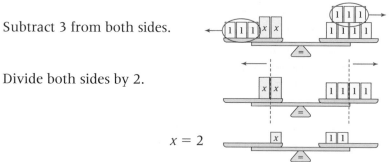

Divide both sides by 2.

$x = 2$

First get the $x$ term on its own on one side. This gives the value of $2x$.

Then divide to find the value of $x$.

- You can solve two-step equations using the **balance method**.

**Example**

Solve these equations.
**a** $4y + 2 = 18$        **b** $4x - 3 = 17$

**a**    $4y + 2 = 18$
   $4y + 2 - 2 = 18 - 2$   Subtract 2 from both sides.
       $4y = 16$
   $4y \div 4 = 16 \div 4$   Divide both sides by 4. This gives the value of $y$.
       $y = 4$

**b**      $4x - 3 = 17$
   $4x - 3 + 3 = 17 + 3$   Add 3 to both sides.
       $4x = 20$
   $4x \div 4 = 20 \div 4$   Divide both sides by 4.
       $x = 5$

You can check using **substitution**. In part **b**
$4x - 3 =$
$4 \times 5 - 3 =$
$20 - 3 = 17$

- You can check a solution by **substituting** the value back into the equation.

**1** Solve these equations using the balance method.
   **a** $2x + 3 = 13$      **b** $2x + 5 = 9$
   **c** $2x + 8 = 20$      **d** $2x + 1 = 21$
   **e** $2x + 3 = 15$      **f** $2x + 7 = 9$
   **g** $2x + 12 = 44$      **h** $2x + 5 = 23$
   **i** $2x + 13 = 21$      **j** $2x + 11 = 51$
   **k** $2x + 12 = 28$      **l** $2x + 36 = 40$

**2** Solve these equations using the balance method.
   Check your answers by substitution.
   **a** $2m - 4 = 16$      **b** $3n - 5 = 10$
   **c** $5 = 2p + 9$      **d** $5 + 3r = 26$
   **e** $13 = 2s - 1$      **f** $4t + 1 = 1$
   **g** $25 - 3x = 10$      **h** $19 - 2y = 7$

**3** Solve these equations.
   **a** $4m + 3 = 5$      **b** $4q - 2 = 2$
   **c** $8 - 6p = 5$      **d** $4r + 2 = 12$
   **e** $12 = 8q + 20$      **f** $6s - 6 = -3$

Check your
answers.

**4** Tom and Sacha both solve the equation

$$5x - 7 = 43$$

Tom's solution is            Sacha's solution is

$x = 8$                 $x = 10$

Check their solutions by substitution.
Who is correct?

**5** The formula for the perimeter of a rectangle is

$$P = 2l + 2w$$

where $l$ = length and $w$ = width.
   **a** Work out the perimeter of a rectangle where $l = 10$ cm and
      $w = 4$ cm.
   **b** Work out the length of a rectangle where $P = 40$ cm and
      $w = 7$ cm.
   **c** Work out the width of a rectangle where $P = 84$ cm and
      $l = 30$ cm.

**6** Amos uses the formula

$$4.5s - 11.2t = r$$

   **a** Work out the value of $r$ when $s = 13$ and $t = 4$.
   **b** Work out the value of $s$ when $t = 5$ and $r = 48$.
   **c** Work out the value of $t$ when $s = 10$ and $r = 4.68$.

Check your answers by substitution.

**Writing and solving equations**

This spread will show you how to:

**Keywords**
Equation
Solution

- Check a solution to an equation by substituting it back into the equation
- Write equations to represent real-life problems

Jenny has $n$ books in her school bag.
Her maths teacher gives her 4 more books for revision.
She now has 7 books in her school bag.
How many books did she have to start with?

You can write an equation for this problem

| Jenny starts with | → | adds 4 | → | total 7 |
|---|---|---|---|---|
| $n$ | | $+ 4$ | $=$ | $7$ |

You can solve the equation $n + 4 = 7$ to find $n$.

$n + 4 = 7$
$n + 4 - 4 = 7 - 4$
$n = 3$

Subtract 4 from both sides.

Jenny had 3 books to start with.

- You can write an **equation** to represent a problem.

- You can solve the equation to find the **solution** to the problem.

**Example**

Marcus spends £$r$ out shopping.
Pritesh spends twice as much as Marcus.
Tariq spends £6 more than Pritesh.

**a** Write an expression for the amount each person spends.

Tariq spends £50 in total.
**b** Write an equation for the amount Tariq spends.
**c** Solve your equation to find $r$.
**d** Work out how much Marcus and Pritesh spend.

........................................................................

**a** Marcus $r$
   Pritesh $2 \times r = 2r$
   Tariq $2r + 6$

**b** $2r + 6 = 50$

**c**     $2r + 6 = 50$
     $2r + 6 - 6 = 50 - 6$
            $2r = 44$
             $r = 22$

Subtract 6 from both sides.
Divide both sides by 2.

**d** Marcus £22

   Pritesh $2 \times £22 = £44$

Substitute $r = 22$ into the original expressions.

**1** For each of these 'think of a number' problems
- write an equation
- solve your equation to find the missing number.

**a** I think of a number. I double it. Then I add 5. My answer is 17.

**b** I think of a number. I multiply it by 4. Then I subtract 8. My answer is 8.

**c** I think of a number. I multiply it by 7. Then I add 1. My answer is 50.

**d** I think of a number. I multiply it by 3. Then I subtract 17. My answer is 13.

**2** A pack of sausages costs £2.

  **a** Write an expression for the cost of $x$ packs of sausages.

  For a barbeque, Charlotte spends £14 on sausages.

  **b** Write an equation for the sausages Charlotte buys.

  **c** Solve your equation to find the number of packs of sausages she bought.

**3** Sarah, Josh and Millie bring sandwiches to a picnic.
Sarah brings $y$ sandwiches.
Josh brings twice as many sandwiches as Sarah.
Millie brings 4 less than Josh.

  **a** Write an expression for the number of sandwiches each person brings.

  Millie brings 12 sandwiches.

  **b** Write an equation for the sandwiches Millie brings.

  **c** Solve your equation to find $y$.

  **d** Work out the number of sandwiches each person brings to the picnic.

**4** Four people go out for a meal.
The meal costs £$x$ each.
The drinks cost £15.

  **a** Write an expression for the total bill for the meal.

  The total bill comes to £65.

  **b** Write an equation for the total bill.

  **c** Solve your equation to find $x$, the cost of one meal.

**5** Rory buys four CDs at £$y$ each and a DVD for £16.
His total bill comes to £60.
Write an equation for Rory's total bill.
Solve your equation to find the cost of one CD.

## Summary

### Check out

You should now be able to:

- Set up simple equations
- Solve linear equations where the unknown appears on either side of the equation
- Check a solution to an equation by substituting it back into the equation

### Worked exam question

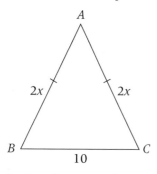

Diagram NOT accurately drawn.

In the diagram, all measurements are in centimetres.

*ABC* is an isosceles triangle.
$AB = 2x$
$AC = 2x$
$BC = 10$

**a** Find an expression, in terms of $x$, for the perimeter of the triangle. Simplify your expression. (2)

The perimeter of the triangle is 34 cm.

**b** Find the value of $x$. (2)

(Edexcel Limited 2006)

**a**

| Perimeter | $= 2x + 2x + 10$ |
|---|---|
| | $= 4x + 10$ |

Simplify the expression.

**b**

$$4x + 10 = 34$$
$$4x + 10 - 10 = 34 - 10$$
$$4x = 24$$
$$4x \div 4 = 24 \div 4$$
$$x = 6 \text{ cm}$$

Set up the equation.

$2 \times 6 + 2 \times 6 + 10 = 34$
Check that $x = 6$ is the correct answer.

# Exam questions

**1** Here is a table for a two-stage number machine.
It multiplies by 2 then subtracts 1.
Complete the missing numbers in the table.

$$\times\mathbf{2} \quad -\mathbf{1}$$

| Input | Output |
|-------|--------|
| 1 | 1 |
| 2 | 3 |
| 3 | ...... |
| 5 | ...... |
| ...... | 15 |

(3)
(Edexcel Limited 2003)

**2 a** Solve $\quad 2x = 12$ (1)

  **b** Solve $\quad 9 = \dfrac{y}{5}$ (1)

  **c** Solve $\quad 6 - x = 2$ (1)

**3 a** Solve $\quad 4x + 1 = 9$ (2)

  **b** Solve $\quad 2y - 1 = 12$ (2)

(Edexcel Limited 2009)

**A03**

**4**

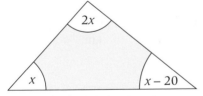

Diagram NOT accurately drawn.

The diagram shows a triangle.
The sizes of the angles, in degrees, are

$x$
$2x$
$x - 20$

Work out the value of $x$. (3)

383

# Introduction

When a ship sails across an ocean it sets course using a bearing. During a typical voyage, constant adjustments are made to the direction to allow for the effects of wind, currents, and other ships.

## What's the point?

If you get lost in a town, you can often use landmarks to find your way. But there are some situations such as crossing an ocean where there are no landmarks to guide you! Understanding angles and bearings allows ships and planes to navigate their way around the world.

**Check in**

1  Convert these measurements to the units stated.

|   |   |   |   |   |
|---|---|---|---|---|
| **a** 10 mm = | cm | **b** 40 mm = | cm |
| **c** 45 mm = | cm | **d** 100 cm = | m |
| **e** 400 cm = | m | **f** 150 cm = | m |
| **g** 1000 m = | km | **h** 6000 m = | km |
| **i** 500 m = | km | **j** 1500 m = | km |

2  **Estimate** these angles.

**a**

**b**
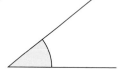

**c**
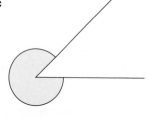

**d**
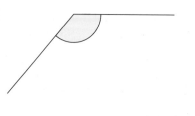

**What I need to know**

**What I will learn**

**What this leads to**

G1 + 2 →

- Draw triangles using a ruler and protractor
- Use and interpret scale drawings
- Give bearings accurately

→ Careers in technical drawing, graphic design and architecture

**Rich task**

Two ships, on the same line of latitude, are both travelling at a speed of 10km/h. The first ship is on a heading of 030° (angle *a*) and the second ship is on a heading of 330° (angle *b*)

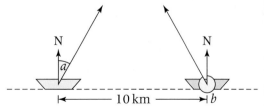

Construct a scale diagram to show where the two ships meet.

On the same diagram construct a diagram to show where the ships would have met if the first ship increased their bearing by 10° and the second ship decreased their bearing by 10°.

Investigate.

This spread will show you how to:

- Draw triangles and other 2-D shapes using a ruler and protractor, given information about side lengths and angles

**Keywords**
Base
Construct
Protractor
Straight edge

Sunita and Emma were asked to **construct** a triangle with angles 50°, 40° and 90°. Here are their answers.

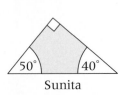

Sunita

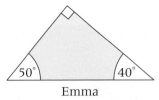

Emma

They are both correct!

They constructed different triangles because not enough information was given.

You will always construct identical triangles if you know:

two sides and the angle between them (SAS)      or      two angles and a side (ASA)

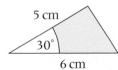

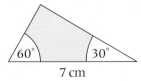

A = Angle
S = Side

You will need a ruler and a **protractor** to construct SAS and ASA triangles.

A ruler is sometimes called a **straight edge**.

---

**Example**

Construct triangle ABC with AB = 6 cm, BC = 4 cm and B̂ = 50°.
What is the length of AC?

········································································

Sketch the shape.      Draw the **base** AB.      Construct angle B using a protractor.      Mark point C. Join it to A.

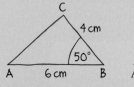

Measuring gives AC = 4.6 cm.

---

**Example**

Construct triangle PQR with angle P = 40°, angle Q = 40° and length PQ = 8 cm.
What sort of triangle is PQR?

········································································

Sketch the shape.      Draw the base PQ.      Measure angle P.      Measure angle Q.

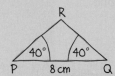

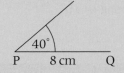

Triangle PQR is isosceles.

**1** Make accurate drawings of these triangles (SAS).
Measure the unknown length in each triangle.

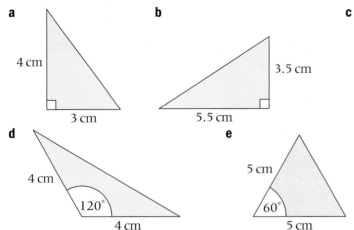

**a** 4 cm, 3 cm

**b** 3.5 cm, 5.5 cm

**c** 3.5 cm, 45°, 6 cm

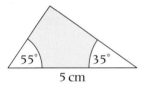

**d** 4 cm, 120°, 4 cm

**e** 5 cm, 60°, 5 cm

**2** Make accurate drawings of these triangles (ASA).
Measure the two unknown lengths in each triangle.
State the units of your answers.

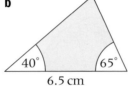

**a** 55°, 35°, 5 cm

**b** 40°, 65°, 6.5 cm

**c** 70°, 70°, 4 cm

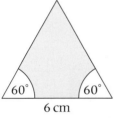

**d** 60°, 60°, 6 cm

**e** 100°, 30°, 6.5 cm

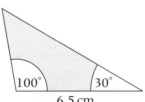

**3** Make accurate drawings of these triangles.
Measure the unknown lengths in each triangle.

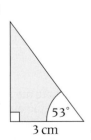

**a** 53°, 3 cm

**b** 120°, 3 cm, 5 cm

**c** 5 cm, 4 cm

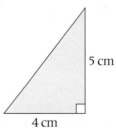

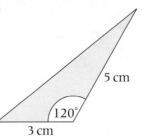

**4** Make an accurate drawing of this parallelogram.

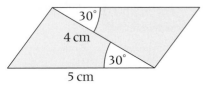

30°, 4 cm, 30°, 5 cm

Unit 3

This spread will show you how to:

- Use and interpret scale drawings
- Understand the implications of enlargement for scale drawings

**Keywords**
Proportion
Reduced
Scale
Scale drawing

Real-life lengths are **reduced** in **proportion** to give a **scale drawing**.

**Real-life**

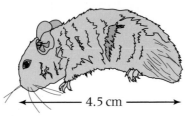

9 cm

**Scale drawing**
Scale: 1 cm represents 2 cm

4.5 cm

**Scale:** 1 cm
represents 1 m

6 cm

Length in scale
drawing = 6 cm
Length in real
life = 6 m

The scale of a drawing gives the relationship between the drawing and the real object.

**Example**

The scale for this drawing of a chessboard is 1 cm represents 10 cm.
**a** Calculate the dimensions of the real chessboard.
**b** Calculate the perimeter of the real chessboard.
**c** How many squares are on the real chessboard?

4 cm

**a** 1 cm represents 10 cm.
4 cm represents 4 × 10 cm = 40 cm.
Dimensions are 40 cm by 40 cm.
**b** Perimeter 40 + 40 + 40 + 40 = 160 cm.
**c** Number of squares = 8 × 8 = 64.

There are exactly
the same number
of squares on
the scale drawing
as on the real
chessboard.

1 The scale on a drawing is 1 cm represents 5 cm.
Calculate the distance represented by
  **a** 2 cm          **b** 4 cm
  **c** 5 cm          **d** 10 cm
  **e** 20 cm

2 The scale on a drawing is 1 cm represents 10 cm.
Calculate the distance represented by
  **a** 2 cm          **b** 5 cm
  **c** 2.5 cm        **d** 0.5 cm
  **e** 4.1 cm

3 The scale on a drawing is 1 cm represents 50 cm.
Calculate the distance represented by
  **a** 4 cm          **b** 5 cm
  **c** 10 cm         **d** 0.5 cm
  **e** 1.5 cm

4 The scale on a drawing is 1 cm represents 1 km.
Calculate the distance represented by
  **a** 2 cm          **b** 2.5 cm
  **c** 3.2 cm        **d** 10 cm
  **e** 0.25 cm

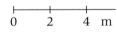

5 The scale on a drawing is 1 cm represents 2 m.
Calculate the distance represented by
  **a** 8 cm          **b** 7.5 cm
  **c** 3.6 cm        **d** 10.8 cm
  **e** 0.45 cm

**A02 Functional Maths**

6 Using this scale drawing of the Eiffel Tower, calculate
   **a** the height
   **b** the width of the base.

Scale: 1 cm represents 60 m

**Unit 3**

## G6.3 | Bearings

This spread will show you how to:

• Understand angle measure using the associated language

• Give bearings accurately

**Keywords**
Bearing
Direction
Scale
Three-figure
  bearing

You can give a **direction** using the compass points to describe P.

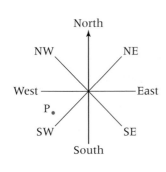

P is between SW and W.
This is not very accurate.

You use a 360° **scale** or a **bearing** to give a direction accurately.

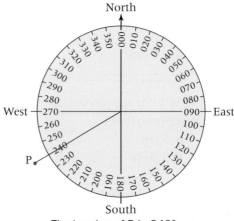

The bearing of P is 240°.
This is very accurate.

000° = North
090° = East
180° = South
270° = West

• To give a bearing accurately you
  – measure from North
  – measure clockwise
  – use three figures.

**Example**

**a** Write the bearing of Lincoln from Sheffield.

**b** Mark the position of Manchester on a bearing of 284° at a distance of 40 miles from Sheffield.

Scale: 1 cm represents 10 miles

*From* Sheffield means centre the protractor at Sheffield.

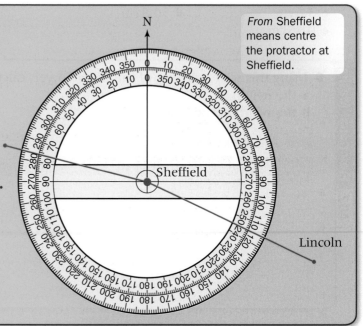

........................................

**a** Place the centre on Sheffield and 0° at North. Read off the direction of Lincoln as 115°.

**b** 1 cm represents 10 miles.
4 cm represents 40 miles

390

**1** **a** Use a protractor to draw an accurate diagram of the compass points.

**b** On your diagram, give the **three-figure bearings** of each of the compass points.

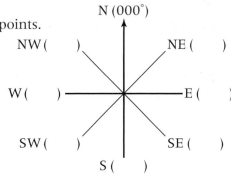

N (000°)

NW (    )          NE (    )

W (    )          E (    )

SW (    )          SE (    )

S (    )

A02 | Functional Maths

**2** Measure the bearing of these places from the Lookout point.
 **a** Battlefield
 **b** Tower
 **c** Church
 **d** Castle
 **e** Buoy
 **f** Yacht
 **g** Needles rocks
 **h** Lighthouse

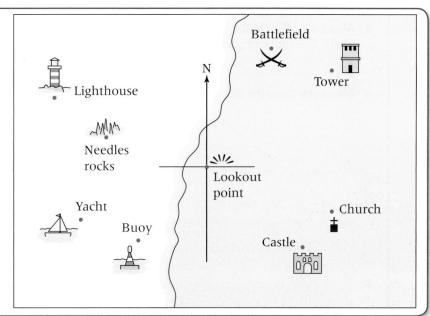

Unit 3

**3** For each question, put a cross anywhere on your page.
 Plot the points and join them to form a quadrilateral.
 Name the shape, then measure and calculate the perimeter.

**a**

| Bearing from the cross | 000° | 050° | 180° | 310° |
|---|---|---|---|---|
| Distance from the cross | 5 cm | 5 cm | 5 cm | 5 cm |

**b**

| Bearing from the cross | 055° | 145° | 235° | 325° |
|---|---|---|---|---|
| Distance from the cross | 5 cm | 5 cm | 5 cm | 5 cm |

**c**

| Bearing from the cross | 000° | 090° | 180° | 270° |
|---|---|---|---|---|
| Distance from the cross | 5 cm | 2.5 cm | 5 cm | 2.5 cm |

**d**

| Bearing from the cross | 000° | 135° | 180° | 225° |
|---|---|---|---|---|
| Distance from the cross | 5 cm | 5 cm | 5 cm | 5 cm |

**e**

| Bearing from the cross | 040° | 120° | 240° | 320° |
|---|---|---|---|---|
| Distance from the cross | 4 cm | 5 cm | 5 cm | 4 cm |

### Check out
You should now be able to:

- Understand and use bearings
- Construct triangles using a ruler and a protractor
- Use and interpret scale drawings

### Worked exam question

**a** Measure the length of *PQ*.
State the units of your answer.

P •————————————————————• Q

(2)

**b** Measure the size of angle *a*.

(1)
(Edexcel Limited 2007)

..............................................................................

**a**

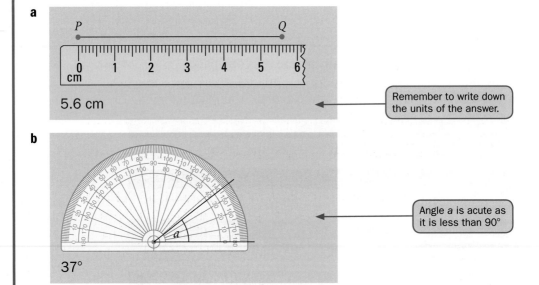

5.6 cm

> Remember to write down the units of the answer.

**b**

37°

> Angle *a* is acute as it is less than 90°

# Exam questions

**1** This is a map of part of England.

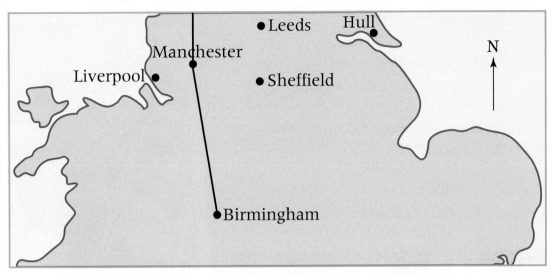

Scale: 1 cm represents 30 km

A plane flies in a straight line from Manchester to Birmingham.

**a** How far does it fly?
Give your answer in kilometres. (2)

**b** Measure and write down the bearing of Birmingham from Manchester. (1)

**2**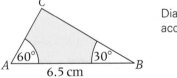

Diagram NOT
accurately drawn

**a** Make an accurate drawing of triangle *ABC*. (2)
**b** Measure the size of the angle at *C* in your triangle. (1)

(Edexcel Limited 2009)

Graffiti artists often sketch their designs before projecting them onto the surface. They sometimes use grids or parts of their body as measuring tools to help them copy the proportions accurately.

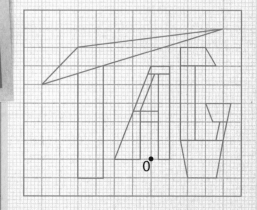

1. A graffiti artist projects an image from a sketchpad of length 20cm and height 14.8cm onto a wall of length 6m.

   a. What scale factor is being used?
   b. What is the height of the graffiti wall?

   The artist's hand-span is 150mm.
   c. What are the dimensions of the wall in terms of hands?

## Grid method  ★ ★ ★ ★

The T is made up of a trapezium and a scalene triangle. The coordinates of its vertices are

(-4, -1), (-4, 4.6), (-6, 4), (-4, 6), (4, 7), (-2.6, 5) and (-2.6, -1).

2. Describe
   a. the shapes used to make up   i. the A  ii. the G
   b. the coordinates of the vertices of  i. the A  ii. the G.

3. The dimensions of the sketch are 12cm × 10cm.
   a. What scale factor would you use to project this image onto a surface of dimensions 24cm × 20cm?
   b. What would the effect be on the area of the image?
   c. Calculate the area of
      i. the original sketch   ii. the enlarged image.
   d. Use a 2cm square grid to draw the enlarged image.

When a grid is being used, it is the shapes that make up the design and their borders that are important.

Here is a sketch of the word TAG drawn on a 1cm square grid. The artist's 'starting position', O, is the reference point (origin):

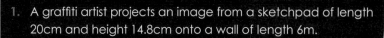

*Sketch your own graffiti tags using geometric shapes. Use the grid method to create enlarged copies of your images.*

Crop circles are geometric patterns that are displayed in crop fields.

# CROP CIRCLES

**This crop circle was found in Wiltshire in 2008. The design is based on an equilateral triangle.**

## You can recreate the pattern using these steps:

1. Use your compasses to draw a circle
2. Choose a point on your circle. Use your compasses (do not alter them) to step round the circle. Mark at each point your pencil touches the circle
3. Join three of the marks to form an equilateral triangle
4. Join the other three marks to form an equilateral triangle in the reverse direction
5. Alter your compasses. Draw a circle, with the same centre, passing through the six intersections of the two triangles
6. Alter your compasses again. Draw a circle, centred at a point of one of the triangles, so that it touches the second circle you drew
7. Construct two more circles as in step 6 at the other two points of that triangle
8. Erase your construction lines.

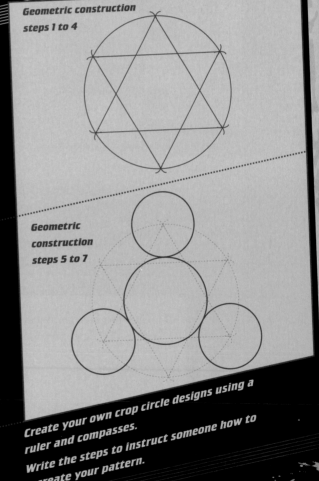

Geometric construction steps 1 to 4

Geometric construction steps 5 to 7

Create your own crop circle designs using a ruler and compasses.
Write the steps to instruct someone how to recreate your pattern.

# Introduction

Many of the man-made shapes we see in everyday life are cuboids, particularly in packaging.

## What's the point?

Cuboids are easy to assemble, and most importantly they stack up without leaving any gaps. This makes them more economical and practical for packaging and transporting goods.

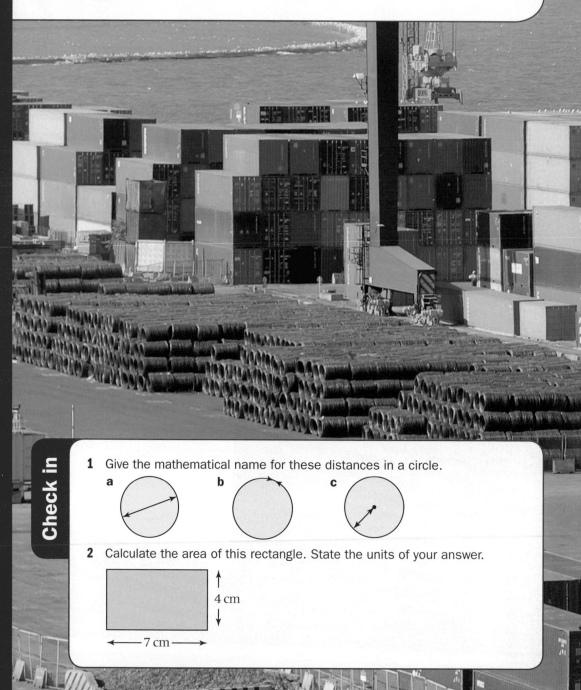

1   Give the mathematical name for these distances in a circle.

a          b          c

2   Calculate the area of this rectangle. State the units of your answer.

4 cm

← 7 cm →

**What I need to know**

**What I will learn**

**What this leads to**

G3 →

- Calculate the circumference and area of a circle
- Calculate the volume and surface area of a cuboid
- Use 2-D representations of 3-D shapes
- Understand congruence
- Find angles in polygons

→ Careers in manufacturing and industrial design

**Rich task**

A drinks company needs to design a container to hold exactly 360 ml. They are aware of environmental issues and want to minimise the surface area of the container.

**a** Design a container, in the shape of a cuboid, to hold exactly 360 ml, with the minimum possible surface area.

**b** Refine your design in the light of any practical considerations.

**Congruent shapes**

This spread will show you how to:
● Understand congruence

**Keywords**
Congruent
Corresponding
  angles
Corresponding
  sides

 p.318  ● **Congruent** shapes are exactly the same size and same shape.

**Example**

Which of these shapes are congruent?

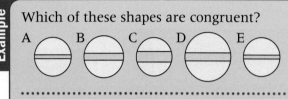

A and E are congruent.

Congruent shapes can be rotated or reflected if necessary.

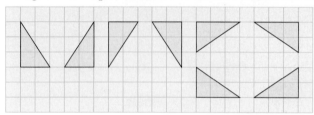

All these triangles
are congruent –
they fit exactly on
top of each other.

● In congruent shapes
  – corresponding angles are equal
  – corresponding sides are equal.

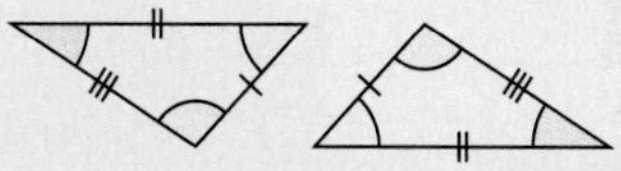

**Example**

This is triangle A.

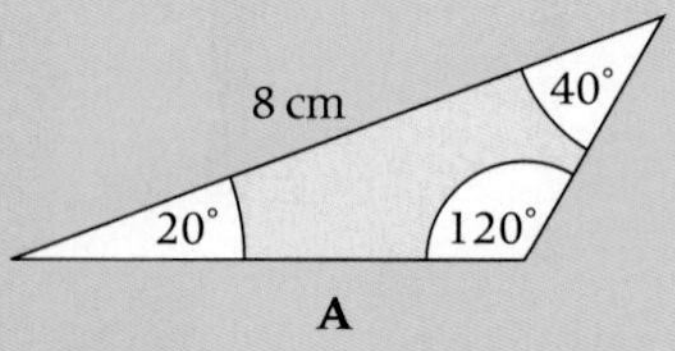

8 cm    40°
20°    120°
**A**

Which triangle is congruent to triangle A?

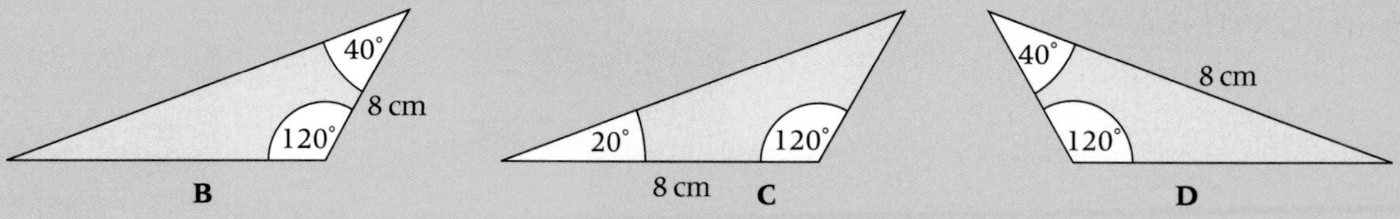

40°
8 cm
120°
**B**

20°    120°
8 cm  **C**

40°      8 cm
120°
**D**

Fill in the missing information.

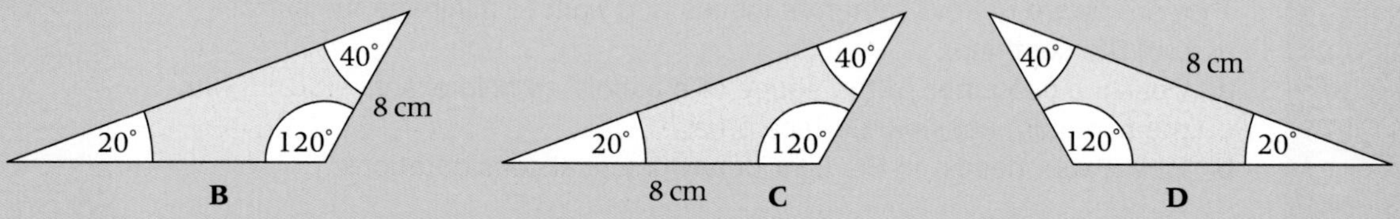

40°
8 cm
20°   120°
**B**

40°
20°   120°
8 cm  **C**

40°   8 cm
120°   20°
**D**

No, 8 cm in the wrong place.    No, 8 cm in the wrong place.    Yes, congruent.

1  State which are the congruent pairs.

**a**

   A        B        C        D

**b**

   A        B        C        D

**c**

   A        B        C        D

**d**

   A        B        C        D

**e**

   A        B        C        D

2  **a** Find **all** the pairs of quadrilaterals that are congruent.
  **b** Give the name of the shape for each pair.

3  Here is triangle A.
Which of these triangles are
congruent to triangle A?

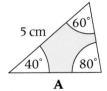

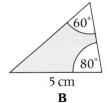 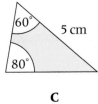 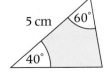 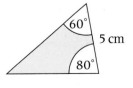

    B             C             D             E

Unit 3

This spread will show you how to:
- Find exterior angles in triangles and quadrilaterals
- Know the names of general polygons
- Understand that regular polygons have equal sides and equal angles

**Keywords**
Isosceles
Polygon
Regular

- A **polygon** is a 2-D shape with many sides and many angles.

You should know the names of these polygons.

| Sides | Name |
|-------|------|
| 3 | triangle |
| 4 | quadrilateral |
| 5 | pentagon |
| 6 | hexagon |
| 7 | heptagon |
| 8 | octagon |
| 9 | nonagon |
| 10 | decagon |

- A **regular** shape has equal sides and equal angles.

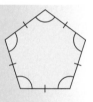

A regular pentagon has 5 equal sides and 5 equal angles.

**Example**

A regular octagon is drawn inside a circle.
There are 8 **isosceles** triangles.
Calculate the values of $x$ and $y$.

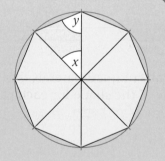

$360° \div 8 = 45°$
$x = 45°$ (angles at a point add to 360°)
$180° - 45° = 135°$
$2y = 135°$
$y = 67\frac{1}{2}°$ (angles in a triangle add to 180°)

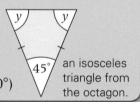

an isosceles triangle from the octagon.

p.260

- For any polygon
  - sum of exterior angles = 360°
  - interior angle + exterior angle = 180°

You can use the example to find the interior and exterior angles of an octagon.

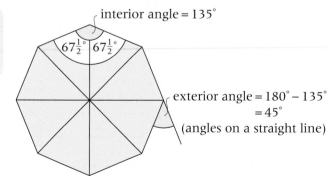

interior angle = 135°

exterior angle = 180° − 135°
= 45°
(angles on a straight line)

**1 a** Use a protractor and a ruler to draw a regular hexagon.

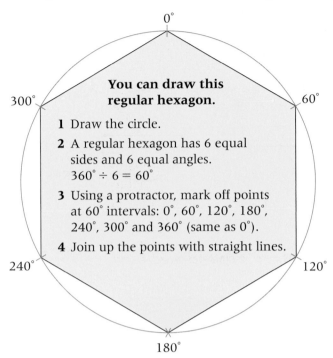

You can draw this
**regular hexagon.**

**1** Draw the circle.

**2** A regular hexagon has 6 equal
sides and 6 equal angles.
$360° \div 6 = 60°$

**3** Using a protractor, mark off points
at 60° intervals: 0°, 60°, 120°, 180°,
240°, 300° and 360° (same as 0°).

**4** Join up the points with straight lines.

**2** A regular pentagon is made from five isosceles triangles.
   **a** Calculate the three angles in an isosceles triangle for a pentagon.
   **b** Use your protractor to measure and check these angles.
   **c** Use your results to work out the interior angle of a regular pentagon.

   **d** Work out the exterior angle of a regular pentagon.

**3** You can split a quadrilateral into two
triangles by drawing a diagonal.
Angle sum of quadrilateral $= 2 \times 180°$
$= 360°$

You can split a pentagon into triangles
by drawing diagonals.

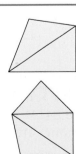

   **a** How many triangles are formed?
   **b** What is the angle sum of a pentagon?
   **c** Find the angle sum of a hexagon in a similar way.

This spread will show you how to:
- Use the vocabulary associated with circles
- Calculate the circumference and area of a circle

**Keywords**
Centre
Circle
Circumference
Diameter
Pi ($\pi$)
Radius

In a **circle**:
- the **radius** is $r$
- the **diameter** is $d$
- the **circumference** is $C$.

$C$, $d$ and $r$ are all measures of length.

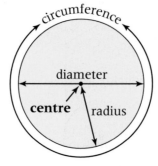

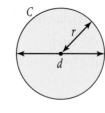

The perimeter of a circle is called the circumference.

---

- Diameter = 2 × radius

- $C = \pi \times$ diameter $= \pi d = 2\pi r$

$d = 2 \times r$

---

**Example**

Calculate the circumference of this circle.

10 cm

$C = \pi \times d$
$= 3.14 \times 10$
$= 31.4\,\text{cm}$

Remember to state the units.

---

- Area of a circle $= \pi \times$ radius $\times$ radius
  $= \pi \times r \times r$   or   $\pi r^2$

$r^2$ means $r \times r$

---

**Example**

A circular lawn has radius 3 metres.
**a** Calculate the area of the lawn. State the units of your answer.
**b** Calculate the length of edging stones needed to fit all round the edge of the lawn.
Give your answer to a suitable degree of accuracy.

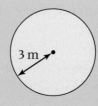

3 m

..........................................................................................................

**a** Area $= \pi r^2$
$= 3.14 \times 3 \times 3$
$= 3.14 \times 9$
$= 28.26\,\text{m}^2$

**b** Circumference $= \pi d$
$= 3.14 \times 6$
$= 18.84$
So 19 m of edging stones are needed.

Area is measured in square units.

Take $\pi = 3.14$ for all questions on this page.

**1** Calculate the circumferences of these circles. State the units of your answers.

**a**
diameter = 10 cm

**b**
diameter = 8 m

**c**
diameter = 12 cm

**d**
diameter = 20 m

**e**
radius = 2 m

**f**
radius = 8 cm

**g**
radius = 1.5 m

**h**
radius = 3.5 cm

**2** Calculate the diameter of a circle, if its circumference is
**a** 18.84 cm    **b** 15.7 m    **c** 28.26 cm    **d** 47.1 m    **e** 314 cm

**3** Calculate the areas of these circles. State the units of your answers.

**a**
radius = 7 cm

**b**
radius = 5 m

**c**
radius = 4 cm

**d**
radius = 3 m

**e**
diameter = 20 m

**f**
diameter = 16 cm

**g**
diameter = 12 mm

**h**
diameter = 18 cm

**DID YOU KNOW?**

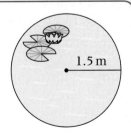

The world's largest tyre, in Michigan, USA, has a diameter of 24.4 m. That's a 76.6 m circumference!

**4** A garden pond is circular.
The radius of the pond is 1.5 m.
**a** Calculate the diameter of the pond.
**b** Calculate the circumference of the pond.
**c** Calculate the area of the pond.
Give your answers to a suitable degree of accuracy.

1.5 m

Functional Maths

AO2

Unit 3

This spread will show you how to:

- Use nets to construct cuboids from given information
- Use 2-D representations of 3-D shapes

p.264 A **solid** is a **three-dimensional (3-D)** shape.

- A **net** is a 2-D arrangement that can be folded to form a solid shape.

The net of a **cube** has 6 squares.

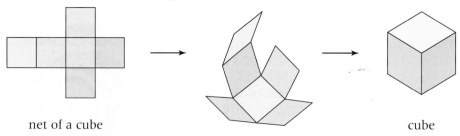

net of a cube                                   cube

There are many other possible nets of a cube.

The net of a **cuboid** has 6 rectangles.

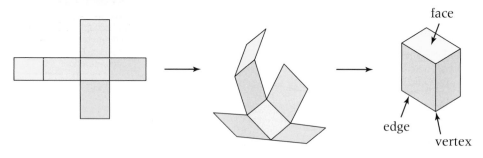

face

edge                vertex

A cuboid has
6 **faces**,
12 **edges**
and
8 vertices.

The plural of **vertex** is vertices.

Here is the net of a cuboid.
**a** State the dimensions of the cuboid.
**b** Calculate the **surface area** of the cuboid.
**c** Calculate the **volume** of the cuboid.

p.266

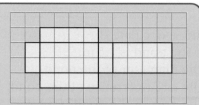

p.268

**a** 1 cm by 2 cm by 4 cm
**b** Surface area = (4 + 8 + 2) × 2
           = 28 cm$^2$
**c** Volume = 2 × 4 × 1
          = 8 cm$^3$

**1** State whether each arrangement of squares is a net of a cube.

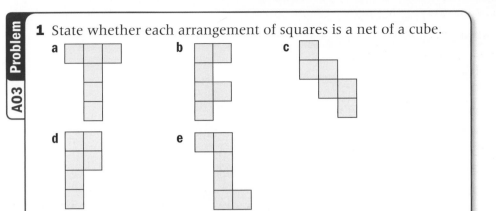

a    b    c

d    e

**2** These nets make cuboids. Copy the nets onto centimetre squared paper and cut them out to make the cuboids. Write the dimensions and calculate the surface area and the volume of each cuboid.

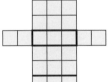  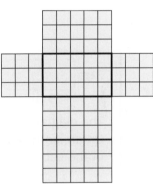

a    b    c

**3** The volume of a cube is 27 cm³.
On square grid paper, draw the net of this cube.

**4** On square grid paper, draw the net for each cuboid.

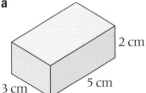 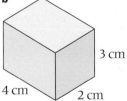 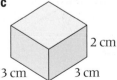

a
2 cm
3 cm    5 cm

b
3 cm
4 cm    2 cm

c
2 cm
3 cm    3 cm

 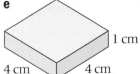

d
1 cm
3 cm    4 cm

e
1 cm
4 cm    4 cm

## Summary

### Check out

You should now be able to:

- Calculate the circumference and area of circles
- Calculate the surface area and volume of cubes and cuboids
- Use 2-D representations of 3-D shapes
- Draw nets and show how they fold to make a solid
- Recognise congruent shapes
- Find interior and exterior angles in polygons

### Worked exam question

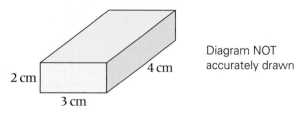

Diagram NOT
accurately drawn

The diagram shows a solid cuboid.
On an isometric grid, make an accurate full size drawing
of the cuboid.

(2)

(Edexcel Limited 2007)

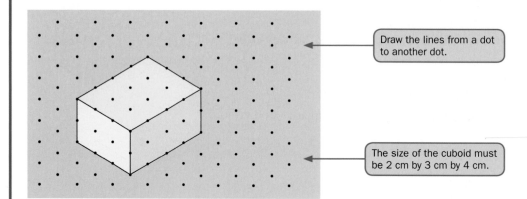

Draw the lines from a dot
to another dot.

The size of the cuboid must
be 2 cm by 3 cm by 4 cm.

## Exam questions

**1**

Here is the net of a 3-D shape.
The diagrams show four 3-D shapes.

 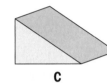 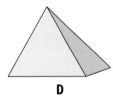

    **A**            **B**            **C**            **D**

Write down the letter of the 3-D shape which can be made from the net.     (1)

(Edexcel Limited 2006)

**2**

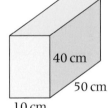

40 cm

50 cm

10 cm

Diagram NOT
accurately drawn

The diagram shows a cuboid.

The length of the cuboid is 50 cm.
The width of the cuboid is 10 cm.
The height of the cuboid is 40 cm.

Work out the volume of the cuboid.     (2)

**3**

8 cm

Diagram NOT
accurately drawn

The radius of this circle is 8 cm.

Work out the circumference of the circle.
Give your answer correct to 2 decimal places.     (2)

(Edexcel Limited 2008)

This spread will show you how to:
- Round numbers to a given number of decimal places
- Round numbers to a given number of significant figures
- Use approximation to estimate an answer

**Keywords**
Approximate
Decimal places
Estimate
Rounding
Significant figures

You can round a decimal number to a given accuracy.

To round 718.394 to 2 **decimal places**, look at the **thousandths** digit.

The **thousandths** digit is **4**, so round down to 718.39.

718.394 = 718.39 (to 2 decimal places).

718.39       718.395       718.40

You can also round numbers to a given number of **significant figures**.

- The first **non-zero digit** in a number is called the **1st significant figure** – it has the highest value in the number.

You only need to know how to round to 1 significant figure for your exam.

**Example**

Round 54.76 to 2 **significant figures**.

Look at the 3rd significant figure.

| Tens | Units | • | tenths | hundredths |
|------|-------|---|--------|------------|
| 5 | 4 | • | 7 | 6 |

The **3rd significant** figure is **7**, so the number is rounded up to 55.

54.76 ≈ 55 (to 2 significant figures).

- When **rounding numbers** to a given degree of accuracy, look at the next digit. If it is 5 or more then round up, otherwise round down.

You can **estimate** the answer to a calculation by rounding the numbers.

**Example**

Estimate the answer to $\frac{6.23 \times 9.89}{18.7}$.

You can round each of the numbers to 1 significant figure.

$\frac{6.23 \times 9.89}{18.7} \approx \frac{6 \times 10}{20} = \frac{60}{20} = 3$

1  Round each of these numbers to the
   **i** nearest 10     **ii** nearest 100     **iii** nearest 1000.
   **a** 3487                   **b** 3389              **c** 14 853 m
   **d** £57 792                **e** 92 638 kg         **f** £86 193
   **g** 3438.9                 **h** 74 899.36

2  Round each of these numbers to the nearest whole number.
   **a** 3.738                  **b** 28.77             **c** 468.63
   **d** 369.29                 **e** 19.93             **f** 26.9992
   **g** 100.501                **h** 0.001

3  Round each of these numbers to the nearest
   **i** 3 dp     **ii** 2 dp     **iii** 1 dp.
   **a** 3.4472                 **b** 8.9482            **c** 0.1284
   **d** 28.3872                **e** 17.9989           **f** 9.9999
   **g** 0.003 987              **h** 2785.5555

4  Round each of these numbers to the nearest
   **i** 3 sf     **ii** 2 sf     **iii** 1 sf.
   **a** 8.3728                 **b** 18.82             **c** 35.84
   **d** 278.72                 **e** 1.3949            **f** 3894.79
   **g** 0.008 372              **h** 2399.9            **i** 8.9858
   **j** 14.0306                **k** 1403.06           **l** 140 306

5  Write a suitable estimate for each of these calculations.
   In each case, clearly show how you estimated your answer.
   **a** $4.98 \times 6.12$            **b** $17.89 + 21.91$

   **c** $\dfrac{5.799 \times 3.1}{8.86}$      **d** $34.8183 - 9.8$

   **e** $\dfrac{32.91 \times 4.8}{3.1}$       **f** $\{9.8^2 + (9.2 - 0.438)\}^2$

C Booster

This spread will show you how to:
● Add and subtract fractions

**Keywords**
Cancel
Common
   denominator
Equivalent
Fraction

It is easy to add or subtract **fractions** when they have the same denominator.

  +    =

$\frac{3}{8}$  +  $\frac{1}{8}$  =  $\frac{4}{8}$

● You can add or subtract fractions with different denominators by first writing them as **equivalent** fractions with the same denominator.

**Example**

Calculate  **a** $\frac{3}{5} + \frac{1}{3}$  **b** $1\frac{3}{4} - \frac{5}{7}$

**a** $\frac{3}{5} + \frac{1}{3}$

$\frac{3}{5} + \frac{1}{3} = \frac{9}{15} + \frac{5}{15}$

$\phantom{\frac{3}{5} + \frac{1}{3}} = \frac{9 + 5}{15}$

$\phantom{\frac{3}{5} + \frac{1}{3}} = \frac{14}{15}$

$\overset{\times 3}{\frac{3}{5} = \frac{9}{15}}$ $\overset{\times 5}{\frac{1}{3} = \frac{5}{15}}$
$\underset{\times 3}{} \qquad \underset{\times 5}{}$

The lowest **common denominator** is the least common multiple of 5 and 3, which is 15.

**b** $1\frac{3}{4} - \frac{5}{7}$

Change the mixed number to an improper fraction:

$1\frac{3}{4} = \frac{7}{4}$

$1\frac{3}{4} - \frac{5}{7} = \frac{7}{4} - \frac{5}{7}$

$\phantom{1\frac{3}{4} - \frac{5}{7}} = \frac{49}{28} - \frac{20}{28}$

$\phantom{1\frac{3}{4} - \frac{5}{7}} = \frac{49 - 20}{28}$

$\phantom{1\frac{3}{4} - \frac{5}{7}} = \frac{29}{28} = 1\frac{1}{28}$

$\overset{\times 7}{\frac{7}{4} = \frac{49}{28}}$ $\overset{\times 4}{\frac{5}{7} = \frac{20}{28}}$
$\underset{\times 7}{} \qquad \underset{\times 4}{}$

The lowest common denominator is the least common multiple of 4 and 7, which is 28.

● You can compare and order fractions by writing them as **equivalent fractions** with the same denominator.

**Example**

Which is bigger: $\frac{3}{7}$ or $\frac{4}{9}$?

You need an equivalent fraction for both $\frac{3}{7}$ and $\frac{4}{9}$.

$\frac{27}{63} < \frac{28}{63}$  so  $\frac{3}{7} < \frac{4}{9}$  $\frac{4}{9}$ is bigger.

$\overset{\times 9}{\frac{3}{7} = \frac{27}{63}}$ $\overset{\times 7}{\frac{4}{9} = \frac{28}{63}}$
$\underset{\times 9}{} \qquad \underset{\times 7}{}$

The common denominator of these equivalent fractions will be $7 \times 9 = 63$.

**1** Work out

**a** $\frac{1}{3} + \frac{1}{3}$    **b** $\frac{3}{8} + \frac{2}{8}$    **c** $\frac{8}{11} - \frac{3}{11}$

**d** $\frac{8}{17} + \frac{5}{17}$    **e** $\frac{14}{23} - \frac{11}{23}$    **f** $\frac{5}{27} + \frac{8}{27}$

**2** Work out each of these, leaving your answer in its simplest form.

**a** $\frac{2}{3} + \frac{1}{3}$    **b** $\frac{8}{9} - \frac{2}{9}$    **c** $\frac{8}{11} + \frac{5}{11}$    **d** $\frac{15}{13} - \frac{8}{13}$

**e** $\frac{14}{9} + \frac{1}{9}$    **f** $\frac{17}{12} - \frac{9}{12}$    **g** $1\frac{2}{3} + \frac{2}{3}$    **h** $4\frac{2}{7} - \frac{5}{7}$

**3** Work out

**a** $\frac{1}{3} + \frac{1}{2}$    **b** $\frac{1}{4} + \frac{3}{5}$    **c** $\frac{3}{5} - \frac{1}{3}$    **d** $\frac{4}{5} - \frac{2}{7}$

**e** $\frac{5}{8} + \frac{1}{3}$    **f** $\frac{4}{9} + \frac{2}{5}$    **g** $\frac{7}{9} - \frac{2}{11}$    **h** $\frac{7}{15} + \frac{3}{7}$

> Write both fractions as equivalent fractions with the same denominator.

**4** Work out each of these, leaving your answer in its simplest form as appropriate.

**a** $\frac{2}{5} - \frac{1}{15}$    **b** $\frac{1}{2} - \frac{1}{3}$    **c** $\frac{2}{5} + \frac{7}{20}$    **d** $\frac{1}{2} - \frac{1}{6}$

**5** Work out each of these, leaving your answer in its simplest form.

**a** $\frac{4}{5} + \frac{2}{3}$    **b** $1\frac{1}{2} + \frac{3}{5}$    **c** $1\frac{1}{3} + 1\frac{1}{4}$    **d** $1\frac{2}{7} + \frac{3}{5}$

**e** $2\frac{2}{5} - \frac{1}{3}$    **f** $3\frac{3}{8} - 1\frac{1}{2}$    **g** $4\frac{1}{3} - 2\frac{3}{4}$    **h** $3\frac{4}{7} - 2\frac{8}{9}$

**A02 Functional Maths**

**6** Work out each of these problems, leaving your answer in its simplest form.

**a** Pete walked $3\frac{2}{3}$ miles before lunch and then a further $2\frac{1}{4}$ miles after lunch. How far did he walk altogether?

**b** A bag weighs $2\frac{3}{16}$ lb when it is full. When empty the bag weighs $\frac{3}{8}$ lb. What is the weight of the contents of the bag?

**c** Henry and Paula are eating peanuts. Henry has a full bag weighing $1\frac{3}{16}$ kg. Paula has a bag that weighs $\frac{4}{5}$ kg. What is the total mass of their two bags of peanuts?

**d** Simon spent $\frac{2}{3}$ of his pocket money on a computer game. He spent $\frac{1}{5}$ of his pocket money on a ticket to the cinema. Work out the fraction of his pocket money that he had left.

**7** Write if each of these statement are true or false.

**a** $\frac{9}{2} < 3$    **b** $\frac{17}{24} > \frac{5}{8}$    **c** $\frac{11}{12} > \frac{8}{9}$    **d** $\frac{2}{3} < \frac{5}{7}$

**e** $\frac{3}{5} > \frac{4}{7}$    **f** $\frac{26}{25} > \frac{16}{15}$    **g** $\frac{5}{4} < \frac{12}{7}$    **h** $\frac{7}{4} > \frac{12}{10}$

> < means less than
> > means more than.

**C Booster**

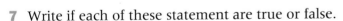

This spread will show you how to:

- Express a number as the product of its prime factors
- Recognise and use the HCF and LCM of two numbers

**Keywords**
Factor
HCF
LCM
Prime factor
Prime number

- A **prime factor** is a prime number that is also a factor of another number.
  Factors of 28 are {1, 2, 4, 7, 14, 28}.   Prime factors are {2, 7}.

- Every whole number can be written as the product of its prime factors.

Here are two common methods to find prime factors.

**Factor trees**
Split the number into a **factor** pair. Continue splitting until you reach a prime factor.

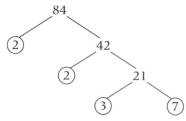

**Division by prime numbers**
Divide the number by the smallest **prime number**. Repeat dividing by larger prime numbers until you reach a prime number.

| 2 | 84 |
| 2 | 42 |
| 3 | 21 |
|   | ⑦ |

$84 = 2 \times 2 \times 3 \times 7 = 2^2 \times 3 \times 7$      $84 = 2 \times 2 \times 3 \times 7 = 2^2 \times 3 \times 7$

- You can find the **highest common factor (HCF)** of a set of numbers by using prime factors.

For example, the HCF of 30 and 135:
$30 = 2 \times 3 \times 5$      $= 2 \times 3 \times 5$

$135 = 3 \times 3 \times 3 \times 5 = 3 \times 3 \times 3 \times 5$

HCF $= 3 \times 5 = 15$

| 2 | 30 |
| 3 | 15 |
|   | 5 |

| 3 | 135 |
| 3 | 45 |
| 3 | 15 |
|   | 5 |

- Write each number as the product of its prime factors.
- Pick out the common factors 3 and 5.
- Multiply these together to get the HCF.

- You can find the **least common multiple (LCM)** of a set of numbers by using prime factors.

For example, the LCM of 28 and 126:
$28 = 2^2 \times 7 = 2 \times 2 \times 7$

$126 = 2 \times 3^2 \times 7 = 2 \times 3 \times 3 \times 7$

HCF $= 2 \times 7 = 14$
LCM $= 2 \times 3 \times 3 \times 14 = 252$

| 2 | 28 |
| 2 | 14 |
|   | 7 |

| 2 | 126 |
| 3 | 63 |
| 3 | 21 |
|   | 7 |

- Write each number as the product of its prime factors.
- Pick out the common factors 2 and 7.
- Multiply these together to get the HCF(14).
- Multiply the HCF by the remaining factors – the remaining factors are 2, 3 and 3.

**1** Work out the value of each of these expressions.
   **a** $3 \times 5^2$   **b** $2^3 \times 5$   **c** $3^2 \times 7$
   **d** $2^2 \times 3^2 \times 5$ **e** $3^2 \times 7^2$

**2** Express these numbers as products of their prime factors.
   **a** 18      **b** 24      **c** 40      **d** 39
   **e** 48      **f** 82      **g** 100     **h** 144
   **i** 180     **j** 315     **k** 444     **l** 1350

**3** In each of these questions, Jack has been asked to write each of the numbers as the product of its prime factors.
   **i** Mark his work and identify any errors he has made.
   **ii** Correct any of Jack's mistakes.
   **a** 126      **b** 210      **c** 221

| 2 | 126 |
| 3 | 63 |
| 3 | 21 |
|   | 7 |

| 2 | 210 |
| 3 | 105 |
| 3 | 21 |
|   | 7 |

| 221 |
|  |
|  |

Answer: $126 = 2 \times 3^2$    Answer: $2 \times 3^2 \times 7$    Answer: 221

**A03 Problem**

**4** The number 18 can be written as $2 \times 3 \times 3$.
   You can say that 18 has three prime factors.
   **a** Find three numbers with exactly three prime factors.
   **b** Find five numbers with exactly four prime factors.
   **c** Find four numbers between 100 and 300 with exactly five prime factors.
   **d** Find a two-digit number with exactly six prime factors.

**5** Find the HCF of
   **a** 9 and 24       **b** 15 and 40      **c** 18 and 24
   **d** 96 and 144     **e** 12, 15 and 18  **f** 425 and 816.

**6** Find the LCM of
   **a** 9 and 24       **b** 15 and 40      **c** 18 and 24
   **d** 20 and 30      **e** 12, 15 and 18  **f** 48, 54 and 72.

**7** Cancel these fractions to their simplest forms using the HCF of the numerator and denominator to help.
   **a** $\frac{6}{8}$   **b** $\frac{12}{18}$   **c** $\frac{60}{96}$
   **d** $\frac{36}{54}$  **e** $\frac{117}{169}$  **f** $\frac{26}{65}$

**C Booster**

# Harder percentage increase and decrease

This spread will show you how to:
● Calculate percentage increase and decrease using a range of methods

Percentages are used in real life to show how much an amount has increased or decreased.

● To calculate a **percentage increase**, work out the increase and add it to the original amount.

● To calculate a **percentage decrease**, work out the decrease and subtract it from the amount.

WORKERS DEMAND A 6% INCREASE
MARKET NEWS

**Example**

**a** Alan is paid £940 a month. His employer increases his wage by 3%. Calculate the new wage Alan is paid each month.
**b** A new car costs £19 490. After one year the car depreciates in value by 8.7%. What is the new value of the car?

· · · · · · · · · · · · · · · · · · · · · · · · · · · · · · · · · · · · · · · · · · · · · · ·

**a** Calculate 3% of the amount.
Add to the original amount.
Increase in wage = 3% of £940 = $\frac{3}{100} \times £940$

$= \frac{3 \times 940}{100} = \frac{2820}{100}$

Increase in wage = £28.20 per month
Alan's new wage = £940 + £28.20 = £968.20

**b** Calculate 8.7% of the amount.
Subtract from the original amount.
Depreciation = 8.7% of £19 490

$= \frac{87}{100} \times £19\ 490$

$= 0.087 \times £19\ 490$

Price reduction = £1695.63
New value of car = £19 490 − £1695.63 = £17 794.37

The percentage calculation has been worked out using a written method.

The percentage calculation has been worked out using a calculator.

Money saved in a bank account usually earns **interest**.

To calculate **compound interest** you work out the amount of money in the bank account at the end of each year. At the end of the next year the interest is paid on **all** the money.

You will not need to know about compound interest for the Foundation exam.

**Example**

Ben puts £1200 into a bank account. Each year the bank pays a rate of interest of 10%. Work out the amount of money in Ben's bank account after 3 years.

| Year 1 amount | Year 2 amount | Year 3 amount |
|---|---|---|
| = (100 + 10)% of £1200 | = 110% of £1320 | = 110% of £1452 |
| = 110% × £1200 | = 1.1 × £1320 | = 1.1 × £1452 |
| = 1.1 × £1200 = £1320 | = £1452 | = £1597.20 |

**1** Calculate these amounts using an appropriate method.
a 25% of 18 kg
b 20% of 51 m
c 15% of 360°
d 2% of 37 cm
e 65% of 510 ml
f 17.5% of 360°
g 28% of 65 kg
h 31% of 277 kg
i 3.6% of 154 kg
j 0.3% of 1320 m²

**2** Calculate each of these using a mental or written method.
a Increase £350 by 10%
b Decrease 74 kg by 5%
c Increase £524 by 5%
d Decrease 756 km by 35%
e Increase 960 kg by 17.5%

**3** Calculate these. Give your answers to 2 decimal places as appropriate.
a Increase £340 by 17%
b Decrease 905 kg by 42%
c Increase £1680 by 4.7%
d Decrease 605 km by 0.9%
e Increase $2990 by 14.5%

**A02 Functional Maths**

**4** These are the weekly wages of five employees at Suits-U clothing store. The manager has decided to increase all the employees' wages by 4%. Calculate the new wage of each employee.

| Employee | Original wage | Increase | New wage |
|---|---|---|---|
| Hanif | £350 | 350 × 1.04 = ? | |
| Bonny | £285.50 | | |
| Wilf | £412.25 | | |
| Gary | £209.27 | | |
| Marielle | £198.64 | | |

Give your answers to 2 decimal places as appropriate.

**5 a** Patricia puts £8000 into a bank account. Each year the bank pays a compound interest rate of 5%. Work out the amount of money in Patricia's bank account after 2 years.

**b** Simone puts £12 500 into a savings account. Each year the building society pays a compound interest rate of 6%. Work out the amount of money in Simone's bank account after 2 years.

**c** Antonio invests £3400 into a Super Saver account. Each year the account pays a compound interest rate of 6%. Work out the amount of money in Antonio's account after 3 years.

Compound interest will not appear in your exam. However it is a good example of maths in everyday life.

# +5 Dividing in a given ratio

**Unit 1**

This spread will show you how to:

- Divide an amount in a given ratio
- Solve multi-step problems involving ratio

**Keywords**
Ratio
Scale

You can divide a quantity in a given **ratio**.

**Example**

Sean and Patrick share £348 in the ratio 5 : 7.
How much money do they each receive?

Sean receives 5 parts for every 7 parts that Patrick receives.

Total number of parts = 5 + 7
$\quad$ = 12 parts
Each part $\quad$ = £348 ÷ 12
$\quad$ = £29

Sean will receive 5 parts $\quad$ = 5 × £29
$\quad$ = £145
Patrick will receive 7 parts = 7 × £29
$\quad$ = £203

Check your answer by adding up the two parts. They should add up to the amount being shared!
£145 ÷ £203 = £348

Some calculations involving ratio and **scale** need to be broken down into smaller steps.

**Example**

A model is made of a truck.
The length of the model is 28 centimetres.
The length of the real truck is 6.3 metres.
Work out the ratio of the length of the model to the length of the real truck.
Write your answer in the form 1 : $n$.

**Step 1**
Express the ratio in equal units.

Length of model : length of truck
$\quad$ 28 cm : 6.3 m
$\quad$ 28 cm : 630 cm
$\quad$ 28 : 630

**Step 2**
Express the ratio in the form 1 : $n$.

The scale is 1 : 22.5.

÷28 ( 28 : 630 ) ÷28
$\quad$ 1 : 22.5

When a ratio is expressed in different units, convert the measurements to the same unit.

416

**1** Solve each of these problems.

   **a** The ratio of boys to girls in a class is 4 : 5. There are 12 boys in the class. How many girls are there?

   **b** In a metal alloy the ratio of aluminium to tin is 8 : 5. How much aluminium is needed to mix with 55 kg of tin?

   **c** The ratio of the number of purple flowers to the number of white flowers in a garden is 5 : 11. There are 132 white flowers. How many purple flowers are there?

   **d** The ratio of Key Stage 3 students to Key Stage 4 students in a school is 7 : 6. There are 588 Key Stage 3 students. How many Key Stage 4 students are there at the school?

> Hint for part **a**:
> For every 4 boys, there are 5 girls.
>   8 boys → 10 girls
>  12 boys → ? girls

**2 a** A map has a scale of 1 : 400. A distance in real life is 4.8 m. What is this distance on the map?

   **b** In a school the ratio of teachers to students is 1 : 22.5. If there are 990 students at the school, how many teachers are there?

   **c** The model of an aircraft is in the scale 1 : 32. If the real aircraft is 12.48 m long, how long is the model?

**3** A map has a scale of 1 : 5000.

   **a** What is the distance in real life of a measurement of 6.5 cm on the map?

   **b** What is the distance on the map of a measurement of 30 m in real life?

**4** Solve each of these problems.

   **a** Divide £90 in the ratio 3 : 7.

   **b** Divide 369 kg in the ratio 7 : 2.

   **c** Divide 103.2 tonnes in the ratio 5 : 3.

   **d** Divide 35.1 litres in the ratio 5 : 4.

   **e** Divide £36 in the ratio 1 : 2 : 3.

**5** Solve each of these problems. Give your answers to 2 decimal places where appropriate.

   **a** Divide £75 in the ratio 8 : 7.

   **b** Divide £1000 in the ratio 7 : 13.

   **c** Divide 364 days in the ratio 5 : 2.

   **d** Divide 500 g in the ratio 2 : 5.

   **e** Divide 600 m in the ratio 5 : 9.

# Expanding and factorising

This spread will show you how to:
- Multiply a single term over a bracket
- Take out common factors

**Keywords**
Brackets
Expand
Simplify

- You can multiply out brackets.
  You multiply each term inside the bracket by the term outside.

$$2(x+4) = 2 \times x + 2 \times 4 = 2x + 8$$

$2 \times 4 = 8$

$2 \times x = 2x$

In the picture, there are normally x cookies in each pack.

**Example**

Expand each expression.
**a** $4(y + 3)$      **b** $2(3x + 1)$      **c** $n(n + 5)$

**a** $4(y + 3) = 4 \times y + 4 \times 3$
$\phantom{4(y + 3)} = 4y + 12$

**b** $2(3x + 1) = 2 \times 3x + 2 \times 1$
$\phantom{2(3x + 1)} = 6x + 2$

**c** $n(n + 5) = n \times n + 5 \times n$
$\phantom{n(n + 5)} = n^2 + 5n$

**Expand** means 'multiply out'.

$n \times n = n^2$

To **simplify** expressions with brackets, expand the brackets and collect like terms.

**Example**

Simplify each of these.
**a** $2(p + 2) + 3p$      **b** $m(m + 2) + m$      **c** $3(x + 1) + 2(4x + 2)$

**a** $2(p + 2) + 3p = 2p + 4 + 3p$
$\phantom{2(p + 2) + 3p} = 2p + 3p + 4$
$\phantom{2(p + 2) + 3p} = 5p + 4$

**b** $m(m + 2) + m = m^2 + 2m + m$
$\phantom{m(m + 2) + m} = m^2 + 3m$

**c** $3(x + 1) + 2(4x + 2)$

$= 3x + 3 + 8x + 4 = 11x + 7$

Like terms have the same power of the same letter.
$m^2$ and $m$ are **not** like terms.

- Factorising is the 'opposite' of expanding brackets.
- To factorise an expression, look for a **common factor** for all the terms.

A common factor divides into all the terms.

$$2(x + 4) \overset{\text{expand}}{\underset{\text{factorise}}{=}} 2x + 8$$

**In number...**
a factor is a number that exactly divides into another number.

2, 3 and 4 are factors of 12.

**In algebra...**
a factor is a number or letter that exactly divides into another term.

3 and $2x$ are factors of $6x$.

**1** Expand the brackets in these expressions.

   **a** $3(m + 2)$    **b** $4(p + 6)$    **c** $2(x + 4)$    **d** $5(q + 1)$

   **e** $2(6 + n)$    **f** $3(2 + t)$    **g** $4(3 + s)$    **h** $2(4 + v)$

**2** Expand these expressions.

   **a** $3(2q + 1)$    **b** $2(4m + 2)$    **c** $3(4x + 3)$    **d** $2(3k + 1)$

   **e** $5(2 + 2n)$    **f** $3(4 + 2p)$    **g** $4(1 + 3y)$    **h** $2(5 + 4z)$

---

**Functional Maths**   **AO2**

**3** At a pick-your-own farm, Lucy picks $n$ apples.

Mary picks 5 more apples than Lucy.

   **a** Write down, in terms of $n$, the number of apples Mary picks.

Nat picks 3 times as many apples as Mary.

   **b** Write down, in terms of $n$, the number of apples Nat picks.

---

**4** Expand and simplify each of these expressions.

   **a** $3(p + 3) + 2p$    **b** $2(m + 4) + 5m$    **c** $4(x + 1) - 2x$

   **d** $2(5 + k) + 3k$    **e** $4(2t + 3) + t - 2$    **f** $3(2r + 1) - 2r + 4$

---

**Functional Maths**   **AO2**

**5** On Monday a shop sells $s$ DVDs.

On Tuesday the shop sells 6 more DVDs than on Monday.

   **a** Write an expression for the number of DVDs it sells on Tuesday.

On Wednesday the shop sells twice as many DVDs as on Tuesday.

   **b** Write an expression for the number of DVDs it sells on Wednesday.

On Thursday the shop sells 7 more DVDs than on Wednesday.

   **c** Write an expression for the number of DVDs it sells on Thursday.

Give your answer in its simplest form.

---

**6** Find all the common factors of

   **a** $2x$ and 6    **b** $4y$ and 12    **c** 10 and $20j$    **d** 6 and $12p$

   **e** 9 and $6q$    **f** $6t$ and 4    **g** $4x$ and 10    **h** $24t$ and 8

**7** Find the highest common factor of

   **a** $3x$ and 9    **b** $12r$ and 10    **c** $6m$ and 8    **d** 4 and $4z$

**8** Find the highest common factor of

   **a** $y^2$ and $y$    **b** $4s^2$ and $s$    **c** $7m$ and $m^3$    **d** $2y^2$ and $2y$

**9** Factorise these expressions.

   **a** $2x + 10$    **b** $3y + 15$    **c** $8p - 4$    **d** $6 + 3m$

   **e** $5n + 5$    **f** $12 - 6t$    **g** $14 + 4k$    **h** $9z - 3$

> Hint for **6a**:
> 2 and $x$ are factors of $2x$.
> 1, 2, 3 and 6 are factors of 6.
> 2 is the common factor of $2x$ and 6.

**C Booster**

This spread will show you how to:

- Plot graphs of functions in which $y$ is given explicitly in terms of $x$

A straight line graph is made up of an infinite number of points.

- All the points on a straight line **satisfy** the equation of the line.

- Where two straight lines cross, the coordinates satisfy the equations of both lines.

The lines $x = 4$ and $y = -1$ are drawn on this graph.

Every point on the line $x = 4$ has $x$-coordinate 4.
Every point on the line $y = -1$ has $y$-coordinate $-1$.

So the point where they cross is $(4, -1)$.

The point P satisfies both equations: $x = 4$ **and**
$y = -1$. It has coordinates $(4, -1)$.

P is the **solution** to the equations $x = 4$ and $y = -1$.

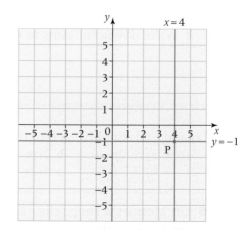

**Example**

a  Draw the graphs of $y = x + 6$ and $y = 2x$
   on the same pair of axes.
b  Write the coordinates of the point where they cross.
c  What can you say about this point?

..................................................................

a  $y = x + 6$

| x | −2 | −1 | 0 | 1 | 2 |
|---|----|----|---|---|---|
| y | 4 | 5 | 6 | 7 | 8 |

$y = 2x$

| x | −2 | −1 | 0 | 1 | 2 |
|---|----|----|---|---|---|
| y | −4 | −2 | 0 | 2 | 4 |

b  Graphs cross at $(6, 12)$
c  $(6, 12)$ satisfies both equations.
   $x = 6$ is the solution to $x + 6 = 12$ and $2x = 12$.

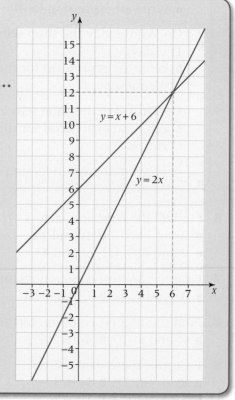

1   Write the coordinates of the points where these lines cross.
    Draw graphs to check your answers.
    **a** $x = 2$ and $y = 3$
    **b** $x = -1$ and $y = -4$
    **c** $x = 3$ and $y = 7$
    **d** $x = -2$ and $y = -4$
    **e** $x = 7$ and $y = -2$
    **f** $y = 1$ and $x = 4$

2   For each pair of equations,
    decide whether the lines
    will cross and then draw the
    graphs on a copy of this grid
    to check your answers.
    **a** $y = 2x + 1$ and $y = 4x + 2$
    **b** $y = 3$ and $y = x + 1$
    **c** $y = 3x + 2$ and $y = 3x - 1$
    **d** $y = x$ and $y = -x$

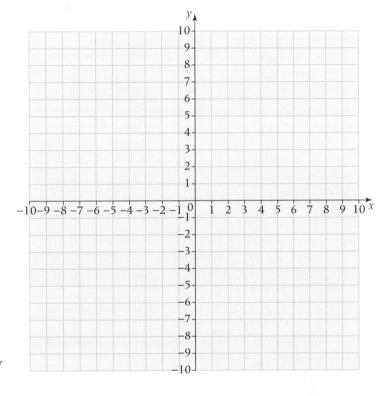

3   For each pair of lines from
    question **2** that cross, write
    the coordinates of the point
    where the lines cross.

4   **a** Draw the graphs of
    $y = -x + 2$ and $y = 2x - 1$
    on the same axes.
    **b** Write the coordinates of
    the point where the two
    lines cross.
    **c** Does the point $(1, 2)$ satisfy
    both of these equations?
    Explain how you know.

5   **a** Draw the graphs of $y = 2x - 4$ and $y = x - 1$ on the same axes.
    **b** Write the coordinates of the point where they cross.

6   **a** Draw the graphs of these two equations on the same axes.
        $x + 2y = 8$
        $x - y = 2$
    **b** Where the two lines cross, the $x$ and $y$ values satisfy both these
    equations.
    Write these $x$ and $y$ values.

# 8

# Equations with brackets and fractions

This spread will show you how to:

● Solve linear equations that require prior simplification of brackets and fractions

**Keywords**

Brackets
Expand

● To solve equations with the unknown on both sides and brackets
   – Expand the brackets
   – Use the balance method.

---

**Example**

Solve each equation.
**a** $2(y + 4) = 4y$
**b** $6r - 2 = 4(r + 3)$

····················································································

**a** $2(y + 4) = 4y$            Expand the brackets.
    $2y + 8 = 4y$            Subtract $2y$ from both sides.
        $8 = 4y - 2y$
        $8 = 2y$              Divide both sides by 2.
        $4 = y$

**b**       $6r - 2 = 4(r + 3)$
        $6r - 2 = 4r + 12$          Subtract $4r$ from both sides.
  $6r - 4r - 2 = 4r - 4r + 12$
        $2r - 2 = 12$           Add 2 to both sides.
           $2r = 12 + 2$
           $2r = 14$           Divide both sides by 2.
             $r = 7$

---

**Example**

Solve each equation.

**a** $\dfrac{x}{4} = -3$                  **b** $\dfrac{x + 3}{2} = 5$

·······································································

**a**    $\dfrac{x}{4} = -3$               **b**    $\dfrac{x + 3}{2} = 5$

   $4 \times \dfrac{x}{4} = -3 \times 4$           $2 \times \dfrac{x + 3}{2} = 5 \times 2$

        $x = -12$              $x + 3 = 10$
                                $x = 10 - 3$
                                $x = 7$

**1** Solve these equations.
   **a** $2(r + 6) = 5r$          **b** $6(s - 3) = 12s$
   **c** $4(2t + 8) = 24t$      **d** $5(v - 1) = 6v$

**2** Solve these equations.
   **a** $2(a + 5) = 7a - 5$     **b** $3(b - 2) = 5b - 2$
   **c** $2(c + 6) = 5c - 3$     **d** $3d + 8 = 2(d + 2)$

**3** Solve these equations.
   **a** $3(2x - 4) = 7x - 18$    **b** $2(3y + 2) = 5y - 2$
   **c** $4(2z + 1) = 6z + 15$    **d** $-4(6m + 1) = -17m - 18$

**4** Solve these equations.
   **a** $2(e + 3) = 4e - 1$     **b** $4f + 3 = 2(f + 2)$
   **c** $4(2g + 1) = 6g + 1$     **d** $3(2h + 3) = 5h + 8$

**5** Solve these equations.
   **a** $\dfrac{x}{3} = 3$     **b** $\dfrac{m}{4} = -2$     **c** $\dfrac{-n}{3} = 6$     **d** $\dfrac{m}{5} = 4$

**6** Find the value of the unknown in each of these equations.
   **a** $\dfrac{s}{3} + 5 = 8$   **b** $4 - \dfrac{t}{2} = 1$   **c** $\dfrac{u}{5} + 7 = 5$   **d** $16 = \dfrac{v}{4} + 13$

**7** Solve these equations.
   **a** $\dfrac{2x}{3} + 5 = 9$   **b** $\dfrac{3y}{2} - 5 = 4$   **c** $3 - \dfrac{2z}{5} = -3$   **d** $\dfrac{3q}{2} + 5 = -7$

**8** Solve these equations.
   **a** $\dfrac{x + 5}{3} = 2$   **b** $\dfrac{x - 3}{4} = 2$   **c** $\dfrac{x + 9}{2} = -4$   **d** $\dfrac{10 - x}{4} = 1$

**9** I think of a number.
I divide my number by 4 and add 6.
   **a** Write an expression for 'I divide my number by 4 and add 6'.
      Use $n$ to represent the number.
   **b** My answer is 10.
      Using your expression from part **a**, write an equation to
      show this.
   **c** Solve your equation to find the number, $n$.

$\dfrac{n}{\square} + \square$

Expression
**a** = 10

**A03** **Problem**

**C Booster**

# The general term

This spread will show you how to:

- Generate and describe integer sequences using position-to-term definitions

- A **position-to-term** rule links a term with its position in the sequence.

For example, the 4 times table: 4, 8, 12, 16, 20, 24, ... can be written as

| 1st term = T(1) | 2nd term = T(2) | 3rd term = T(3) | 4th term = T(4) | 5th term = T(5) | 6th term = T(6) |
|---|---|---|---|---|---|
| 4 | 8 | 12 | 16 | 20 | 24 |

$T(1) = 1 \times 4$
$T(2) = 2 \times 4$
$T(3) = 3 \times 4$
$T(10) = 10 \times 4$

The **general term** or ***n*th term** of the 4 times table is $T(n) = n \times 4$ or $4n$.

You can generate a sequence from the general term.

**Example**

Find the first three terms and the 10th term of the sequence with general term $3n + 2$.

- - - - - - - - - - - - - - - - - - - - - - - - - - - - - - - - - - - - - - - - -

1st term $3 \times 1 + 2 \rightarrow 5$
2nd $\quad 3 \times 2 + 2 \rightarrow 8$
3rd $\quad 3 \times 3 + 2 \rightarrow 11$
10th $\quad 3 \times 10 + 2 \rightarrow 32$

- To find the general term of a linear sequence.
  - work out the common difference
  - write the common difference as the coefficient of *n*
  - compare the terms in the sequence to the multiples of *n*

A linear sequence has an equal spacing between terms.

**Example**

Find the general term of the sequence
5, 8, 11, 14, 17 ...

- - - - - - - - - - - - - - - - - - - - - - - - - - - - - - - - - - - - - - - - -

The common difference is $+3$.
The *n*th term contains the term $3n$.
Compare the sequence to the multiples of 3:

| 3*n* | 3 | 6 | 9 | 12 | 15 |
|---|---|---|---|---|---|
| Term | 5 | 8 | 11 | 14 | 17 |

Each term is 2 more than a multiple of 3.
The general term is $3n + 2$.

Check:
$n = 1 \rightarrow 3 + 2 = 5$
$n = 2 \rightarrow 6 + 2 = 8$
$n = 3 \rightarrow 9 + 2 = 11$
...

**1** Find the first three terms and the 10th term of these sequences.

    **a** $5n + 1$     **b** $3n + 8$       **c** $8n - 4$       **d** $6n - 8$

    **e** $24 - 2n$    **f** $15 - 5n$     **g** $7n - 20$    **h** $4n - 6$

**2** Copy and complete the table of results for each sequence.

    **a** $3n + 8$                            **b** $6n - 15$

| Term number | Term |
|:---:|:---|
| 1 | 11 |
| 2 | |
| 3 | |
| 5 | |
| 10 | |
| $n$ | $3n + 8$ |

| Term number | Term |
|:---:|:---|
| 1 | $-9$ |
| 2 | |
| 3 | |
| 5 | |
| 10 | |
| $n$ | $6n - 15$ |

**3** Write the first five terms of the sequences with $n$th term

    **a** $n^2 + 4$     **b** $n^2 - 2$       **c** $2n^2$         **d** $12 - n^2$

**4** **a** Find the common difference for the series 5, 9, 13, 17, 21, ...

    **b** Copy and complete this statement:

           The $n$th term contains the term $\square n$.

    **c** Copy and complete this table to show the sequence and the multiples of $n$.

| Sequence | | | | |
|:---:|:---|:---|:---|:---|
| $\square n$ | | | | |

    **d** Compare the terms in the sequence to the multiples of $n$ and write the general term for the sequence.

**5** Follow the steps in question **4** to find the general terms for these sequences.

    **a** 11, 17, 23, 29, 35, ...       **b** 1, 10, 19, 28, 37, ...

    **c** 15, 22, 29, 36, 43, ...     **d** $-10, -6, -2, 2, 6, ...$

    **e** 20, 17, 14, 11, 8, ...      **f** $15, 11, 7, 3, -1, ...$

    **g** $16, 8, 0, -8, -16, ...$    **h** $31, 23, 15, 7, -1, ...$

**6** Find the $n$th term for each of these arithmetic sequences.

    **a** 7, 11, 15, 19, 23, ...       **b** $-6, -2, 2, 6, 10, ...$

    **c** $32, 23, 14, 5, -4, ...$     **d** $15, 9, 3, -3, 9, ...$

**C Booster**

This spread will show you how to:
• Solve linear inequalities in one variable

• In an **equation**, the left-hand side equals the right-hand side.

• In an **inequality**, the left-hand and right-hand sides are not necessarily equal.

 An inequality usually has a range of values.

You use one of these signs to show the relationship between the two sides of an inequality.

| < | less than | > | greater than |
|---|---|---|---|
| ≤ | less than or equal to | ≥ | greater than or equal to |

You can show inequalities on a number line.

| $x < 2$ | $x$ is less than 2 | |
|---|---|---|
| $x > 2$ | $x$ is greater than 2 | |
| $y \leqslant 4$ | $y$ is less than or equal to 4 | |
| $y \geqslant 4$ | $y$ is greater than or equal to 4 | |

The open circle shows that 2 is not included.

The filled-in circle shows that 4 is included.

Inequalities can have more than one term, for example $3x + 4 < 19$.

You can solve an inequality to find a set of values for $x$.

**Example**

**a** Solve the inequality $3x + 4 < 19$
**b** Show the **solution set** on a number line.

........................................................................................

**a** $$3x + 4 < 19$$
$$3x + 4 - 4 < 19 - 4$$
$$3x < 15$$
$$x < 5$$

**b**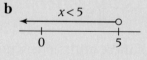

The solution set is $x < 5$.

Sometimes a letter is bounded by two inequalities.

**Example**

List the whole numbers that satisfy the inequality $-3 < x \leqslant 2$.

........................................................................................

$-3 < x$ means '$-3$ is less than $x$,' or '$x$ is greater than $-3$'.
$x \leqslant 2$ means '$x$ is less than or equal to 2'.
The whole numbers that satisfy the inequality are $-2, -1, 0, 1, 2$.

**1** Show these inequalities on a number line.
   **a** $x < 1$          **b** $x \geqslant 1$          **c** $x \geqslant 5$          **d** $x < -2$
   **e** $x < 1.5$          **f** $x > -4$          **g** $x \leqslant 3$          **h** $x \leqslant -1.5$

**2** **a** If $x > 5$, what can you say about   **i** $2x$   **ii** $4x$?
   **b** If $y \leqslant 6$, write an inequality for   **i** $3y$   **ii** $5y$.
   **c** If $x \geqslant -4$, write an inequality for $5x$.
   **d** If $m < -3$, write an inequality for $6m$.

**3** Solve these inequalities and show the solution sets on number lines.
   **a** $2x \leqslant 4$          **b** $2x < 10$          **c** $3x > -6$          **d** $4x \geqslant -16$

**4** Match each inequality to a number line.

**a**

**i** $x < -3$

**b**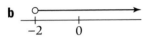

**ii** $x \leqslant 3$

**c**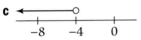

**iii** $x - 1 \leqslant -3$

**d**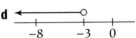

**iv** $x \geqslant -3$

**e**

**v** $x - 1 > -3$

**f**

**vi** $x + 2 < -2$

**5** Copy and complete these inequalities.
   **a** If $3x + 2 > 11$ then $3x > \square$ and $x > \square$
   **b** If $7x - 4 > 31$ then $7x > \square$ and $x > \square$
   **c** If $2x + 9 \leqslant 11$ then $2x \leqslant \square$ and $x \leqslant \square$
   **d** If $5x - 3 \geqslant 12$ then $5x \geqslant \square$ and $x \geqslant \square$

**6** Solve each of these inequalities.
   Show each solution on a number line.
   **a** $x + 7 \leqslant 12$          **b** $x - 2 \geqslant 4$          **c** $3x + 5 \geqslant 11$          **d** $2x - 5 < 3$
   **e** $5x + 1 \geqslant -4$          **f** $6x - 2 \leqslant 16$          **g** $3x + 2 > 11$          **h** $2x - 9 \leqslant -5$

**7** List the whole numbers that satisfy each of these inequalities.
   **a** $-3 \leqslant x < 2$          **b** $-2 < x \leqslant 3$          **c** $-1 \leqslant x \leqslant 4$
   **d** $0 < x \leqslant 5$          **e** $-3 \leqslant x \leqslant -1$          **f** $0 < x < 2$

This spread will show you how to:

- Use the formula to find the area of any parallelogram
- Use formulae of rectangles, triangles and parallelograms to find the area of any trapezium

**Keywords**
Area
Base
Parallelogram
Perpendicular
height
Trapezium

You can find the formula for the **area** of any **parallelogram**.

For this parallelogram ...

cut off one triangle ...

and fit it on the other end ... to make a rectangle.

height

base

- **Area of parallelogram = base × perpendicular height.**

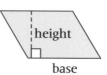

height

base

The height must be perpendicular to the base.

You can find the formula for the area of any **trapezium**.

You can fit two **congruent** trapeziums together to make a parallelogram.

Congruent means identical.

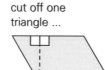 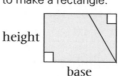 

The base of the parallelogram is $a + b$ and the height is $h$.
Area of parallelogram $= (a + b) \times h$
Area of trapezium = half area of parallelogram.

- **Area of trapezium $= \frac{1}{2} \times (a + b) \times h$**

height

The height is the perpendicular distance between the parallel sides.

**Example**

Calculate the area of each shape.

**a**

3 cm

5 cm

**b**

3 cm

4 cm

7 cm

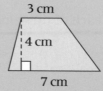

· · · · · · · · · · · · · · · · · · · · · · · · · · · · · · · · · · · · · · · · · · · · ·

**a** Area of parallelogram $= 5 \times 3$
$= 15 \, \text{cm}^2$

**b** Area of trapezium $= \frac{1}{2}(3 + 7) \times 4$
$= 5 \times 4$
$= 20 \, \text{cm}^2$

**1** Calculate the area of each parallelogram.

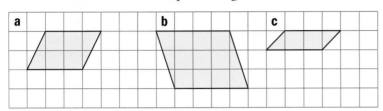

Give your answers in square units.

**2** Calculate the area of each trapezium.

**3** Calculate the area of each parallelogram. State the units of your answers.

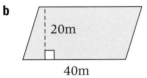 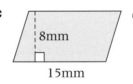 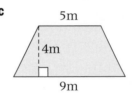 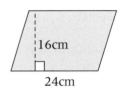

a 8cm, 10cm  b 20m, 40m  c 8mm, 15mm  d 16cm, 24cm

**4** Calculate the area of each trapezium. State the units of your answers.

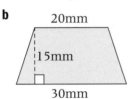 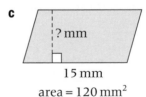 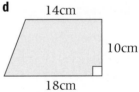 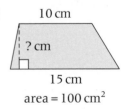

a 8cm, 5cm, 12cm  b 20mm, 15mm, 30mm  c 5m, 4m, 9m  d 14cm, 10cm, 18cm

**5** The areas of these shapes is given. Calculate the unknown lengths.

a ? m, 12 m, area = 72 m²  
b square, ? cm, area = 196 cm²  
c ? mm, 15 mm, area = 120 mm²  
d 10 cm, ? cm, 15 cm, area = 100 cm²

**6 a** Calculate the area of this shape using the formula for the area of a trapezium.
**b** Calculate the area by adding the areas of the triangles and the square.

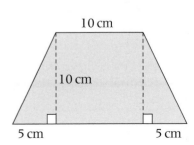

10 cm, 10 cm, 5 cm, 5 cm

429

This spread will show you how to:
- Use parallel lines and alternate angles

**Keywords**
Alternate
Corresponding
Parallel
Vertically
  opposite

When two lines cross, four angles are formed.

- **Vertically opposite** angles are equal.

When a line crosses two **parallel** lines, eight angles are formed.

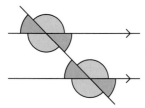

The four red **acute** angles are equal.

The four purple **obtuse** angles are equal.

Acute + obtuse = 180°

Parallel lines are always the same distance apart.

An acute angle is less than 90°. An obtuse angle is more than 90° but less than 180°.

- **Alternate** angles are equal.

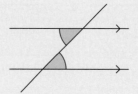

These are sometimes called 'Z angles'.

- **Corresponding** angles are equal.

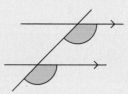

These are sometimes called 'F angles'.

**Example**

Find the unknown angles in these diagrams.
Give reasons for your answers.

**a** 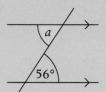  **b** 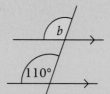  **c**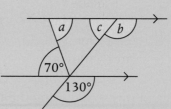

..............................................................................................

**a** $a = 56°$
  (alternate angles)

**b** $b = 110°$
  (corresponding angles)

**c** $a = 70°$          (alternate angles)
  $b = 130°$      (corresponding angles)
  $c = 180° - 130°$
     $= 50°$       (angles on straight line add to 180°)

**1** Calculate the size of the angles marked by a letter in each diagram. Give a reason for each answer.

The diagrams are not drawn to scale.

**a**

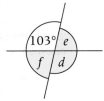

**b**

**c**

**d**

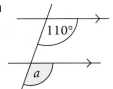

**e**

**2** Find the value of each angle marked with a letter. Give a reason for each answer.

**a**

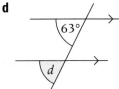

**b**

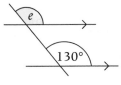

**c**

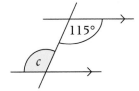

**d**

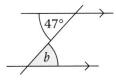

**e**

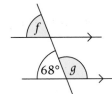

**f**

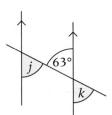

**g**

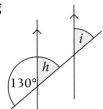

**h**

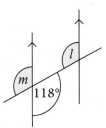

**i**

**3** Find the value of each angle marked with a letter. Give a reason in each case.

**a**

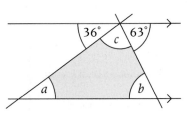

**b**

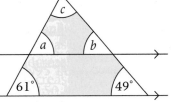

**c**

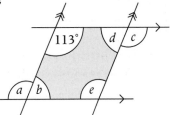

This spread will show you how to:

- Identify the scale factor of an enlargement as a ratio of the lengths

**Keywords**
Enlargement
Scale factor
Similar

- In an **enlargement**, the object and the image are **similar**,
  - the angles stay the same
  - the lengths increase in proportion.

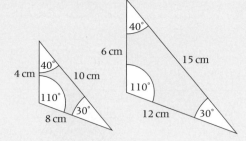

You use corresponding lengths to find the **scale factor**.

- Scale factor $= \dfrac{\text{length of image}}{\text{lengh of object}}$.

**Example**

These triangles are similar.
Find the length $x$.

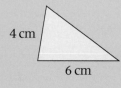

................................................................................

The scale factor is $\frac{15}{6} = 15 \div 6 = 2.5$
$x = 4\,\text{cm} \times 2.5 = 10\,\text{cm}$

**Example**

**a** Show that triangle ABE is similar to triangle ACD.
**b** Calculate the value of $x$.

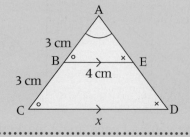

................................................................................

**a** Angle B = angle C    (corresponding angles are equal)
Angle E = angle D    (corresponding angles are equal)
Angle A is common to both triangles.
So ΔABE and ΔACD are similar.

**b** The scale factor is $6 \div 3 = 2$
$x = 4\,\text{cm} \times 2 = 8\,\text{cm}$

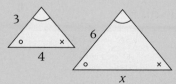

Similar shapes have the same angles but are different sizes.

**1** In each question, the two triangles are similar.
Find the value of the unknown angles.

**a**

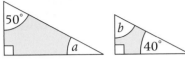

Angles in a triangle add to 180°.

**b**

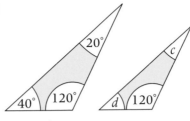

**c**

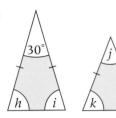

**d**

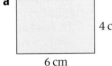

**2** Which of these rectangles are similar to the green rectangle?

For the ones that are similar, give the scale factor of the enlargement.

2 cm

3 cm

**a**
4 cm

6 cm

**b**
10 cm

15 cm

**c**
4 cm

5 cm

**d**
3 cm

6 cm

**e**
8 cm

12 cm

**f**
2 cm

2 cm

**3** In each question, the two triangles are similar. Calculate the scale factor of the enlargement and the unknown length.

**a**

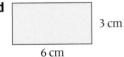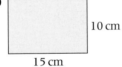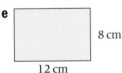

3 cm

6 cm

4 cm

? cm

**b**

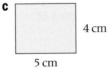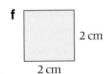

3 cm

9 cm

4 cm

? cm

**4** Calculate the value of each unknown length.

**a**

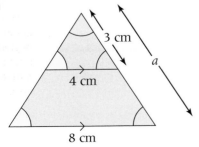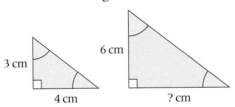

3 cm

4 cm

a

8 cm

**b**

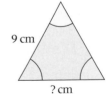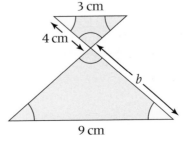

3 cm

4 cm

b

9 cm

This type of question is unlikely to appear in the Foundation tier exams.

This spread will show you how to:

- Calculate the midpoint of the line AB

**Keywords**
Coordinates
Line
Midpoint

- The **midpoint M** of a line **AB** is halfway along it.

A    M    B

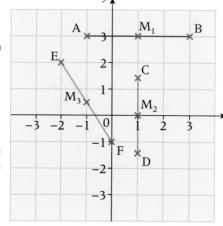

If A = (−1, 3)
and B = (3, 3)
then $M_1$ = (1, 3)

If C = (1, $1\frac{1}{2}$)
and D = (1, $−1\frac{1}{2}$)
then $M_2$ = (1, 0)

If E = (−2, 2)
and F = (0, −1)
then $M_3$ = (−1, $\frac{1}{2}$)

**M** is the midpoint.

- If **A** = $(x_1, y_1)$ and **B** = $(x_2, y_2)$ then **M** = $\left(\dfrac{x_1 + x_2}{2}, \dfrac{y_1 + y_2}{2}\right)$.

The midpoint of AB is the mean of the **coordinates** of points A and B.

**Example**

Calculate the coordinates of the midpoint between the points
**a** (7, 1) and (−3, 5)
**b** (4, −1) and (2, −2)

........................................................................................

**a** (7, 1) = $(x_1, y_1)$ and (−3, 5) = $(x_2, y_2)$

Midpoint = $\left(\dfrac{7 + -3}{2}, \dfrac{1 + 5}{2}\right)$

= $\left(\dfrac{4}{2}, \dfrac{6}{2}\right)$

= (2, 3)

**b** (4, −1) = $(x_1, y_1)$ and (2, −2) = $(x_2, y_2)$

Midpoint = $\left(\dfrac{4 + 2}{2}, \dfrac{−1 − 2}{2}\right)$

= $\left(\dfrac{6}{2}, \dfrac{−3}{2}\right)$

= (3, $−1\frac{1}{2}$)

**1 a** Draw the points A(1, 3) and B(5, 1) on a copy of the grid.

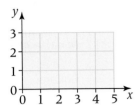

**b** M is the midpoint of the line AB.
Find the coordinates of the point M.

**2** Calculate the coordinates of the
midpoint between the points
  **a** (3, 1) and (3, 5)
  **b** (0, 4) and (4, 4)
  **c** (2, −2) and (2, 4)
  **d** (3, 1) and (7, 7)
  **e** (−2, −1) and (6, 7)
Use a copy of the grid to help you.

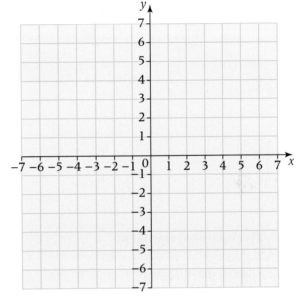

**3** The point (3, 4) is the midpoint between (x, 6) and (1, y).
Find the values of x and y.

**4** The point $(1\frac{1}{2}, 5\frac{1}{2})$ is the midpoint between (x, 4) and (2, y).
Find the values of x and y.

**5** The point (0, 2) is the midpoint between (x, 6) and (−4, y).
Find the values of x and y.

**A03 Problem**

**6** The coordinates (−1, 2), (−3, 0), (−1, −2) and (1, 0) are the
midpoints of each side of a square.
  **a** Find the coordinates of the vertices of the square.
  **b** Find the area of the square.

This spread will show you how to:

- Understand, recall and use Pythagoras' theorem

The longest side of a **right-angled triangle** is called the **hypotenuse**.
The hypotenuse is always opposite the right angle.

hypotenuse

This is a right-angled triangle.

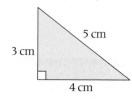

Draw the **squares** on each side.

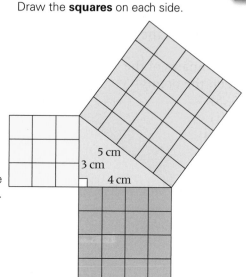

Area of yellow square $= 3 \times 3 = 9\,cm^2$
Area of red square $= 4 \times 4 = 16\,cm^2$
Area of orange square $= 5 \times 5 = 25\,cm^2$

Area of orange square = area of yellow square
+ area of red square.

This is **Pythagoras' theorem**.

- In a right-angled triangle, $c^2 = a^2 + b^2$ where $c$ is the hypotenuse.

**Example**

Calculate the unknown lengths in these triangles.

**a**

$c$
5 cm
12 cm

**b**

1.5 m
$c$
2 m

. . . . . . . . . . . . . . . . . . . . . . . . . . . . . . . . . . . . . . . . . . . . . . . . . . . .

**a** Label the sides.

**b** Label the sides.

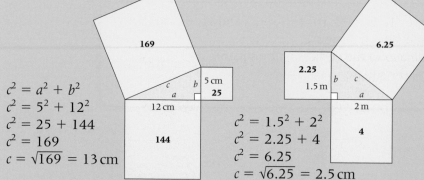

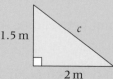

$\sqrt{\phantom{x}}$ means
**square root**.

$\sqrt{169} = 13$
because
$13 \times 13 = 169$.

$c^2 = a^2 + b^2$
$c^2 = 5^2 + 12^2$
$c^2 = 25 + 144$
$c^2 = 169$
$c = \sqrt{169} = 13\,cm$

$c^2 = 1.5^2 + 2^2$
$c^2 = 2.25 + 4$
$c^2 = 6.25$
$c = \sqrt{6.25} = 2.5\,cm$

**1** Calculate the area of these squares. State the units of your answers.

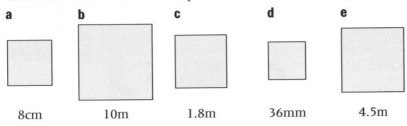

a   b   c   d   e

8cm   10m   1.8m   36mm   4.5m

**2** Calculate the length of a side of these squares.
State the units of your answers.

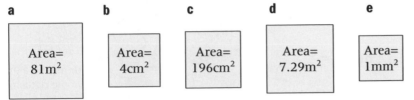

a   b   c   d   e

Area= 81m²   Area= 4cm²   Area= 196cm²   Area= 7.29m²   Area= 1mm²

**DID YOU KNOW?**

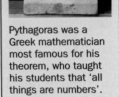

Pythagoras was a Greek mathematician most famous for his theorem, who taught his students that 'all things are numbers'.

**C Booster**

**3** Calculate the unknown area for these right-angled triangles.

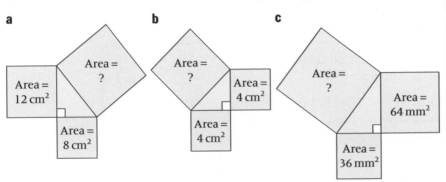

a   b   c

a: Area = 12 cm², Area = ?, Area = 8 cm²

b: Area = ?, Area = 4 cm², Area = 4 cm²

c: Area = ?, Area = 64 mm², Area = 36 mm²

**4** Calculate the length of the hypotenuse in these right-angled triangles. State the units of your answers.

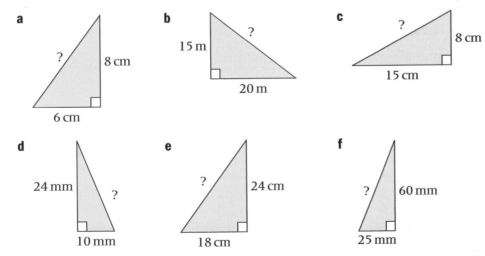

a   b   c

a: ?, 8 cm, 6 cm

b: 15 m, ?, 20 m

c: ?, 8 cm, 15 cm

d   e   f

d: 24 mm, ?, 10 mm

e: ?, 24 cm, 18 cm

f: ?, 60 mm, 25 mm

This spread will show you how to:
- Identify different mutually exclusive outcomes
- Know that the sum of the probabilities of all the outcomes is 1

The possible **outcomes** when a dice
is rolled are 1, 2, 3, 4, 5, 6.

These outcomes are **mutually exclusive**
because if you get one outcome,
you cannot get another one.

The probability of rolling a 4 = $\frac{1}{6}$

The probability of rolling a 5 = $\frac{1}{6}$

The probability of rolling a 4 **or** a 5 = $\frac{2}{6}$

$P(4) = \frac{1}{6}$

$P(5) = \frac{1}{6}$

**Or** means either
of the outcomes
4 or 5.

Notice that

$P(4 \text{ or } 5) = P(4) + P(5)$

$\frac{2}{6} = \frac{1}{6} + \frac{1}{6}$

**Example**

A spinner is made from a regular pentagon and
numbered from 1 to 5. Calculate

**a** $P(3)$     **b** $P(3 \text{ or } 4)$     **c** $P(3 \text{ or an odd number})$

..........................................................................

**a** There is one 3. There are 5 possible outcomes. $P(3) = \frac{1}{5}$

**b** $P(3) = \frac{1}{5}$       $P(4) = \frac{1}{5}$

The outcomes are mutually exclusive and so

$P(3 \text{ or } 4) = \frac{1}{5} + \frac{1}{5}$

$= \frac{2}{5}$

**c** $P(3) = \frac{1}{5}$       $P(\text{odd}) = \frac{3}{5}$

The events are not mutually exclusive so you can't just add their
probabilities.
A list of the 5 possible outcomes is

$\begin{pmatrix} 1 \\ \text{odd} \end{pmatrix}$    $\begin{pmatrix} 2 \\ \text{even} \end{pmatrix}$    $\begin{pmatrix} 3 \\ \text{odd} \end{pmatrix}$    $\begin{pmatrix} 4 \\ \text{even} \end{pmatrix}$    $\begin{pmatrix} 5 \\ \text{odd} \end{pmatrix}$

$P(3 \text{ or an odd number}) = \frac{3}{5}$

There are 3
outcomes that
are OK.

**1** Events are mutually exclusive if they cannot occur at the same time.
State if these events are mutually exclusive.
  **a** spinning a Head and spinning a Tail with a coin
  **b** rolling a 2 and rolling a 3 with a dice
  **c** rolling a 2 and rolling an even number with a dice
  **d** rolling a 2 and rolling an odd number with a dice
  **e** rolling a 2 and rolling a prime number with a dice
  **f** winning and losing a game of chess
  **g** sunny and rainy weather
  **h** taking out a red ball and taking out a blue ball, when taking out
   one ball from a bag.

**2** This is a net of a tetrahedral dice. The dice is made and
rolled. What is the probability of rolling

  **a** a 3
  **b** a 2
  **c** a 2 or a 3?

**3** A bag contains 4 red discs, 5 blue discs and 1 white disc.
One disc is taken out.
Calculate the probability that the disc is

  **a** red
  **b** blue
  **c** white
  **d** red or white
  **e** blue or white
  **f** red or blue or white

**4** Five names are written on cards and placed in a bag.
One name is taken out of the bag at random.
Calculate the probability that
  **a** the first letter on the card is H
  **b** the first letter on the card is G
  **c** the first letter on the card is H or G
  **d** the card has 5 letters written on it
  **e** the card has 5 or 6 letters written on it.

HENRY
EDWARD
JAMES
CHARLES
GEORGE

**C Booster**

439

This spread will show you how to:

- Understand and use relative frequency
- Compare experimental data and theoretical probabilities

**Keywords**
Biased
Equally likely
Estimate
Experiment
Fair
Relative
  frequency
Trial

- A dice is **fair** if the numbers are all **equally likely** to be rolled.
  You would normally expect a dice to be fair, as each face is identical.
- A spinner is **biased** if the colours are **NOT all equally likely to happen**.
  This spinner is not fair as the size and shape of each colour are
  not identical.

It is not always possible to calculate the theoretical probability.

- You can **estimate** the probability from experiments.

**Example**

Sam knows the probability of a Head when spinning a coin should be $\frac{1}{2}$ (or 0.5).
She thinks the coin is biased and so she spins the coin
50 times. The results are shown in the frequency table.

| | Frequency |
|---|---|
| **Head** | 35 |
| **Tail** | 15 |

**a** Estimate the probability of getting a Head when
spinning the coin.

**b** Do you think the coin is biased? Explain your answer.
.......................................................................................................

**a** Sam got a Head on 35 out of 50 occasions.
Estimated probability of getting a Head = $\frac{35}{50} = \frac{7}{10} = 0.7$

**b** The spinner could be biased as 0.7 is significantly larger than 0.5. However, Sam
needs to spin the coin a lot more times before she can make the decision.

- Estimated probability is called the **relative frequency**.

Each spin of the
coin is called a
**trial**.

In the example, if
Sam calculated the
relative frequency
of getting a Head
after each spin, she
could graph the
results.

Highest relative
frequency is 1.

Lowest relative
frequency is 0.

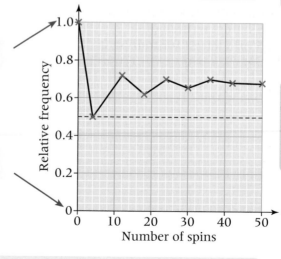

P(Head) = $\frac{1}{2}$
= 0.5
This is the
theoretical
probability of
spinning a Head.

- The estimated probability becomes more reliable as you increase the number of trials.

**1** The colours of 50 cars are recorded. The colours are shown

| Blue | Red | Other | Silver | Blue | Red | Silver | Silver | Blue |
|------|-----|-------|--------|------|-----|--------|--------|------|
| Other | Red | Silver | Silver | Blue | Red | Red | Other | Silver |
| Silver | Red | Red | Silver | Silver | Blue | Blue | Silver | Silver |
| Red | Red | Other | Blue | Red | Red | Other | Red | Red |
| Red | Silver | Blue | Blue | Blue | Other | Silver | Other | Other |
| Other | Silver | Red | Red | Blue | | | | |

**a** Copy and complete the frequency chart to show the 50 colours.

**b** State the modal colour.

**c** Give an estimate of the probability that the next car will be

  **i** blue      **ii** red      **iii** silver.

| Colour | Tally | Frequency |
|--------|-------|-----------|
| Blue | | |
| Red | | |
| Silver | | |
| Other | | |

**2** A spinner is made from a regular pentagon. The scores are recorded

| 1 | 2 | 3 | 4 | 3 | 5 | 1 | 2 |
|---|---|---|---|---|---|---|---|
| 5 | 4 | 2 | 1 | 3 | 1 | 5 | 4 |
| 2 | 2 | 3 | 1 | 4 | 5 | 4 | 2 |
| 3 | 1 | 2 | 2 | 4 | 4 | 5 | 5 |
| 1 | 2 | 3 | 4 | 2 | 4 | 1 | 1 |

**a** Draw a frequency chart to show the scores.

**b** State the modal score.

**c** How many times is the spinner spun?

**d** Estimate the probability of scoring

  **i** a 1    **ii** a 2    **iii** a 3    **iv** a 4    **v** a 5.

**e** If the spinner is fair, how many times would you expect to spin a 3 from 100 spins?

**3** There are 10 coloured balls in a bag.
One ball is taken out and then replaced in the bag.
The colours of the balls are shown in the frequency table.

| Colour | Red | Green | Blue |
|--------|-----|-------|------|
| Frequency | 9 | 14 | 27 |

**a** How many times was a ball taken out of the bag?

**b** Estimate the probability of taking out

  **i** a red ball    **ii** a green ball    **iii** a blue ball.

**c** How many balls of each colour do you think are in the bag?

**d** How could you improve this guess?

# Frequency tables and the mean

This spread will show you how to:

- Use a data collection sheet for discrete data
- Understand and use frequency tables

**Keywords**

Data
Data collection
  sheet
Frequency table
Tally chart

- You can collect data using a **data-collection sheet**.

  This one is a **tally chart**.

| Coin face | Tally | Frequency |
|-----------|-------|-----------|
| Head | 卌 卌 ‖‖ | 13 |
| Tail | 卌 卌 ‖ | 12 |

卌 = 5

Data can also be shown using a **frequency table**.

**Example**

The number of televisions in each house in my street is shown in the frequency table.

| Number of TVs | Number of houses |
|---------------|------------------|
| 0 | 1 |
| 1 | 5 |
| 2 | 12 |
| 3 | 9 |
| 4 | 1 |

**a** Calculate the number of houses in my street.

**b** Calculate the total number of televisions in my street.

**c** Calculate the mean number of televisions per house.

••••••••••••••••••••••••••••••••••••••••••••••••••••••••••••••••

The numbers in the table are:

0, 1, 1, 1, 1, 1, 2, 2, 2, 2, 2, 2, 2, 2,
2, 2, 2, 2, 3, 3, 3, 3, 3, 3, 3, 3, 3, 4

Add an extra column to the table

| TVs | Houses | TVs × Houses |
|-----|--------|--------------|
| 0 | 1 | $0 \times 1 = 0$ |
| 1 | 5 | $1 \times 5 = 5$ |
| 2 | 12 | $2 \times 12 = 24$ |
| 3 | 9 | $3 \times 9 = 27$ |
| 4 | 1 | $4 \times 1 = 4$ |

**a** $1 + 5 + 12 + 9 + 1 = 28$ houses

**b** $0 + 5 + 24 + 27 + 4 = 60$ televisions

**c** $60 \div 28 = 2\frac{1}{7}$ televisions per house.

**A02 Functional Maths**

**C Booster**

**1 a** Copy and complete the tally chart to find the frequency of the vowels a, e, i, o, u in this sentence.

**b** Which vowel occurs the most often?

**c** Which vowel occurs the least often?

**d** Calculate the total number of vowels in the sentence.

**e** Find a paragraph of writing in a newspaper and complete a similar tally chart.

| Vowel | Tally | Frequency |
|-------|-------|-----------|
| a | | |
| e | | |
| i | | |
| o | | |
| u | | |

**2** Rainfall, measured in millimetres, is recorded daily for the month of April.

```
4  2  1  0  0  1  2  2  3  5
7  8  5  3  3  2  0  0  0  1
2  3  2  4  6  7  8  8  1  2
```

**a** Copy and complete the tally chart to show this information.

**b** State the number of completely dry days in April.

**c** Calculate the total amount of rain to fall throughout April. State the units of your answer.

| Rainfall (mm) | Tally | Number of days |
|---------------|-------|----------------|
| 0 | | |
| 1 | | |
| 2 | | |
| 3 | | |
| 4 | | |
| 5 | | |
| 6 | | |
| 7 | | |
| 8 | | |

**3** Nails can be bought in bags. There are approximately 20 nails in each bag. The numbers of nails in 40 bags are recorded.

```
19  20  19  21  20  20  20  21
22  19  19  19  21  20  20  21
19  21  21  22  20  19  20  21
20  20  21  21  20  20  22  21
19  19  20  20  21  20  20  20
```

**a** Copy and complete the tally chart to show this information.

**b** Calculate the total number of nails in all 40 bags.

NAILS

Approximately 20 nails in this bag

| Number of nails | Tally | Number of bags |
|-----------------|-------|----------------|
| 19 | | |
| 20 | | |
| 21 | | |
| 22 | | |

**4** Sophie did a survey to find the number of CDs owned by the students in her class. The results are shown in the frequency table.

**a** Calculate the number of students in Sophie's class.

**b** Calculate the total number of CDs owned by the whole class.

**c** Calculate the mean number of CDs for each student.

| Number of CDs | Number of students |
|---------------|--------------------|
| 0 | 1 |
| 1 | 8 |
| 2 | 6 |
| 3 | 8 |
| 4 | 2 |
| 5 | 3 |

This spread will show you how to:

- Draw and use scatter graphs, and compare two data sets
- Understand correlation and use lines of best fit

**Keywords**
Correlation
Line of best fit
Relationship
Scatter graph
Variables

You can use a **scatter graph** to compare two sets of data, for example, height and weight.

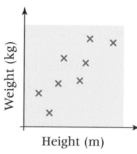

The data can be discrete or continuous.

- The data is collected in pairs and plotted as coordinates.
- If the points lie roughly in a straight line, there is a **linear relationship** or **correlation** between the two **variables**.

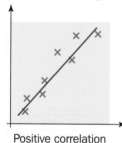

Positive correlation

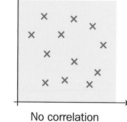

No correlation

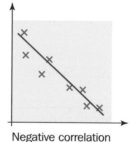

Negative correlation

Plotted points are not joined on a scatter diagram.

The straight line is the **line of best fit.**

The correlation is strong if the points are close to the line of best fit.

**Example**

The exam results (%) for Paper 1 and Paper 2 for 10 students are shown.

| Paper 1 | 56 | 72 | 50 | 24 | 44 | 80 | 68 | 48 | 60 | 36 |
|---------|----|----|----|----|----|----|----|----|----|----|
| Paper 2 | 44 | 64 | 40 | 20 | 36 | 64 | 56 | 36 | 50 | 24 |

**a** Draw a scatter graph and line of best fit.

**b** Describe the relationship between the Paper 1 results and Paper 2 results.

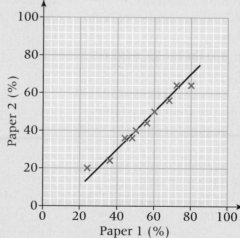

**a** Plot the exam marks as coordinates. The line of best fit should be close to all the points, with approximately the same number of crosses on either side of the line.

**b** Students who did well on Paper 1 did well on Paper 2. Students who did not do well on Paper 1 did not do well on Paper 2 either.

The line of best fit does not have to pass through (0, 0).

444

**1** Describe the type of correlation for each scatter graph.

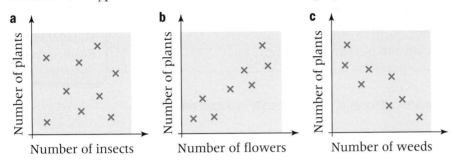

a — Number of plants vs Number of insects
b — Number of plants vs Number of flowers
c — Number of plants vs Number of weeds

**2** The table shows the amount of water used to water plants and the daily maximum temperature.

| Water (litres) | 25 | 26 | 31 | 24 | 45 | 40 | 5 | 13 | 18 | 28 |
|---|---|---|---|---|---|---|---|---|---|---|
| Maximum temperature (°C) | 24 | 21 | 25 | 19 | 30 | 28 | 15 | 18 | 20 | 27 |

**a** Copy and complete the scatter graph for this information.

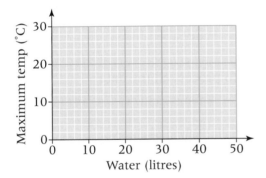

**b** State the type of correlation shown in the scatter graph.
**c** Copy and complete these sentences:
  **i** As the temperatures increases, the amount of water used _____.
  **ii** As the temperature decreases, the amount of water used _____.

**3** The times taken, in minutes, to run a mile and the shoe sizes of ten athletes are shown in the table.

| Shoe size | 10 | $7\frac{1}{2}$ | 5 | 9 | 6 | $8\frac{1}{2}$ | $7\frac{1}{2}$ | $6\frac{1}{2}$ | 8 | 7 |
|---|---|---|---|---|---|---|---|---|---|---|
| Time (mins) | 9 | 8 | 8 | 7 | 5 | 13 | 15 | 12 | 5 | 6 |

**a** Draw a scatter graph to show this information.
  Use 2 cm to represent 1 shoe size on the horizontal axis.
  Use 2 cm to represent 5 minutes on the vertical axis.
**b** State the type of correlation shown in the scatter graph.
**c** Describe, in words, any relationship that the graph shows.

# Databases and random sampling

This spread will show you how to:
- Gather data from secondary sources
- Use effective methods for random sampling
- Identify sources of bias and plan to minimise it

**Keywords**
Biased
Database
Equally likely
RAN#
Random sample

- A **database** is an organised collection of data, especially in a form that can be used by a computer.

An example might be the records of the Year 11 students in a school. You can sort a computer database
- alphabetically
- numerically.

You can sort using any or several of the columns (fields).

| Number | Surname | Forename | Form | Gender |
|--------|---------|----------|------|--------|
| 0001 | Smith | Thomas | 10E | Male |
| 0002 | Jones | Michaela | 10B | Female |
| 0003 | Chapham | Leah | 10A | Female |
| 0004 | Clark | Alan | 10B | Male |

This database has been sorted by number.

Sometimes there is too much data in a database to process all the data, and so a **random sample** is used.

- In a random sample, each person or item must be **equally likely** to be chosen.

If each person is not equally likely to be chosen, the sample is **biased**.

**Example**

Describe a method to choose a random sample of 30 students from a year group of 120 students.

·········································································

- Number each student from 1 to 120.
- Generate 30 random numbers, by either
  - picking 30 numbers from a bag of 120, numbered 1 to 120, or
  - using the RAN# key on a calculator.
- You can generate random numbers on a calculator using the  random function. RAN# generates random numbers from 0.000 to 0.999.
- You can generate a random number from, say, 1 to 120 by using 120 × RAN#.

Use the first three digits of the display.

**Functional Maths**

**A02**

**1** Sanjit wants to buy a laptop. He creates a database of the 10 laptops he is considering buying.

| Laptop number | Speed of processor | RAM memory | Size of hard drive | Screen size | Warranty | Cost |
|---|---|---|---|---|---|---|
| 1 | 2.16 GHz | 1 GB | 120 GB | 15.4" | No | £275 |
| 2 | 2.0 GHz | 2 GB | 160 GB | 14.1" | 1 year | £500 |
| 3 | 1.6 GHz | 1 GB | 120 GB | 8.9" | 1 year | £220 |
| 4 | 1.8 GHz | 2 GB | 120 GB | 17" | 1 year | £350 |
| 5 | 2.0 GHz | 2 GB | 64 GB | 12.1" | 3 years | £600 |
| 6 | 2.0 GHz | 2 GB | 160 GB | 15.4" | 2 years | £310 |
| 7 | 2.16 GHz | 1 GB | 120 GB | 15.4" | 3 years | £345 |
| 8 | 2.0 GHz | 4 GB | 320 GB | 15.4" | 3 years | £437 |
| 9 | 1.8 GHz | 2 GB | 160 GB | 15.4" | 1 year | £402 |
| 10 | 2.53 GHz | 5 GB | 500 GB | 15.6" | No | £549 |

**a** Write down the costs of the laptops in order of price, smallest first.
**b** Write down the speeds of the processors in order of size, smallest first.
**c** Which laptop has the smallest processor speed?
**d** Which laptop has the largest RAM memory?
**e** List the laptops that have
  **i** a screen size of 15" or more
  **ii** at least 160 GB of hard drive memory
  **iii** a 2-year or 3-year warranty.
**f** Sanjit wants a laptop with a screen size of 15" or more, at least 160 GB of hard drive memory and one with a 2- or 3-year warranty. Which laptop is the cheapest option?

**2** A class of 30 students decide to elect a class representative by a random process. State whether these methods of selection are random or biased. Give a reason for each answer.
**a** Arrange the class list into alphabetical order and select the first name on the list.
**b** Arrange the class list into alphabetical order and select the last name on the list.
**c** Put the names of the students on cards of equal size. Put the cards into a bag and pick out one card.
**d** Arrange the students in order of height and select the smallest student.
**e** Hide a gold star in the classroom, and select the student who finds the star.
**f** Number the students from 1 to 30. Roll a dice and select the student with that number.
**g** Number the students from 1 to 30. Use a calculator to find $30 \times$ RAN# and take the first two digits on the display.

**C Booster**

# GCSE formulae

In your Edexcel GCSE examinations you will be given a formula sheet like this on this page. Here are the formulae that you are given in your exams.

**Area of a trapezium** $= \frac{1}{2}(a + b)h$

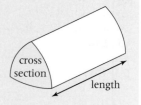

**Volume of prism** = area of cross section × length

Here are some other formulae that you should learn.

**Area of a rectangle** = length × width

**Area of a triangle** $= \frac{1}{2} \times$ base × height

**Area of a parallelogram** = base × perpendicular height

**Area of a circle** $= \pi r^2$

**Circumference of a circle** $= \pi d = 2\pi r$

**Volume of a cuboid** = length × width × height

**Volume of a cylinder** = area of circle × length

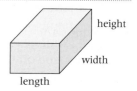

**Pythagoras' theorem states,**

For any right-angled triangle, $c^2 = a^2 + b^2$
where $c$ is the hypotenuse.

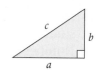

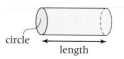

# Answers

## N1 Check in

1  304
2  **a** 70          **b** −12
   **c** 5
3  −7°C

## N1 Summary

1  **a** Seven thousand three hundred and sixty
   **b** 14 000     **c** 40
2  28, 45, 56, 79, 121
3  **a** Huntingdon     **b** 3     **c** 1005
4  **a** 8°C          **b** 22°C
5  £36

## D1 Check in

1  **a** 0.2, 0.25, 0.3
   **b** 0.7, 0.75, 0.8
   **c** 0.8, 0.85, 1
2  **a** $\frac{3}{4}$          **b** $\frac{3}{8}$
3  **a** 1     **b** 1     **c** $\frac{1}{10}$     **d** $\frac{1}{5}$     **e** $\frac{1}{4}$
4  **a** 0.8     **b** 0.3     **c** 0.1

## D1 Summary

1  **a** Impossible     **b** Even
   **c** Certain
2  **a** around 1     **b** zero
3  $\frac{7}{20}$

## D2 Check in

1  **a** 6, 17, 19, 26, 29, 30, 37, 42
   **b** 106, 115, 118, 121, 130, 135
   **c** 144, 145, 154, 155, 156, 165, 166
2  **a** 121          **b** 144
   **c** 252          **d** 413
   **e** 68          **f** 23
   **g** 49          **h** 82
   **i** 189          **j** 266
3  **a** 04 : 58     **b** 20 : 45

## D2 Summary

1  (left to right, top to bottom):
   55, 190, 17, 10, 88, 78
2  **a** e.g. no time period; labels too vague
   **b** not enough people; not a representative
      sample
3  47

## N2 Check in

1  **a** 3000     **b** 2900     **c** 2920
2  **a** 48          **b** 105
   **c** 815          **d** 229

3  **a** 30          **b** 6          **c** 72
   **d** 141          **e** 168          **f** 13

## N2 Summary

1  29
2  5 cm
3  644
4  18
5  **a** 4          **b** 2          **c** 9
6  £19.50

## D3 Check in

1  **a** 180     **b** 90     **c** 36
   **d** 72     **e** 60     **f** 30
   **g** 2     **h** 4
2  **a** 25, 29, 30, 31, 36, 41, 43, 49
   **b** 234, 243, 324, 342, 423, 432
   **c** 12.3, 13.2, 21.3, 23.1, 31.2, 32.1
3  150°

## D3 Summary

1  **a** 3          **b** Cat          **c** 22
2  **a** 9 a.m.     **b** It went down

## D4 Check in

1  **a** 26, 29, 31, 35, 36, 40, 41, 48
   **b** 91, 92, 98, 101, 102
   **c** 4, $4\frac{1}{2}$, 6, $7\frac{1}{2}$, 8
2  **a** 80, 80 ,80, 82, 83, 83, 84, 84, 84, 84
   **b** 45, 45, 46, 48, 48, 48, 48, 49, 49, 49

## D4 Summary

1  **a** frequencies: 7, 4, 2, 1, 2
   **b** 2          **c** 4
2  30 mm
3  Range = 9 (mode = 0), mean = 2.7
   (median = 2.5)
   sensible comment e.g. mean number of
   absences is only 2.9 students but it varies a lot

## N3 Check in

1  **a** $\frac{3}{4}$          **b** $\frac{3}{5}$          **c** $\frac{3}{5}$
2  **a** 0.75          **b** 0.4          **c** 1.25
3  **a** $\frac{3}{5}$          **b** $\frac{1}{4}$          **c** $\frac{1}{5}$

## N3 Summary

1  **a** 6 shaded     **b** 2 shaded
2  **a** 35%          **b** 8%          **c** $\frac{3}{10}$
   **d** 0.09          **e** 280          **f** 2%
3  €900

## D5 Check in

1  **a**  2, 3, 5 or 7  **b**  1, 4 or 9
   **c**  1, 3, 6 or 10  **d**  4 or 8
   **e**  1, 2, 5 or 10

2  **a**  $\frac{2}{3}$  **b**  $\frac{4}{5}$  **c**  $\frac{1}{4}$
   **d**  $\frac{3}{5}$  **e**  1

3  **a**  $\frac{3}{4}$  **b**  $\frac{3}{10}$  **c**  $\frac{2}{5}$

4  **a**  10  **b**  40  **c**  200

## D5 Summary

1  $\frac{5}{12}$

2  6 ways: (2, 6), (3, 5), (3, 6), (4, 4,), (4, 5), (4, 6)

3  **a**  $\frac{1}{2}$
   **b**  valid reason e.g. it's a random process

## G1 Check in

1  **a**  7.8  **b**  9.4  **c**  5.5
2  **a**  400  **b**  14 000  **c**  31
   **d**  1340  **e**  6300  **f**  40
   **g**  60  **h**  4.3  **i**  0.64
   **j**  0.31
3  **a**  45 mm  **b**  4.5 cm

## G1 Summary

1  Around 4.5 m.
2  **a**  60 cm  **b**  200 cm²
3  centimetres, miles, kilograms

## A1 Check in

1  **a**  9  **b**  4  **c**  16
2  15
3  **a**  7  **b**  −1
   **c**  2  **d**  −3
4  **a**  −6  **b**  −8
   **c**  −2  **d**  4

## A1 Summary

1  **a**  $n - 3$  **b**  $2n$
2  **a**  $3c$  **b**  $3e + 2f$  **c**  $5a$
   **d**  $4xy$  **e**  $2a + 7b + 8$
3  **a**  17.6  **b**  20
4  $30x + 50y$
5  Two possibilities are: 4 cm, $(x + 3)$ cm
   or 2 cm, $(2x + 6)$ cm

## N4 Check in

1  $\frac{2}{3}$
2  e.g. $\frac{2}{4}, \frac{3}{6}$

## N4 Summary

1  **a**  £10.75  **b**  7  **c**  £1.55
2  **a**  $\frac{3}{4}$  **b**  6 shaded
   **c**  0.3  **d**  $\frac{39}{100}$

## A2 Check in

1  **a**  3  **b**  8
   **c**  2  **d**  5
2  **a**  8  **b**  5
   **c**  8  **d**  $3\frac{1}{2}$
3  **a**  5  **b**  −4
   **c**  1  **d**  11
4  **a**  −1  **b**  −5
   **c**  1  **d**  −7

## A2 Summary

1  **a**  **i**  (0, 2)  **ii**  (4, 3)
   **b**  Should be at $\left(2, 2\frac{1}{2}\right)$
2  **a**  −5, 1, 4, 7
   **b**  Straight line passing through (0, 1) and (2, 7)

## G2 Check in

1  **a**  57 mm  **b**  5.7 cm
2  **a**  around 40°
   **b**  around 130–140°

## G2 Summary

1  **a**  A and D
   **b**  E
2  **a**  **i**  135°  **ii**  Angles on a straight line add
                              to 180°
   **b**  40°
3  Two possible answers: (3, 1) or (5, 5)

## N5 Check in

1  **a**  49  **b**  8
   **c**  1000  **d**  0.32
2  5
3  Yes, because it will halve twice over (122, 61)

## N5 Summary

1  **a**  6, 8 or 10  **b**  9
   **c**  8  **d**  7
2  **a**  2 numbers from 5, 7, 9, 11
   **b**  5, 7 or 11
   **c**  8
3  **a**  48  **b**  4
4  10
5  12
6  36 seconds

## A3 Check in

1  **a**  3  **b**  9
   **c**  4  **d**  3
2  1, 4, 9, 16, 25, 36, 49, 64, 81, 100
3  **a**  5  **b**  4
   **c**  7  **d**  6
4  **a**  2  **b**  2
   **c**  3  **d**  3
5  **a**  8  **b**  6
   **c**  12  **d**  10

**A3 Summary**

1 **a** Pattern with 9 sticks
   **b** 9, 11    **c** 25
2 **a** 23, 27    **b** 43
3 **a** $1 + 3 + 5 + 7 + 9 + 11 = 36$
   **b** square
4 Possibilities include 8, 16 or 7, 11

**G3 Check in**

1 **a** 180°    **b** 180°    **c** 360°
2 **a** 50°    **b** 70°

**G3 Summary**

1 **a** and **b** Correct drawings
2 **a** cylinder
   **b** cone
   **c** Square-based pyramid
3 **a** 4    **b** 6    **c** 4
4 Possibilities include $4 \text{ cm} \times 3 \text{ cm} \times 7 \text{ cm}$
   and $2 \text{ cm} \times 2 \text{ cm} \times 21 \text{ cm}$

**A4 Check in**

1 **a** $4x$    **b** $m^2$
   **c** $4p$    **d** $6x$
2 **a** $5p + q$    **b** $5x + y$
   **c** $-m + 5n - 4p$ (or $5n - m - 4p$)
3 Grid with points correctly plotted.

**A4 Summary**

1 **a** 18    **b** 8
2 **a** 100 miles    **b** 5 hours
   **c** 33.3 miles per hour

**N6 Check in**

1 $\frac{1}{3}$
2 £24
3 £5
4 10

**N6 Summary**

1 £1.50
2 **a** £2.40    **b** £2
   **c** €1.25
3 21 : 4
4 £12

**G4 Check in**

1 **a** 180°    **b** 270°
   **c** 90°    **d** 180°
2 **a** clockwise    **b** anticlockwise

**G4 Summary**

1 **a** vertices at (5, −1), (6, −2), (6, −4), (4, −4)
   and (4, −2).
   **b** vertices at (−1, 3), (−2, 4), (−2, 6), (0, 6)
   and (0, 4).

2 **a** vertices at (−2, 1), (−6, 1) and (−2, 3).
   **b** vertices at (−2, −1), (−2, −3) and (−6, −1).

**A5 Check in**

1 **a** 6    **b** 15
   **c** 11    **d** 3
2 **a** 4    **b** 6
   **c** 8    **d** 5
3 **a** 3, 4    **b** 5, 7
4 **a** 7    **b** −1
   **c** 12    **d** $2\frac{1}{4}$

**A5 Summary**

1 **a** 30    **b** 4    **c** 32
2 14
3 **a** 6    **b** 10    **c** 24

**N7 Check in**

1 47
2 **a** 1.3    **b** 0.3
3 **a** 3.56    **b** 8.04    **c** 0.06

**N7 Summary**

1 £3.00, £2.50, £24.00, £42.00
2 945 francs
3 17.9867
4 Around 20

**G5 Check in**

1 **a** $x = -2$    **b** $y = 1$
2 **a** 90°    **b** 270°    **c** 180°

**G5 Summary**

1 **a** G or C
   **b** F and A
   **c** 2
2 **a** $6 \text{ cm}^2$
   **b** Shape correctly drawn on grid

**A6 Check in**

1 **a** −3    **b** +6
   **c** ÷5    **d** × 4
2 **a** $2x + 2y$    **b** $5p + 2$
   **c** $\frac{m}{8}$
3 **a** 12    **b** 11
   **c** 4    **d** 13
4 **a** $x = 2$    **b** $x = 5$
   **c** $y = 2$    **d** $y = 7$

**A6 Summary**

1 5, 9, 8
2 **a** $x = 6$    **b** $y = 45$    **c** $x = 4$
3 **a** $x = 2$    **b** $y = 6.5$
4 $x = 50°$

**G6  Check in**

1  a  1　　　b  4　　　c  4.5　　　d  1
　　e  4　　　f  1.5　　g  1　　　h  6
　　i  0.5　　j  1.5
2  a  35–45°　　b  160–170°
　　c  220–230°　d  125–135°

**G6  Summary**

1  a  120 km　　b  170°
2  a  Accurate drawing　　b  90°

**G7  Check in**

1  a  diameter　b  circumference　　c  radius
2  28 cm²

**G7  Exam question**

1  A
2  20 000 cm³
3  50.27 cm